HÉLOÏSE AND ABÉLARD

HÉLOÏSE AND ABÉLARD

by George Moore

LIVERIGHT PUBLISHING
CORPORATION
PUBLISHERS   NEW YORK

First Printing
BLACK AND GOLD LIBRARY
July, 1932
Second Printing, January, 1934
Third Printing, November, 1938
Fourth Printing, May, 1942
Fifth Printing, January, 1945

PRINTED IN THE UNITED STATES OF AMERICA

A MADAME X

Héloïse et Abélard fut composé pour
célébrer mon amour. Les épreuves sont
corrigées, les brouillons au panier,
l'encrier est à sec. Erreur! J'en tire
une dernière goutte et avec une plume
estropiée je vous écris cette petite épître
dédicatoire. Je vous prie de l'accepter,
Madame, sans trop me chicaner sur un
mot qui semblera trop fort à certains
sots, pauvres êtres, qui voudraient rem-
placer le mot amour par celui d'amitié,
ne sachant pas que le cœur ne connait
que l'amour.

G. M.

HÉLOÏSE AND ABÉLARD

VOLUME ONE

HÉLOÏSE AND ABÉLARD

CHAP. I.

PHILIPPE, the Canon's brother, was among the first to enlist in the army that Raymond assembled to rescue the Holy Sepulchre from the Infidel. He was leaving behind him Jeanne, his wife, and his daughter, a child of ten; to both he was devotedly attached, to his wife by memories of a romantic marriage (and to these were added memories of months of care bestowed upon her, for her health was now failing), and to his daughter, Héloïse, he was not less attached, a child so unusually intelligent that he had begun to dream of a great future for her (a father's hope takes wing quickly), and he was also leaving his career, for Philippe was a physician of no small repute. He was leaving all that he loved and all those that claimed him, and in the belief that he would not return. But he did not mention his forebodings to the Canon when he repaired to his house in the rue des Chantres to bid him good-bye. For why, he asked himself, should he speak of things that would be painful for his brother to hear, wounds and death and burial, things of which he had no certain knowledge, only a vague premonition?

So very little was settled during the meeting of the brothers, who almost without words paced the room or stood by the window overlooking the Seine watching the water flowing past, perplexed by the apparent strangeness of their destinies; for while Philippe was fighting

9

stiff battles with the Saracen, Fulbert would be going
to and forth from the rue des Chantres to the Cathedral
of Notre-Dame.   To offer up the sacrifice of the Mass,
Philippe interjected and Fulbert acquiesced, serving
God, he said, in different modes, but always the one true
and living God.

The low and irritating ripple of the Seine reached
their ears and it seemed to remind the Canon that he preferred the part he had chosen from the beginning of his
life, knowing well that it would secure to him the same
circumstance and the same hope always, rather than this
adventure that had befallen his brother suddenly and from
which there was no escape, for it would be a family dishonour if there was not one member of the family at least
to answer the call—Jerusalem for Christendom.   They
spoke to each other in snatches of the ships that were
assembled in the ports of Marseilles and Toulon to carry
the Crusaders to Acre, a lengthy voyage of many weeks
even if the winds should prove favourable, but God
would see they were; unless, indeed, he wished to try the
faith of the Crusaders in their enterprise by delaying them
with contrary winds; yet God was good, and it was natural that he should wish the city to be given back to the
faith for which his Son had perished, nor could the war
be a long one.   Jerusalem will fall speedily and thou'lt
kneel in the Sepulchre, and we shall see each other again,
the Canon said.   Philippe did not answer him, and the
perplexed Canon returned to the window, thinking that
if his brother did not come back from the Holy City
Jeanne and Héloïse would fall to his charge.   I shall
have to bring them here to live with me, he said to himself, and the fear grew upon him of daily attendance on
an ailing woman, and that the life he had sought and
found in the rue des Chantres would be plucked from him,

and his house be no longer his own. Even if Jeanne did
not live very long, Héloïse and her future would become a
business from which he could not escape any more than
Philippe could from the Holy Land; for all the choir
and chapter would look upon him with contempt if his
whole life were not dedicated to the widow and child of
a man who had given his life to the service of Our Lord
Jesus Christ. And while Fulbert was thinking of these
things Philippe sat on one of the oak chests along the
wall that served as seats, all expression having faded
from his face, pale at the thought that he might never
see his brother again, and Fulbert said to himself: He
is thinking that if he should turn round suddenly and take
my hands in his he might get a vow from me that his wife
and child shall want for nothing as long as I live. But it
will make little difference whether he asks me or not;
my life is pledged to his service.

That he should feel so much unwillingness to stand by
his sister-in-law alarmed him, and he tried to find consolation in the thought that the irksome task would be
approved in the sight of God and in the sight of men and
in his own sight because of its irksomeness. For it is no
small thing to ask a man to give up his life; God is asking
as much from me as he is asking from Philippe; and I will
do my duty as Philippe does his. And the Canon vowed
to slough the sensual coil when the time came for him to
choose between shame and honour. But it might never
come; if it did, Philippe would be dead. His brother's
footsteps startled him from his reverie and he turned
from the window to bid him good-bye abruptly, unable to
bear the strain of the parting any longer; he heard the
clink of the mail on the staircase, and still seeing the
spare figure of the Crusader in his mind's eye, Fulbert
could not do else than contrast the narrow, helmeted skull

with his own great bald head, its rim of reddish hair rising
no higher than the ears, and meditate on his canonical
belly swelling under the purple robe, whose rustling silk
reminded him of his own increasing vanity.

But we are never at quarrel with ourselves for long,
and his thoughts soon passed from Philippe to Jeanne,
who could not live more than six months; if so, his care
of her could be borne without hardship, and he began to
compose the picture, saying to himself that if he were to
sit by her bedside twice a week he would be doing all that
could be expected of him. Two visits in the week, he
said, I shall not be able to manage; a weekly visit, however, did not seem to conflict with his work in the Cathedral, but life is always more exacting than we think for,
and it fell out that despite his intentions the Canon did
not succeed in crossing the Little Bridge more than four
times during the three months Jeanne lingered between
life and death. The fourth time he went to Sainte-Geneviève was to hear her last message to her husband, if he
should return, and to administer the last sacrament to
her. All hope of saving her is at an end, he said, on his
way home; and a little later, as he passed the Cathedral,
he muttered: Things have not fallen out as evilly as they
might have; I shall only have the girl to contend with, and
the hardship of the burden may not prove too great, for
Héloïse may be all Philippe thinks she is, and if she be
no more than half she deserves education and the best that
can be given to her.

Jeanne died even sooner than was expected; she did
not outlive the week, and on returning from the funeral
he remembered that three learned women had joined the
Benedictine convent at Argenteuil lately, and he asked
himself as he strolled if he could do better than place
Héloïse in their charge. Some carts were going thither

next morning; would it not be well to avail himself of
them? Nothing will be gained by delay, he said to himself, and to his serving-woman: Madelon, I will give thee
a letter to the Prioress; and thou'lt take Héloïse to Argenteuil to-morrow. He spoke firmly, for he was afraid that
Madelon would raise objections and begin to argue with
him, saying that his niece ought to pass a few days in
the rue des Chantres, long enough to recover from the
shock of her mother's death, and that Latin and Arith-
metic were not like green vegetables, they could wait. All
the way down the staircase I shall hear her muttering, he
said; she'll make me pay for this in many little ways.
And he fell to thinking. But so convinced was he that
it would be for Héloïse's good to go straight to the convent without tarrying in his house, that he overruled Madelon, surprising her not a little by his firmness. Never have
I seen him so stubborn, she growled, pausing at her kitchen
door, uncertain if she should return; and next morning
when the carts stopped in the street the Canon heard her
still muttering: A fine hurry indeed he is in to get rid
of the child; frightened, I suppose, lest anything should
come between him and his books. Madelon, the carts
are waiting, Canon Fulbert cried up the staircase;
Héloïse is waiting, no doubt, expecting thee; the carts
will call for her. Madelon continued to mutter, and his
ear catching certain words—cruel, selfish old fellow—he
began to think that he was no longer master in his own
house. But the thought of separating himself from Madelon and throwing himself upon the charity of a new
servant, who, though she might not have the faults that
Madelon had, would have other faults, intervened, and
the thought of Madelon's dismissal was dropped almost
as quickly as it had come. Madelon has her faults, he
said; everybody has, none is without faults; all the same,

it is strange that she mistrusts me, for she should know that I always act thoughtfully. On listening again, it seemed to him that he heard the words: Not even for one night! That is how it seems to her, for she is not able to look ahead; the actual moment in front of her is all that she apprehends. Madelon does not see that if Héloïse were here for one night I should have to keep her several. Why one night rather than two—why not a week? And at the end of a week it would be hard to get her away, for children are propense to acquire habits; and he imagined Héloïse drifting about the house, in and out of the kitchen, dabbling in the silt with the ducks along the river's edge (to the great danger of her life), for to whose care could he confide her? There was no one in the house except Madelon, and Madelon's work occupied all her time. If he kept his niece in the house for a week, she would wish to return to it. He would receive letters asking if she might come for holidays. . . . Holy Virgin! would that packing upstairs never come to an end? And once more he ran up half-a-dozen steps and called to Madelon to hasten, saying: the carts will not wait any longer. Madelon paid no heed to his warnings. It may be, he said to himself, that she hopes to gain her point, thinking that if the carters refuse to wait any longer I shall never summon enough courage again to do what I am doing now. The carters reassured him, and once more he picked up the thread of his thoughts, that servants do not see farther ahead than a day; two or three days at most. If Madelon were a gossip! But he never heard Jeanne complain of Madelon carrying stories to and fro. She had her faults, of course, but she was trustworthy; and the Canon fell to thinking how this excellent woman came into the family. About ten years ago it was, soon after Héloïse was born: he was certain of the year, but could not remember if Madelon had come from Brittany before Héloïse was born or a few weeks later. However, it doesn't matter, he said; what is certain is that she came hither to suckle Héloïse. Alas! one of the many sad cases of girls led astray. But she had to leave on account of the drying up of her milk, and he recalled Jeanne's despair, how she had come to him to ask if he knew anybody who could replace Madelon. He didn't, but he was glad to overlook Madelon's fault and—— A smile gathered about his lips, but he did not linger unduly over the first years that he and Madelon lived together, but passed on to some years later, when he discovered that Madelon always looked upon herself as his niece's mother. So it was only natural that she should not like Héloïse to be hurried off to a convent the day after her mother's funeral. His thoughts fell once more on the short-sightedness of servants. Governed always, he said, by the seeming need of the moment, unable to weigh and consider the alternatives, whether it would be wiser for her to spend a few idle days in the rue des Chantres or to go to the convent with the impression of her mother's death fresh in her memory, for if she were as Philippe believed her to be, and as himself believed her to be, a child of very rare mind, it would be well to prepare her for the acceptance of the religious life. For outside the religious life, he said, there is nothing but trouble and anxiety, nor is advancement possible except through the Church. It was then, remembering his age (he was fifty), that he asked himself what would become of this orphan at his death. Not many years remained in front of him; ten or fifteen, twenty at the most! His meditation on life's brevity was interrupted by Madelon coming down the stairs with her packages; a great relief it was, and having instructed the carters, he returned into his house soothed, for he knew now of a certainty his life would continue flowing in the same even current for several years at least. By going to the convent as a child, she will not carry with her any memories of the world, and rubbing his hands cheerfully he continued his thoughts: Madelon's chatter is full of danger; a good woman, but one without foresight, always speaking her mind without knowing that she is speaking it, which would not matter if Héloïse were a common child; a common child might have stayed here for a few days; but being exceptionally quick she would have been influenced, and have gone to the convent with her memory a store of undesirable thoughts; so there could be no doubt that I acted rightly, none whatever.

But however sure the Canon was at times that he had acted rightly, a doubt rose up from the depths occasionally, and once it almost compelled him to mount his nag and ride to Argenteuil to see his niece. But he had fallen into fat; horse-riding was not to his taste, and as he sat in his chair trying to balance the advantages and the disadvantages that would accrue from a ride to Argenteuil, it occurred to him suddenly that his visit could not fail to remind her of two things: that as a Canon of Notre-Dame he would have money to leave, and that his money would eventually come to her, she being his nearest relative. But he had sent her to the convent the day after her mother's funeral; and for that she thinks harshly of me, he said, and the nuns think the same and maybe have put the thought into her head. A word is enough to poison her mind, and of all a word spoken casually. On the other hand, they might like to keep her; convents are always agog to catch a clever girl and the Prioress will understand—— All the same I ought to have asked her to spend the holidays here, and yet . . . His thoughts

melted away, and three days after a letter came from
the convent that restored to the Canon confidence in his
own wisdom. Héloïse was already more proficient in
Latin than anybody else in the convent and should prove
a great ornament to the Church if it were her lot to be
called to the religious life. She will discover a vocation
if left undisturbed, he said, and was more than ever
certain that he had acted rightly in sending her to Argenteuil and allowing his niece's mind to ripen altogether
in the influence of those holy women. And with such
thoughts and reflections he continued to cajole his conscience, now and then troubled by a fear that Philippe,
on his return from Jerusalem, would think it strange,
even harsh, that Héloïse had been left all this time at
Argenteuil. It was true that Philippe had sent a letter saying that he approved of putting Héloïse to school
at Argenteuil, but the Canon's conscience was not easy;
he was afraid that when Philippe returned from Palestine he would be grieved to hear that his brother had not
been once to see his charge, nor once sent for her to spend
a few days of her holidays under his roof. I shall tell
him that I wished to remove Héloïse from all worldly
influences, so that she might discover a vocation in herself. For what would her position be if I were to die
suddenly and thou in Palestine? I mean, he continued,
addressing his brother's supposed shade, if God chose
to ask for thy life.

It was painful to the Canon to contemplate his brother's
death, for what was most real in him, most true and
fundamental, was his love of Philippe; and when the
news came to him that his brother was killed in the siege
of Jerusalem, he wrote a letter to the Prioress acquaint-
ing her of the fact, saying that he relied upon her to
break the news to Héloïse, and to tell her that if he did

not come to see her it was because he was too broken-
hearted. Not to speak to her of her father would be
impossible, and to speak of Philippe was, he said, beyond
his power, he would break down; so he begged the Prioress to make these things plain sooner or later to his niece,
expressing a hope that she would understand and not
judge harshly his absence from her at this terrible moment
of their lives. He paused to ask himself if he were finding excuses for not doing things that were inconvenient
for him to do. As likely as not he was, for alas! selfishness is the human lot. Be this as it may (he was writing
the exact truth so far as he knew it), he could not talk
about Philippe to Héloïse. Nor to anybody, he said,
springing out of his chair, and going to the kitchen he gave
a solemn order to Madelon that she was never to speak his
brother's name in his presence; and when his colleagues
became aware of his reticence they paid silent respect to
the Canon's grief, without, however, giving their approval
to this closing up of the heart and treating it as a sort
of mortuary-chamber. For we are but houses and require
fresh air; ghosts choose deserted houses for their dwelling-
places; were remarks that were often made behind the
Canon's back. It was also said that the Canon never
sought to discover any new fact from the soldiers who
were returning from Jerusalem telling stories about everybody.

The Canon was fond of good living, assemblies of his
friends and lute-playing, but after Philippe's death his
door was forbidden to all; and the talk about him often
was that he sat alone in the evening thinking how Philippe
died, and that if he came upon Philippe's name in a book
he turned the page. But if he never spoke of Philippe, he
was always thinking of his brother, not however as a
warrior but as a handsome young man of agreeable mien

and bearing, with whom the daughter of a great noble
had, against the wishes of her family, run away, and
against whom the influence of the family was directed so
persistently that Philippe had been obliged to enlist in
Raymond's army—— That was the reason, or part of
the reason, of Philippe's enlistment, he often said to himself, turning over the leaves of a book. It was not till
Madelon told him (in defiance of his order) that it was
Philippe who had gotten tidings of the whereabouts of
the Holy Spear that the Canon began to associate his
brother with the clashing of swords in breached walls and
the sacking of cities. He was angry with Madelon for
mentioning his brother's name, but shrank from telling
her again that she must keep it off her tongue. All the
same he could not bear to see her with her arms akimbo,
talking to him of his brother by the hour. An almost
unendurable trial she was, yet he was glad she had told
him, for now he knew that Philippe was chosen by God;
Philippe was therefore with God, and his belief in his
brother's spiritual life seemed to unite them both in spirit
till the only hours he cared to live were those that he spent
thinking of Philippe, despite the fact that these meditations were broken by misgivings as to whether he was
acting exactly as Philippe would wish by leaving his niece
in the Argenteuil convent.

On looking up and turning his eyes towards a certain
corner of the room one night it seemed to him that the
smile had vanished out of Philippe's eyes. She must be
now sixteen, going on for seventeen, he said to himself,
and sought out the Prioress's letter in the hope that it
would again set flowing a pleasant current of meditation;
but he had hardly opened it when his brother came out
of the corner of the room, and while he looked at Philippe
the thought came into his mind that perhaps he appeared

at this moment so strangely visible because he disapproved of his daughter passing from the schoolroom to the novitiate in ignorance of the world, no choice having been given to her. He looked again (he had never been sure that he was reading Philippe's face truly), but the apparition had faded; he was now looking into his memory of it and could not rid himself of the thought that Philippe's eyes seemed to protest against the handing over of his daughter to the Church in her first youth. Héloïse, a voice said, was thrust into a convent school at ten years of age, and had seen nobody but the nuns. Never once, Fulbert, hast thou been to see her. Fulbert was not certain with what eyes he saw his brother, nor with what ears he heard the words. Did he see with the mind's eye, did he hear with the mind's ear? He did not know, and tried to attribute the appearance and the voice to nervousness or ill-health. For why should a devoted son of the Church object to his daughter taking the veil? he asked himself, getting back for answer that Philippe did not object to his daughter taking the veil if she were so disposed, but did not like her being tricked into accepting it. I am being driven, he said, as if Philippe's sword were behind me all the time prodding, prodding me in the rue des Chantres, prodding me as I sit over my books reading, prodding me in the Cathedral. I am being compelled at the point of a sword to send Madelon for her. He strove against his conscience as long as he could, but one day in the Cathedral it seemed to him, as he was laying out some vestments, that he could not do else than send Madelon to Argenteuil with instructions that she was to bring Héloïse back with her. He could not understand how it was he had delayed so long, and then of a sudden he began to feel that he could not interrupt the pleasant tenor of his life by bringing another person into it; and

no sooner had he come to a new resolve not to send for
Héloïse than he began to feel that he could not bear any
longer the anguish of his conscience, and that the only
way to end it was to send for Héloïse. It is a long time
since we have seen Héloïse, he said one day to Madelon,
turning back as he was going to leave his house.

Troth and faith, it is a long time since you have seen
her, well-nigh six years, Madelon answered. But I sent
thee with some presents last year. I went myself, Canon,
bringing her a cake last year. Now what are you thinking of? Madelon asked, standing before him, her arms,
as usual, akimbo. Of sending me to fetch her back? If
you aren't, it's time you were! Be sure of one thing,
that I'm not asking for thy thoughts on this subject or
any other, the Canon answered, and Madelon began to
laugh and the Canon walked out of the house. But though
he could leave Madelon, he could not escape from the torment within him, and at the end of the week he said: the
die is cast; Madelon must go for her. And next day at
the same hour he stood at his window hearing the cart
groaning through the rutted street on its way to the Great
Bridge, almost helpless, thinking that his life had come
to an end, but unable to do otherwise than he had done.
It had to be, he said to himself, and I couldn't have acted
otherwise, even if I knew that Héloïse would refuse to
return to Argenteuil at the end of the week. She will go
back willingly if she doesn't stay too long, and a three
days' visit will be enough. But Madelon will not hear
of less than a week, not a day less will satisfy her, and
six evenings with a prattling girl seemed an unmerited
punishment. Good-bye, dear books; good-bye, dear
friends, he cried, gathering up his books. The separation
is a hard one, but peace of mind is better than books;
without it books are of no avail. I shall return to you

as I once was, and never to part again, he added, as he
locked his books into a cupboard and fell into a chair,
himself seeming to himself the unhappiest man in the
world.

CHAP. II.

BUT time does not stand still, he said, starting from his
chair, because I am unhappy; I must hasten or I shall be
late for vespers. Now what can be keeping them? he
asked himself as he hastened up the rue des Chantres.
Argenteuil is but six miles from Paris, and they might
walk as many in a couple of hours if Madelon were not
so fat . . . like myself; and should they meet a cart on
the way back it will bring them hither in an hour and a
half. I shall find them for sure in the rue des Chantres
when I return.

And resting his head against the carvings of his stall,
which he could do without hurting himself, his hood
being comfortably padded, the Canon gave his thoughts
to the difference there would be between the present week
and the preceding week, and again between the present
week and the week that was to come. For Héloïse would
not stay more than a week with him. And a week's soon
over, he added thoughtfully within himself, as he left the
Cathedral, stopping to admire the outlines of the street,
as was his custom. Spreading, he said, into great bulk
as the houses ascend in overhanging, jutting storeys, an
architecture following the whims of the builders, telling
a varied tale that I never weary of reading. And his
thoughts going back to Roman times, he meditated that
if the Moderns had lost skill in literature they had acquired an architecture that was all their own. Virgil
would understand the beauty of my street, though the

peaked gables would seem strange to him at first; and he
could not help thinking that Virgil would like a certain
corner house with windows overlooking the street and
windows overlooking the Seine, however little it might
remind him of a Roman villa.   He began to count his
steps.   A dozen more and it will come into view, he said,
and was disappointed to find that he had miscalculated
the distance by three steps.   But never had his house
presented so charming an appearance as it did at this
moment, standing amid strong lights and shadows.   What
a pretty house, he muttered; prettier than I thought for;
and he remained for some moments forgetful of Héloïse,
lost in admiration of the cut-stone façade and the appearance of the balcony high up under the overhanging roof,
where Madelon dried her linen.   She has not a great
deal of washing this week, he said; and I hope the sheets
she will put upon Héloïse's bed will be aired.   But whatever her faults are, and they are many, she does not
forget these things.   They ought to be back by this from
Argenteuil; and he hastened up the flight of steps that
led to his house and kept it free from the Seine, which
in winter flowed into the street if the thaw was sudden.
At the top of the steps was the front door, and on pushing
it open the Canon found himself in a passage, and facing
him was the staircase leading to the first storey.   No
doubt Madelon is showing her round the house, and he
ran up the stairs.   No, she is not here, he said, looking
round the room known as the Canon's company-room.
They must be in the parlour.   And he hastened to the
room in which he had his meals and which served him
also as a sitting-room in the winter, fuel not being plentiful enough to have fires in more than two rooms.   No,
they are not here; she must have taken Héloïse into my
study.   And as he expected, he found Madelon and

Héloïse waiting for him in his study, having no more
than half-an-hour since returned from Argenteuil.

We have not touched your books, Canon, so there is no
reason to look round the room, Madelon cried, jumping
to her feet, a small Breton woman somewhere between
thirty and forty, nearer forty than thirty, a sack tied
in the middle with string, whose two rather witty little
eyes justified her sharp tongue and lighted up her brown
face so pleasantly that the low, ill-shaped forehead and
the coarse black hair dragged up from it were overlooked.
Nothing has been touched, we just sat down quiet as
two children in a story book; but I have been telling
Héloïse of your Latin books stored away in those cupboards. The Canon's face darkened, but Madelon, quite
undaunted, turned to Héloïse, saying: Thou seest how
black he is getting, but we are used to these little changes
in the rue des Chantres; thou mustn't let thine uncle
frighten thee; always remember that his bark is worse
than his bite. At which words the Canon's feet began
to move angrily, and thinking she had said enough Madelon hastened through the door leading from the Canon's
study into the kitchen. The Canon called her back, but
she did not heed the order; he was about to follow her,
but remembering suddenly that his niece was present,
he stopped. Madelon has been with me for many years,
so long that she forgets herself and speaks to me as
if—— A devoted servant, Héloïse interrupted, who
thinks of no one but you, uncle, so pray do not be angry
with her. Fulbert barely heard, for at that moment it
seemed to him that he could not bear any longer with
Madelon's familiarity. Insolent familiarity, he muttered,
and for a moment seemed of a mind to follow his servant
into the kitchen; and thinking that if he did so he would
take her by the arm and put her out of the house, Héloïse

said: Uncle, I have not been in your house half-an-hour, but you will not think it an impertinence if I tell you that Madelon's words are mere words, not worth a second thought. I have not been in your house—— caught the angry Canon's ear, and he stood looking at his niece, whom he was beginning to see, his anger having prevented him from seeing her till now. And half conscious of his rudeness in not speaking to her before, yet unable to command his thoughts, he stood looking at his almost forgotten niece, seeing in the first glance a small, thin girl, whose bright dark face, full of youth's pretty colouring, began to lessen his aversion for his visitor. It is easy to see why the nuns thought highly of her, he reflected; a wide brow and grey, wistful eyes that tell a taste for learning. But after speaking to her for a little while the thought came into his mind that her pale, spirit eyes told of something more than a taste for lessons, and he fell to thinking of his niece's thick brown hair combed into smooth braids and rolled into a knot above the nape of a fine upright neck, for this tire showed to advantage the line of a shapely head. He liked the long blue robe she wore, with sleeves tight at the wrists, and the satchel hanging by cords from an embroidered girdle, and an interest in his niece began to awaken in him. After speaking to her again for a little while a strange discrepancy in her face claimed his attention, her large, loose mouth not seeming to match her eyes. But whom does she take after? Her face droops at the chin like Philippe's and—— Madelon tells me that your closets are full of books. May I look at your books, uncle? Without waiting for an answer she danced rather than walked across the room and picked up a book that the Canon had overlooked. She breaks into speech like a bird, he said to himself, a ringing voice like her mother's, the same alert step; and he began to regret that he had made his niece's acquaintance after so many years in the midst of a sordid quarrel with Madelon, and to blot out any unfavourable opinion that she might have formed of him, he said: It is difficult to keep one's temper sometimes. Madelon at times—— Forget her, uncle, or you will lose your temper again. A reproof this was, and embarrassed he stood looking into Héloïse's far-away eyes. So thou hast come at last to the rue des Chantres, Fulbert said, and not sorry to leave thy convent for a while? What answer do you think I should make to you, uncle? Would it please you to hear that I was happy in the convent but am very glad to be in Paris with you and Madelon? What a pretty house you have. I had almost forgotten it, or had taken it all for granted more likely, for I was but a little thing when I came here one day with mother. Do you remember, uncle? Yes, I do, and it is odd that thou shouldst speak to me about my house, or rather it is not odd at all, for as I returned from the Cathedral it struck me as being a very pretty house. But has Madelon shown thee our company-room, or what was once a company-room? No, uncle; we have only just arrived. This room is my study, said Fulbert, and the room on the other side of this wall, the room off the hall, is the room in which I have my meals. Supper is at eight. I suppose thou wilt have supper with me, Héloïse? Héloïse restrained a smile, and the words that rose to her lips were: I suppose I shall, unless I am going to bed supperless. Come and I'll show thee the house, for I see that thou hast an eye for a house, he continued, speaking like one who desires to please. Two windows, she said, as they passed out of the study into the living-room; and both looking out on to the street. Without two windows the room would be very dark, the

Canon replied; but the windows in the convent are glazed, aren't they? And she answered: I think that more light comes through your glass than through ours. The words—through ours—reassured Fulbert and predisposed him to admire Héloïse as she ascended the stairs, and to foresee a future abbess in her. Her gait is too brisk, but time will correct that, he said to himself, and to her at the head of the stairs: Here is thy bedroom, niece; while thou'rt here, he added, and opened ι door, saying: Here is the company-room, or used to be, for of late years I find my books better company than my fellow-canons.

He expected her face to tell him that she must not wear out her welcome, but her face did not tell him anything; his hints passed unheeded or were not perceived enough to check her admiration of the really handsome room in which she found herself—a long room occupying the full length of the house, with a vast fireplace and chimney-piece, from which she withdrew her eyes reluctantly. On turning from the chimney-piece, walls stretched with a faded silk, old rose, met her eyes, and on raising her eyes she saw a ceiling prettily composed of gaily painted joists. You have a handsome room, uncle; and had I one like it I should never feel inclined to leave it; whereupon she passed her eyes over the furniture, which was spare, leaving plenty of space for the company to walk about. Oak chests that served as seats stood against the walls, and tall oak cupboards with long iron hinges and elaborate locks and keys interested and detained Héloïse, and when she turned from them it was to admire the great oaken table, with carved stools about it. And all this oak furniture was shining in the quiet light diffused through the round windows, filled in with thick glass like those in the room on the ground floor.

What room is this? Héloïse asked, going towards the door. A guest room, the Canon said; no one has slept in it yet, but if it be to thy taste—— I like my room at the head of the stairs, she answered, and walked over to the window that overlooked the Seine. Why, there is the Seine, and bordered with groves of willows and poplars almost like Argenteuil.

Paris was more like Argenteuil in my spring days, Fulbert replied; and they stood together at the window talking of the land on the right bank, now the Lombard quarter. It had gained that name from the number of Italian merchants who had settled there. May I have a table, a small one, uncle? See if you can spare me one, one that I can put in the window, for while I am with you I should like to read there. My house seems to have taken thy fancy, niece, Fulbert answered. It has, indeed, uncle, but may I have the table, and will you lend me your books to read? Lend my books! the Canon replied; young girls are not careful with books; and then he added, as if he did not wish to exhibit himself in too selfish a light on the day of her return from Argenteuil: We shall see; we shall see. Thou'rt fond of reading? I hear that speaking Latin and writing it come easy to thee, so the nuns tell me. Héloïse did not answer, for she was beginning to feel averse from her uncle, and the thought had just come into her head that if he would not lend her his books, she would ask Madelon to give her needles and wool and begin a piece of tapestry. But why should he think she would crumple the leaves of his books? Why speak of the nuns' praise of her Latin with contempt? She was beginning to dislike her uncle, and had resolved not to speak till he spoke to her, however long the silence. Goose, said he, as they descended the stairs. Dost smell it, niece? Yes, I can

indeed, Héloïse answered. Goose is an excellent bird
if properly cared for, the Canon replied, in a tone that
helped her to overlook his partial refusal to lend her his
books. An excellent bird, he repeated, as none knows
better than Madelon, who was a goose-girl in Brittany
before she came to live with your mother; and if we were
not so short of room, if we had a garden, we might keep
some poultry. It would amuse her to look after poultry,
and carry her thoughts back to days that have gone.
According to her the goose is rarely killed at the right
moment, when the fat is healthy and plentiful, but she
tries to make the best of the geese that the market
supplies, and the bird that comes so odoriferously from
underneath the door of my study has been hanging in
the larder under Madelon's special care for the last three
days, in the hope that thou'rt partial to goose, and of
all, that thou'lt not keep the bird waiting. I wonder,
uncle, if she would like me to go to the kitchen to help
her with the cooking? I don't think that she would
like it at all; she says it always tries her temper to have
anybody in the kitchen when she is preparing the dinner.
But Madelon and I, uncle—— Héloïse stopped on seeing her uncle's face darken, and to pass over an awkward
moment she said: I will spend the hour before dinner by
the river, watching the swallows floating up and down.

It must have been something in the temper of her voice
that reminded Fulbert that he was not receiving his niece
with the courtesy which she had a right to expect from
him, and to make amends he proposed that they should
go for a little walk before dinner. Dinner, he called to
Madelon, will not be ready for nearly an hour, and on
hearing that she hoped they would be back in three-
quarters, he said: We shall have time to walk to the
Cathedral and round the King's Gardens. But come

first to the river. So pleasant was the sunset that they walked bareheaded, admiring the stillness of the evening, unbroken except when a solitary rook flew overhead and cawed, or a long narrow leaf detached itself and fell through the branches of the willows into the stream. The Seine flows here almost silently, as it does at Argenteuil, said Héloïse; whispering as it goes by as if afraid that somebody should hear its secret. No river flows more silently: a deep, narrow stream, more suited for navigation than the Loire, the Canon answered her; however dry the summer may be there is water enough in the Seine for the biggest boats that come up to Paris; the Seine is the source of much wealth to Paris. It was the Seine that brought us the rich merchants, and he pointed to the Lombard quarter, which he had already shown her from the room in which she had asked if she might sit and read. Few of those houses were built before thy schooldays, Héloïse, if I remember right; others are building, the city is extending on both sides, and it is by the Little Bridge that hundreds of students come to the Cathedral cloister to attend lectures. The left bank is known as the Latin quarter; because of the bad Latin the students speak there, he added, laughing. And the bridge we are now standing on is known as the Great Bridge—you may remember it. It allows the merchants to come to our services at Notre-Dame without enduring the hardship of the ferry. But, said Héloïse, the right bank has two churches, Saint-Germains-l'Auxerrois and Saint-Gervais. The Canon smiled, Héloïse thought a little ironically, and after complimenting her upon her memory he spoke of the selfishness of the prelacy of these two churches. It is hardly to be believed, he said, that men could be so selfish, yet a great deal of opposition was raised to the building of

the bridge; the case of the ferryman was put forward,
but the cause at the back, the real opposition to the bridge,
was the fear that the bridge would rob the churches
yonder of their congregations, a fear (again Héloïse saw
the ironical smile appear upon her uncle's lips) that has
partly been justified by events. After all, uncle, the
churches yonder would like to retain their congregations.
Fulbert did not answer, and for some time they loitered
listening to the whispering river, watching its eddies
curling almost invisibly on the deep current, till that
sense of sadness inseparable from a river turned them
away from it, and they were glad to find themselves again
in the rue des Chantres.

The Canon drew his hood over his head and bade
Héloïse do likewise, and she admired the storeyed houses,
now so visible against the sky, and the purple-robed
ecclesiastics passing each other with ceremonious smiles
and salutes. Is the street as full at all times as it is
now? Héloïse asked. I never knew it quieter than it
is now, the Canon replied. In the morning the cries
of the tradespeople calling their wares keep one from
sleep if one is not accustomed to noise. A group of
students emerging suddenly from a wine-shop, singing and
shouting and falling over each other, rough gambols that
bewildered the peaceable passenger, provoked the Canon
into mild expostulation. All countries send their students
to us; Paris is becoming not only a centre of commerce
but also of learning; but our students are not only bois-
terous, they are dangerous at nightfall—— The anec-
dote which he was about to tell was interrupted by the
sudden appearance of Notre-Dame, a long, low, Romanesque church with round arches and twin towers, and
after expanding upon it in terms of admiration the Canon
said: Paris is not only the centre of commerce and

science; Paris is also the centre of Christianity, in one
sense more even than Rome, for it was we that gathered
an army to send into Palestine to win the Sepulchre of
Our Lord from the Infidel. England came to the aid
of Christendom later. Paris is the birthplace of ideas,
he added, and they stood at gaze, seeing a city of a
thousand cries projecting its grey profile into the sunset;
a multitude of towers and spires and thronging roofs
above streets so narrow that they were already in
twilight. Paris has many churches, Héloïse said; I see
them all around me. Not so many churches as cries,
the Canon answered; but no city equals Paris in the
beauty and the number of the churches that we see from
where we stand. Grouped about Notre-Dame like chickens
about a hen, Héloïse said, and approving the remark, the
Canon compared the long, narrow island to the carcass
of a stranded ship. And Héloïse said: But why stranded,
uncle? For since commerce and science are collected in
Paris it were surely a pity to represent Paris as a wreck.
As a ship at anchor then, he answered, with a slight irritation in his voice, which Héloïse interpreted to mean
that for the future she must not call his similes in question. To atone for her indiscretion she begged of him
to tell her the names of the churches on the left bank,
and whither led the Little Bridge. He answered that
it led to the Abbey of Sainte-Geneviève. How nobly, she
said, it crowns the hill-top. In the plain about the hill
the students find lodgings, for the city cannot contain
them all, the Canon said; and they come into Paris by
this bridge to attend the lectures of Champeaux, the
great Realist, and Abélard, who—— But that is another
matter and one that would lead us from the pleasant
contemplation of our churches. In the morning the air
is alive with their bells, like larks singing aloft, I have

often thought. The bells of Saint-Germains-l'Auxerrois and Saint-Gervais answer the bells of Notre-Dame, and the bells of Notre-Dame answer again, and in the distance are heard the bells of the old Abbey of Saint-Germains des Prés; nor is that all, for out of the dim west comes to us in the still morning the sound of the bells of the church of Saint-Victor; many other churches, too—fifteen in all. ' But it seems to me now, Héloïse, that if we remain talking about churches any longer we shall hear complaints from Madelon that all the trouble she has taken with the goose in thine honour has been wasted. The churches are tokens to every eye that Paris is a centre of religion, and having said that, Héloïse, let us return to our goose, for in this world little things are often as important as great; indeed, sometimes great things would not be accomplished without the help of little things, so let us give thanks for our goose.

And Héloïse, finding a cheerfulness in her uncle that she had not suspected, began to hope that her visit to Paris might not prove a failure after all. Let that be as might be, the goose awaited them and hunger indisposed them from further chatter as they walked through the crowd of prelates and clerks that still filled the rue des Chantres.

We have not stayed away longer than we said we would, the Canon cried, throwing open the kitchen door. You have come back none too soon, Madelon answered. And none too late; I wouldn't say that five minutes earlier—— But five minutes to a goose—— answered the Canon. Five minutes to a goose is as much as five minutes to a man, Madelon replied; and for Héloïse, who may not enjoy goose as much as we do, I should have liked to have had a plate of gudgeons, but if something isn't done to catch those glittering birds for ever flying up and down the river, we shan't know a plate of gudgeons when we see them.

Héloïse and I have no stomach for anything but the goose, so bring it quickly and tell us what thy tart is. If gudgeons are so rare that there are seldom any in the market, Madelon answered, we have a finer share of honey this year than for many a year past; the bees have been good to us if no one else has. The bees have always been good to men, the Canon answered, in the days of the great Virgil as to-day. He praised bees as no man has ever praised them before. And would have praised them again were he here to share with you the tart I have prepared for you, honey and cream, cream as good as I have ever whipped. Now what do you be saying to my goose? she asked, her little short arms akimbo on her podgy hips, seeming to relish the goose as much as the Canon and his niece, who both had their mouths full. Be sure to fill thy mouth very full, niece, said the Canon, else thou'lt fail to get the taste of it. It is good, Madelon, as good as thyself, which is saying much. The Canon has returned to his humour, Madelon answered. The bird eats tender, don't he? and Héloïse, after her long journey, must be hungry; so am I. Argenteuil and back is a long journey for the day, and my teeth will fasten lovingly on what you leave behind of that goose. We shall leave plenty, the Canon answered. But I don't see thee drinking, Héloïse; and the goose must not allow us to forget the wine. Madelon filled their cups and said: Now is there anything that you want? You have bread enough, and don't neglect my spinach, for it was cooked in the finest butter, and the cauliflower too. I have done my best, but the best is not much when one has been away three parts of the day backwards and forwards to Argenteuil. All the same, I hope my supper will not fall short of the suppers they gave thee in the convent. Ah, they look after their bellies in those convents! and I must look to my honey tart. In a few minutes she was back again, the tart in her hands, proud of the show that it made on the table. I see my goose has received a hearty welcome from you both, but two legs remain, which will do well for Madelon, and there are pickings elsewhere. I am as hungry as you were, and will run away with the goose. Madelon's pastry is excellent, the Canon said, his eyes filled with memories of tarts eaten in the years gone by. Hast thou ever eaten a better one? How flaky it is; wilt have some more? Héloïse would have liked a second helping, but she thought her uncle might like a third, and conquered the temptation. There are nuts on the table, and apples and pears, but there is no fruit like grapes. Look at this bunch, the small, white sweet-water grapes that grow nowhere but in France; these have come up from Fontainebleau. And when each had finished a great bunch he said: They eat well, don't they? Bread and grapes go well together, and none bakes better than Madelon. Do you always sup like to-day, uncle? Héloïse asked, and the Canon answered somewhat tartly that the supper she had eaten was prepared for her: Let us go upstairs, he said.

So that he might better consider Madelon's supper, the Canon lay back in his chair outstretched, his toes in the air, his fat, heavy hands clasped over his belly, and Héloïse bethought herself of his books as a safe subject for discussion, to be broached as soon as he was rested. He is not yet done with his supper, she said to herself, for the Canon had just roused himself from his chair and was returning to it from the table, whither he had gone for a handful of nuts and a tankard of wine;

and he sat cracking and skinning the nuts and drinking large draughts in silence, till Héloïse began to think it would be wise for her to plead the fatigue of her journey and ask leave to retire to her room. Once more the Canon rose, and returning from the table to her, a full tankard in his hand, he began, to her very great surprise, to talk to her of her mother. Thou'rt like her in many ways, he said: in thy voice and gait. Jeanne was a good woman, he muttered, half to Héloïse and half to himself; a good woman, a very good woman. Wives usually love their husbands, but my mother loved hers more deeply than many women, and sacrificed all things to marry father. The words passed her lips incontinently, and no sooner were they gone from her than she held her breath, frightened, remembering that Madelon had told her that she must not speak of her father. So it was to her great surprise, and to his own, that Fulbert began to talk of his brother, like one whose mind has been relieved of a great weight. It seemed as if he almost enjoyed talking of Philippe, or was it, she asked herself, that he could not do else but tell me of my father, or is it the wine that has loosened his tongue? Indifferent as to the cause of her uncle's sudden loquacity, she listened eagerly to his telling of her family history, that some twenty years ago the Comte and Comtesse of an old Breton family came to him, Canon Fulbert, to ask him if he knew any doctor who would go and live in Brittany in special attendance on Madame la Comtesse, who was in delicate health. A valetudinarian is my wife, he said, and I answered him truthfully that the only doctor I knew was my own brother, a young man of great repute, one excellently well learned in every branch of his craft, but a young man who was once, I was careful to add, fond of hunting and falconry.

These sports are out of his mind long since, so you need
not be afraid that—— And while I was looking for
the words the Comte found them for me: Afraid that
your brother will be distracted from his duty towards
the Comtesse by his love of hunting? Something of that
kind was in my mind, no doubt, Comte, but—— I can't
recall what answer I made the Comte, but I am sure
he answered me: Your brother will be able to combine
both science and sport, for in our forests there are
wolves and boars, and I have hounds and peregrine
falcons and goshawks in great number. Your brother
will be appreciated by us both, Canon Fulbert, he said,
for the Comtesse likes to hear that she is not so ill as
she thinks she is from time to time. A woman's imagination, you know, Canon; the confessional must have taught
you much about women. That is how he spoke, and
I told him that Philippe was fond of singing and playing the lute. Better and better, the Comte said, for
the Comtesse loves music. I must meet your brother.
It was not in the course of things that I should say nay
to the Comte; but I could not put aside the thought that
if Philippe were to follow the Comte to Brittany the
end of it would be—— I didn't know what the end
would be, but scented danger, as well I might, Philippe
being a young man and the Comtesse still a young
woman, not yet forty. So I sought to dissuade him, saying that he would not be wise to abandon his patients
for a sinecure; and many other things of the same kind
I said, but to no avail. And now that I come to consider
it after many years it seems to me that the Comte could
not have failed to take heed of my warning if he had not
been what he was, a feeble man, altogether in his wife's
power and blind to the danger I foresaw, which was not
long in coming, for very soon, at the end of the year, it

was plain to everybody that the Comtesse was in love
with Philippe. But thy father, Héloïse, was not of the
shameless sort who eat a man's bread and betray him
with his wife, and from what fell out afterwards it's
easy to guess how hard Philippe's life must have been
in the Castle, lute-playing and hawking with the Comtesse, always by her side, and her private physician at
home, consulting upon ailments that did not exist and
having to close his eyes to the one ailment which he
could cure, her love of him. Philippe would have fallen
—for sooner or later a man is bound to fall to a woman
if she persists and no other woman comes to save him.
The woman that came to save Philippe, Héloïse, was
thy mother, the Comtesse's own daughter. Now whether
thy mother knew of the passionate story unravelling
day by day before her eyes, or whether it was for love
of thy father or a desire to save her mother, we shall
never know. My belief is that woman never loved a
man more truly than thy mother loved her husband and
that she knew nothing of her mother's shameless passion.
The Coetlogons are great nobles, and my brother would
not have spoken to Jeanne of his love for her had he not
been told that he would be accepted. I don't know from
whom he had the news, and it is no great matter; enough
that he learnt it and that the marriage took place in a
forest in a hermit's hut. Once married always married
(thou knowest that, Héloïse, for thou'rt well brought up),
but thy grandmother didn't think like that, not she, but
of revenge only, and thy mother was put out of the
Castle in the gown she wore and no money in the pocket.
The Canon could not continue the story without going
to the table for more wine, and when he came back he
began to tell of the lovers' journey to Paris on foot and
their arrival at his house. A poor creature thy grand-

father, Héloïse, never daring to say nay to his wife, and
believing her story, the old story of Potiphar's wife.
This is how it was, and the Duke of Brittany, Huet IV.,
to please the Comte expelled thy father from the duchy.
Not altogether a bad man, the Duke, for when thou wast
born, Héloïse, he tried for a reconciliation. Thy grand-
father would fain have seen his daughter and his grand-
child, but thy grandmother couldn't forgive; a hard
woman, Héloïse, thy grandmother was, a harlot at heart
and in practice, too, and cruel in her lust. The Coetlogons, said she, that marry beneath them are no longer
worthy of the name.

Thy mother proved herself a true Coetlogon by never
complaining of her poverty, and—listen to me, Héloïse
—I don't believe she ever looked across the table at
thy father putting the question to herself: Was Philippe
worth the sacrifice that I made for him? A good woman,
as good as any I have known, who parted from her husband, when he joined the standard to rescue the Holy
Sepulchre from the Infidel, telling him to go and do his
duty, not an easy thing for a woman to say to a man
like Philippe. Ah! to do one's duty; I tried to do mine
by thee, Héloïse, and hope that I did it. Now what was
I saying? We were standing by this window watching
the Seine flowing past, an emblem of our lives, when Philippe came to bid me good-bye; for, my dear Héloïse, we
are but eddies in a great current; thou'rt too young to
have thought of these things, but as we get on in life . . .
Ah, well, thy father and I loved each other. Be to them
as if they were thine own, he seemed to say. Why he
didn't speak the words I have no means of knowing;
why should I? for thou must see that the emotion of
parting with one's brother is beyond words, and we
parted without many words, never to see each other

again. That is as God willed it. I loved thy father
so dearly that it was painful to me to hear his name
spoken; my friends respected my grief, it was never
spoken in my presence, nor by me till now. And it was
lest it might not be his will to see thee an abbess and
head of a great community that I sent for thee, though
I may be wronging my brother by thinking such a thing.
A good Catholic, thy father, good son of the Church,
laid down his life for it. Three learned women had
joined the convent of Argenteuil, the Prioress, Mother
Ysabeau and the nun that had a baby three years ago——
her name has slipped out of my head—— Sister Paula,
Héloïse interrupted. The Canon acquiesced that it was
of her he was thinking. And my hope, he said, has
always been that thou shouldst discover in thyself a
vocation for the religious life, that I was doing thy
father's will in sending thee to Argenteuil. But one is
never sure one is doing right; my point is——

They could hear the low ripple of the Seine going by,
and Fulbert did not break the silence, hoping that Héloïse
would break it with the words: Uncle, I have found the
vocation that you would have me find, and hope that
you will live long after I have been elected Prioress of
the convent of Argenteuil. But Héloïse said nothing,
and after trying to read her thoughts through her eyes
the Canon continued: It may be thou hast not heard
that it was thy father who pointed out the Spear to
Raymond and jumped into the trench saying: all
wounds shall be cured by its touch and all evils disappear. I didn't know that my father was the finder of
the Spear, and am overjoyed. The news that it was
being brought to France in a ship reached the convent;
we have often spoken about it as we sat at our work in
the cloister. Asking thyself, perchance, Héloïse, why

thine uncle never came to see thee, never sent thee a letter, and to all appearances had forgotten thee? No, uncle. Sometimes I did think it strange, but I think that I always knew that there were reasons. I'm glad of that, Héloïse; my anxiety to see thee a great abbess, perhaps of Sainte-Geneviève or some greater convent, kept me away, and the nuns writing to say that thou wast their best pupil; and perhaps I thought too much of thee as a great abbess, mayhap was too ambitious for thee.

And so he talked on, saying things that he would wish to have left unsaid, but he could not help speaking, though he felt that by saying these things he was putting to the hazard all his fine schemes for her welfare. But since he had sent for her she must be allowed to choose between the world and religion, and that was why he must speak to her of the nobles who came up to Paris from the provinces at Easter. But Easter is six months hence, Héloïse interjected, and the Canon could find no more subtle answer than: Quite true, I had forgotten. To retrieve his mistake he added: But at Easter thou'lt return hither if thou'rt in doubt, and, my dear Héloïse, believe me, it shall be according to thy good wishes whether thou shalt accept or reject the world. But if I return to the convent I hope you will not be kept away by scruples lest I should be tempted to say: Uncle, have me back in the rue des Chantres. It has often seemed to me that I could do well enough in the religious life as it is practised in the convent at Argenteuil, for one is detached there from the world more than it is her lot to be. The Canon was tempted to ask in what measure the nuns were detached from life, but he was beginning to notice a certain thickness in his speech and that his tongue ran away with him, so to speak. It might be that he had drunk more wine

than usual, or it might well be that Madelon had substi-
tuted a headier wine than he was used to, in honour of
Héloïse's return, without warning him; and a little annoyed with himself, and perhaps a little with Madelon, he
began to speak of the fatigue of the journey to Argenteuil. Madelon has been there and back and has already
gone to bed. What thinkest thou, niece——? His eyelids fell over his eyes. He is asleep, she said, and
began to ask herself what she should do in the event of
his not awakening. As she sat considering whether
she should sit and watch by him or steal away to her
bed, his eyelids raised themselves slowly and he started
to his feet. It must be bedtime; Héloïse forgive me
if I seemed to have fallen asleep; it was but an appearance. I heard thine every word. Good-night to thee.
Héloïse, I have had a long day's work at the Cathedral,
a great deal of unnecessary work, for So-and-so (I cannot
remember his name for the moment, but it doesn't matter,
I am too sleepy to think). I was saying—— Don't
trouble, uncle, to fatigue your brain. No, no, it's no
fatigue, I'll get it out; that fellow likes work for its
own sake, a thing that I hope I shall never do. But I
have enjoyed my evening. Yes, I have; I'm telling thee
that I've enjoyed my evening. We shall still see each
other again, so perhaps it's just as well not to say everything, to leave something over for to-morrow evening.
To-morrow thou'lt tell me about the books they gave thee
to read.

CHAP. III.

AFTER helping her uncle downstairs to his bedroom
Héloïse returned to hers at the top of the stairs, perplexed by the reasons her uncle gave her for never

having been to see her and by his refusal to lend her
his books. She lay awake thinking what manner of man
he was, only to forget him in the sway of a sudden memory
of her mother's romantic marriage to a young physician,
and her thoughts returning from Palestine to Brittany
she recalled her memories of her father, associating him
with many little facts that she had heard from her
uncle, his love of falconry and his love of her mother,
a Coetlogon. As the story came from her uncle's lips
she had barely apprehended its meaning, but now lying
in her bed it became clear to her; it was nothing less
than a mother coming between her daughter and her
daughter's lover, striving to undo love with lust. How
terrible! And failing in her wicked endeavour, this
woman, her grandmother, had never ceased to avail herself of the great influence of the Coetlogons against her
father, driving him in the end out of France to Palestine,
and no doubt rejoicing in his death. How terrible!
And then her thoughts passing from these sins of long
ago she began to ask herself if she were her mother's
true daughter, or set more store than her mother had done
on the lineage and the power of the Coetlogons. She had
barely heard the name before this evening and knew no
more of them than that she was allied on her mother's side
to this great family. For her mother had not told her
the story, out of shame, no doubt. Was she less spirited
and adventurous than her mother? She knew nothing
of herself, but that she was good at her lessons, and
fell to thinking in a sudden mood of sadness that if the
nuns had heard her uncle's story they would have gone
away chuckling, asking if a mother and a daughter were
ever more different. One runs out of a castle to marry
her lover in a forest, the other prefers a pile of books
o all else. She was sure that that was what the nuns

would have said if they had heard the story, and the old
joke would have been put on her again, that she couldn't
go to the village to see Sister Paula's baby, so deep was
she in St. Augustine. But she had not said anything of
the kind and had been to the village to see the baby once,
which was enough, for she couldn't find time always to
be running to the village and was as weary of the baby
as of the joke, and sometimes thought that all this talk
about the baby was worse than having one. A curiosity
about the baby's father possessed them all; even the
school children in her charge had begun to ask her questions: Had the baby been found under a gooseberry bush,
or was it a currant bush? Her thoughts ran on incontinently, all the talk of the children coming up in her mind.
Will you tell us, Héloïse, who found the baby? Everybody says it was Sister Paula, and if she found it does
not the baby belong to her much more than it does to
the Prioress or the Sub-Prioress? Nuns, she answered,
do not have babies. And the children replied: Why do
nuns not have babies? Because nuns say their prayers
and have learned their lessons well, she said, not knowing what else to say, but rued her words, for the children
began very soon afterwards to make a false application
of them, thinking, perchance, that if they said their
prayers thoughtlessly and failed to learn their lessons
they, too, would find babies under the gooseberry bushes
in the garden.

It was very unfair of the nuns to think that she was
not like her mother, but merely an earnest girl who was
fond of her books, caring to match St. Augustine's Latin
against St. Jerome's more than for anything else, and
to argue by the hour with Sister Josiane whether rhymed
Latin was more beautiful than unrhymed. She had
thoughts for these things and always would have. Why

not indeed? For it was no shame surely to strive after a good Latinity. Surely not. Nor did it follow that because she didn't care to gossip about Sister Paula's baby, she might not outdo her mother's adventure in the forest if it befell her to meet a man like her father; and then contrasting her mother's marriage with Sister Paula's sin, she fell to thinking that Sister Paula's baby was a mere fact, like her uncle's tipsiness. Nuns did not drink as much as priests, but even nuns were different after wine from what they were before; nor was her uncle the first prelate to drink too much wine, nor would he be the last, nor was Sister Paula the first woman to transgress the moral law. And turning over restlessly on her pillow she asked herself if Sister Paula was going to keep her awake all night. And folding her arms and closing her eyes she availed herself of all the known devices to bring sleep. The sheep were counted as they jumped through the gap, and she tried to put a spell upon her brain with the words: go to sleep, go to sleep, go to sleep. But sleep seemed farther than ever from her eyelids, and she caught herself thinking again of Sister Paula, saying to herself that she hoped the Sister would not transgress again and that the baby's father would repent; she hoped, too, that her uncle would repent, and not drink too much wine again, and said a prayer that he might be given strength to keep himself from it.

A few minutes later she caught herself thinking that she would prefer him to give way to wine rather than that he should refuse to lend her his books. For why had he done this? she asked herself, in a tone that was almost one of anguish, adding that I would turn down the leaves and soil them. Now why did he say such hurtful things of one of whom he knew nothing? Would it not have been better for him to allow her to read and watch her, and at the slightest sign of carelessness to take the book out of her hand?

And it was while grieving over her uncle's unjust suspicions of her care for books that she fell asleep. On awaking it seemed to her that she must have been asleep for a long while. But the room was dark, so she could not have been asleep more than an hour or two. Some noise in the house had awakened her, and she lay listening eagerly, afraid that a robber was within doors, that somebody was on the stairs. At last the awful silence was broken. Was somebody coming in or was it merely her clothes falling from the chair on which she had thrown them? Sounds seemed to come from every side, and in the streets voices came nearer and then died away; voices collected and then divided. Was she in dream or in reality? She did not know, and as the dream dissolved she lay staring through the darkness of the room, unable to escape from an extraordinary mental clarity in which everything was written so clearly that she seemed to have been blind until this night. She understood now why her uncle had put her into a convent as soon as her mother died, and that he had never come to see her so that she might be forced to take the veil. She could not believe, yet she must believe, for there it was written on the wall, and frightened literally out of her senses she recalled how a few hours ago she was reading in the convent library when the news was brought to her that Madelon was waiting in the parlour. She expected a cake and some fruit, for it was autumn, but Madelon brought neither, only the strange news that her uncle wished her to come to Paris for a week's visit, and when she asked for a reason, Madelon answered: I can see there is no thought in thee for Paris. Now why had Madelon said this?   And why had her uncle sent Madelon for her without writing to the nuns? He must have some purpose in view, and Madelon must know of it.   And why had Madelon not told her? Was her old nurse, whom she had known always, going to betray her? It looked like it.   And she felt like a trapped animal, without power to escape from her uncle and Madelon. And why had Madelon's face changed when she said she was sorry to leave her reading? Some plan was in her mind. Were they about to force her into an abhorrent marriage? Perhaps! And Héloïse was so frightened that it was only the silence of the house that kept her in bed. She would have run into the street, she thought, but she did not dare face the staircase and the shadows about the doorways, but lay listening and remembering that Madelon had promised to come to her room to see her before she went to bed, to hear what she had thought of her uncle, to talk things over with her. But Madelon hadn't come. Why hadn't she come?

She turned from the right to the left side without ridding herself of the nightmare till at last sleep fell upon her.   It fell deeply, and when she opened her eyes Madelon was standing beside her. Did I wake thee? I am sorry, for thou must be tired after coming all the way from Argenteuil. Héloïse tried to answer, but she could not recall the circumstances to remembrance. Sleep out thy weariness, she heard Madelon say, but she called her back to the bedside. Do not go, I am not sleepy any longer. I didn't hear thee come into the room but just awoke of myself. The sun coming into the room must have awakened me; the room is light and a great part of the morning must have gone. I came to ask if I might bring thee a glass of wine and a biscuit before I go out marketing, Madelon answered. But may I not go with thee and see the shops and learn the prices? Madelon said she could. And a great help it will be to me to escape the marketing, as I shall do if thou shouldst stay with us and learn the prices. Call to me when thou hast washed thyself and I'll come and help thee with thy dressing, for to do it will be like old times again.

An hour later they were in and out of the shops like bees among flowers, talking of the price of provisions, which had gone up alarmingly, a fine chicken costing as much as threepence—as much as a sheep in the days gone by in Brittany, Madelon was saying, as they returned home through the thronging streets, excited by the pleasant air full of sunshine and thrills. . . . Now the nuns are walking in their convent garden finding young spiders weaving glittering threads from spray to spray, Héloïse said. And I'll warrant startling the ring-doves out of the winter wheat—terrible ravagers of crops, Madelon replied. Why, there's the Canon, looking up at the peaked gables as usual. So it is, Héloïse replied, and raising her eyes she admired the gables showing aloft against the autumn sky. Shining, she said, like—— Like newly varnished paint, Madelon answered, and began to complain that the Canon never wearied of gaping and gazing up and down the street. See him now, his eyes wandering from balcony to balcony. So you went out without your milk, Madelon said, interrupting the Canon's dreams, and he heard from them of the high prices that had to be paid for food in the market. I didn't forget my milk, he said; my mouth was parched and I drank some water instead.

They returned home together, and leaving the Canon to his business in his study, Héloïse followed Madelon to the kitchen, saying that she would like to help her to get dinner ready. But thou'rt more thyself with a book in thy hands than washing vegetables with me. Maybe so, Madelon, Héloïse answered, and then a second thought prompted the words: but not always; I like house work and have done some in the convent. Thou'lt find me handy. We'll come to understand each other better before long, Madelon said. Dost think we shall, Madelon? Héloïse asked, and the tone of her voice was cheerful, implying a hope that in time she might come to understand her uncle better, if she did not return to the convent. I don't know why he doesn't give thee the key of his library, Madelon said, breaking the silence. Thou wouldst not harm his books, if I know thee at all, and who should know thee better than myself? Héloïse asked Madelon where the scullery was, an excuse to avoid committing herself to an opinion, and the Breton woman guessing, as an animal guesses, that Héloïse did not wish to say whether she liked her uncle or disliked him and was waiting for ideas about herself —not knowing if her instinct led her to the cloister or to the world—put no questions to her. Poor child, how should she know her road, having come from a convent only yesterday, where all is different, she said to herself, as the peel of the last apple fell into the bowl. The talk turned upon last year's crop of apples, and Héloïse enjoyed her morning's work, and would have preferred to dine with Madelon in the kitchen, but that could not be. She must face her uncle, of whom she was now afraid. But during dinner he asked her questions that were pleasant to answer. What Latin had she read? We have read all the Fathers. When I say we, uncle, I mean myself and some three or four nuns. I am afraid that there are not many pages in St. Augustine that would not prove a stumbling-block to the greater number

of our community.   So St. Augustine presents difficulties
to the majority of the convent—— the Canon began, and
afraid that he was about to speak contemptuously of the
nuns of Argenteuil before Madelon (who was bringing in
the apple-dumpling at that moment), Héloïse began to
speak in Latin, fetching, she could see, a darkness into
Madelon's face, for she liked to share in the conversation
as a listener, sometimes contributing to it herself.   She
did not like being cut off from communication, looking
upon herself as part of the family.   But any blame cast
upon the nuns at Argenteuil would be painful to Héloïse,
so she continued in Latin, astonishing her uncle, who, forgetful of the nuns at Argenteuil and their ignorance, broke
in suddenly: but thy Latin is excellent, niece; now how
was it that we have been speaking jargon till this minute?
A question that Héloïse avoided answering, ingeniously
saying that she was thinking of Virgil and had dropped
into Latin accidentally.   We shall speak Latin henceforth together, said the Canon.   In Latin I shall have to
say thou to you, uncle.   The second person is without
importance in Latin, and he began to praise the nuns
for having taught his niece the language of Virgil and
Cicero so thoroughly, saying that he would write to
thank them for their learning and assiduity.   And thy
script must be as good as thy speech, I can tell that
without seeing it, he said, and asked her what her reading
had been outside of Augustine and Jerome, what poetry
she had read.   She answered Prudentias.   A worthy man,
the Canon said.   By the word worthy expressing thy
contempt, Héloïse answered.   But why is he contemptible?
And she began to compare him with Augustine, asking
if there were not beautiful things in Augustine, recalling
to his mind a celebrated passage in which the Saint
stands at a window overlooking the Tiber.   Well enough,

well enough, the Canon replied, for one who lived after
the Roman prime, but bearing traces of his indebtedness
to Plotinus and his school; for you know that St.
Augustine was a convert, if not to Christianity at least
to the only true Church. There are beautiful things in
the *Confessions*, no doubt, but—— But what, uncle? And
why standest thou looking at me with wondering eyes?
I am thinking, the Canon said, that thou'rt fortunate
indeed not to have read the divine Virgil, for what
wouldn't I give to have my first reading of Virgil before
me instead of behind me. But Virgil is never behind one,
there is always new beauty to be discerned in him. But
why divine, uncle? It might have been better, Héloïse,
if I had said the blessed Virgil, for besides being the
great poet of all times, past and present, Virgil knew by
the light of his own genius that the Redeemer was to
be born unto us. And he recited the prophetic passage,
saying that he did not see how it could be held to be else
than God-inspired. Yet to admit a pagan among the
prophets is hardly orthodox, he added, his thoughts almost
away, and Héloïse did not speak, afraid to disturb her
uncle's meditation. When she asked him of what he was
thinking he answered that he was thinking of the great
store of delight in the cupboards for her, comparing the
room to a hive filled with honey, layer upon layer of
honeycombs; and going to one of the cupboards, he lifted
down his books with absurdly careful hands and placed
them before her on the table. Come, sit by me, and I'll
show them to thee: here are Virgil, Ovid, Horace, Tibullus,
Cicero, Seneca. Never to have read Virgil! O Héloïse,
what joy awaits thee! Eclogues! Æneid! Georgics! At
which end wilt thou begin? With the story of Dido, doubtless. But if I shall find so much pleasure in this literature, why is it locked away in cupboards? Héloïse asked.

And walking up and down the room he told her that he
had foreseen in her visit but six evenings of silly chatter.
But the convent wrote, uncle, that I was advanced in
learning for my age. The talk of nuns, he replied, is of
little weight. But since thou'rt speaking Latin with me,
and good Latin, my books are thine for the time that
thou'rt with me. But be careful of them; do not turn
down the leaves; read with clean hands. Now, with which
wilt thou begin? With Virgil, the divine Virgil, Héloïse
cried, and receiving the volume from him she opened it,
and his face lighting up with pleasure, he walked to and
fro, saying: how strangely things come about. I thought
to listen to a girl's babble every evening and I have come
upon one who speaks Latin, a slightly battered Latin,
it is true, but still a language that Virgil would have
understood. Making wry faces, perchance, as he listened
to us, Héloïse answered, raising her head from the book.
How beautiful it is; may I go on reading, uncle? Yes, go
on reading; I have stayed too long talking to thee. But,
uncle, thou'lt instruct me? Translate this for me. The
meaning of the passage is, the Canon said: Dost think
the ashes of thy husband or his buried shade care for thy
desolation? But buried shade is a strange expression,
said Héloïse. Virgil, the Canon answered, had a more
lively sense of man's soul than any other writer of his
time; he knew it to be different from the body, of an
ethereal substance, if substance be not a wrong word to
use in connection with the soul. But to-day I am expected
early at the Cathedral; give me the book to put away.
To-morrow thou shalt find it ready for thee as soon as
thou returnest from market and thy work be done in the
house, for I would not have Virgil come between thee
and thy work, lest Madelon be annoyed. Héloïse promised him that her thoughts would be on her marketing

till midday; I will not come hither till the day's work
is finished. My work is finished for to-day, she said,
holding out her hand to receive back the precious volume.
But I should like to see thee in the Cathedral this afternoon, and Madelon too, who has come to tell me that
I must hasten if I would not be late for vespers, would
do well to accompany us.

Now, Canon, it is always the same with you, no change,
always the same, the sturdy and courageous little Breton
replied. After doubts and fears lest you might disturb
your niece's vocation you sent for her, but instead of
leaving the poor child at home to read, you want to take
her to the Cathedral for your own pleasure. If she is
only to be here for a few days why not let her enjoy
them in her own fashion, according to her whim? Her
whim is reading, like your own. Madelon, I will not
have thee come, as I have told thee before many times——
Told me what, Canon? Giving advice that is not asked
for. But you are always asking my advice, Canon, and
though you do not always like it, you often take it. And
now let the poor child have her read and go yourself
to the Cathedral and let me look after the supper; which
I swear will be to your taste this evening. Now what is
it going to be? the Canon asked, and they went down
talking amiably, leaving Héloïse with the volume in her
hand, eager to read in the pleasant company-room, by its
window overlooking the river, the soft airs coming up
through the willow-trees, tossing her hair as she sat, won
almost at once by the romantic story of the Trojan who
fled with his comrades in a galley while Troy was still
smoking, to meet with many adventures by sea and
land, in deserts and in caves, before arriving in Carthage
to love Dido yet abandon her in obedience to the gods,

who bade him depart for Italy, their will being the
greatest and the world's need being Rome.

And for long hours Héloïse sat reading, and was
soothed by Virgil's evident sorrow for Dido, even though
the gods had bidden the flight of Æneas for their great
purposes. Even a goddess pities her, she said, Iris, her
wings showing a thousand colours in the sun as she wheels
above the smoke of the pyre, preparing to liberate the
soul from the body. But to give way like this is silly,
she said, and after a brief effort to master her feelings
she rose to her feet, and after walking back and forth
she said: I must go and speak to somebody. And descending the stairs, she talked with Madelon, telling her the
story she had been reading, to which Madelon gave all
the attention she could spare from the vegetables. But
such casual attention did not satisfy Héloïse's enthusiasm
and, disappointed, she returned to the window overlooking the Seine; and unable to take up the book again, she
fell to thinking instead of the poet whom Christianity
unites with paganism to honour, trying to conclude that
Christianity had prepared the world for a better understanding of Virgil than any he had found in the century
he lived in, and reasoning gently with herself but never
to be convinced of it. For it seemed to her easier to
believe that the world was returning whence it came,
not to paganism but to a sympathy with our life in this
world, which we would do well to lead without repining;
and her eyes returning to the page, she reread how Iris,
with her wings showing a thousand colours in the sun,
descended to liberate the soul from the body. But why
liberate the soul from the body? she asked, since the two
are inseparable as we know them; and putting this question of liberation aside, she gave thanks to Virgil for his
recognition of the soul, more intimate than of any other

pagan writer. But why consider the soul or the body?
The beauty of Latin itself is enough, she said, and sat
asking herself why Virgil's skies and seas should please
her more than St. Augustine's exordiums of faith; and
little by little she fell to thinking that though the decrees
of the ancient gods seemed hard to Virgil they were less
stern in his mind than St. Augustine's conception of his
duty to Christ, till forgetful of gods and goddesses,
she said: the language he writes is born of his subject.
His story is of the world's beauty, of the skies by day
and night and of the seas, and of the heroes, who, returning from Troy in the galleys, were driven almost on
the coasts where the Cyclops would have devoured them
had not a man, worn with uttermost hunger and of piteous
mien, stretched suppliant hands to them from the shore
and told them that he was a man of Ithaca, a luckless
companion of Ulysses, left behind when Ulysses escaped
with his band from the ogre's cavern. Nor had he done
speaking when the ogre came down from the mountain,
followed by his flocks, his only joy, guiding himself to
the well-known shore with his staff, a young pine-tree
lately lopped, and began to wash his wound. But the
splashing of the oars reached his ears and he strode into
the sea seeking the galley, and not finding it he let off
a mighty roar, rousing the Cyclops till they rushed to
the harbour and thronged the shores.

Héloïse sat thinking, asking herself if it were all true.
If in the old time Cyclops haunted the Sicilian coasts;
if Polyphemus ate human flesh; if Ulysses drove out
his single eye with a stake hardened in the fire; asking
herself if the story were a fable or if life had changed,
becoming smaller and meaner than it was. If there had
been Cyclops they must have left their bones behind.
But Troy was, Æneas loved Dido and left her to found

Rome in obedience to the will of the gods. Whereat she fell to seeking for the first time a meaning in life, asking herself whence it came and whither it went. She had accepted the daily doings of the convent as life and received the life she found in her uncle's house as thoughtlessly. The Canon went to the Cathedral and returned from it every morning, reminding her of her father, who started forth at the same hour day by day to see his patients. But Virgil put the thought into her mind that the hearth and the home were not the whole of life, and that another life followed the quiet, uneventful, religious and domestic life, with which she was acquainted, like a shadow, meeting it at every turn like a reflection. Was not her father a hero like Æneas when he enlisted in Raymond's army? Heroism was not over and done with, but Virgil's story of the fugitives from Troy kindled her imagination, and she could not tell whether the spell was one of language or a sudden sympathy for adventure. And she was so absorbed in her dream that neither the opening of the door nor her uncle's footsteps awakened her.

Héloïse, of what art thou thinking? She uttered a little cry. How thou didst frighten me, uncle! for I was far away in Carthage. Ah, but thou must read from the beginning and not skip, else thou'lt miss the chief beauty, the unfolding of the story, clouds rising out of clouds and melting into clouds. But there are no rules for reading. I begin at the beginning of a book and read line by line, and however tiresome the book may be I should have a scruple in laying it aside when halfway through. Each must love the Mantuan according to his mind, and read him, too, in the same accordance. But why, uncle, do we not write as the pagans wrote? On the subject of the difference between their Latin and the Latin of the

Roman poets there was much to say, and they talked till
it was time to go down to supper, and they descended
the stairs talking in Latin. Héloïse tried to turn the
conversation into jargon many times unsuccessfully, for
without noticing the change the Canon continued in Latin,
thinking intently of what he was eating and drinking
and casually of the evening he was going to spend with his
niece upstairs reading Latin, talking Latin, helping her,
perchance, with some construction foreign to Christian
Latin, saying: Come read me the passage aloud and
thou'lt understand it, and if that method did not prevail
and Héloïse still found the passage dark, going over to
her and standing behind her chair helping away the difficult constructions, his finger on the text and a word of
explanation on his tongue. Besides certain constructions
difficult for one unacquainted with the ancient language
there were the mythology and the ritual that Virgil has
made part of the poetic substance of his poem as much
as the story he tells; the story of Pentheus seeing two
suns and a double Thebes would have to be explained to
Héloïse, else she would lose a great part of the beauty
of the poem, and the dreams too of Dido in which Æneas
appears to her with cruel aspect and she is compared to
Pentheus or Orestes agitated by the Furies.

To talk of these things was always delightful to the
Canon and to tell her that all the Roman poets knew
Greek was an added pleasure, and when they went upstairs he watched her face lighting up and envied the
pleasures in store for her, for though Virgil was the
greatest of all poets, there were others, and he was fortunate to possess them all. She must remain with him
till she had read Virgil, Ovid and Tibullus. His thoughts
seemed to melt away, and to bring him back from his
dreams, whatever they might be, she asked him if the

stars know the destinies they bring. Most of the ancient poets and philosophers, he answered, thought they were animated beings with minds of moral intelligence, a mistake, no doubt, but—— But what, uncle? With the exception of Virgil, he replied, who may be regarded as a Christian prophet, we must not ask more of paganism than it can give; its gift is beauty. But thou'lt soon have learned all that I can teach thee; in another six months thou'lt have no questions to ask me. There was a little sadness in this, and Héloïse thought it well to say: In six months I shall understand Virgil's Latin, but he is not the only poet, and I have heard you say that Horace's Latin is more difficult than Virgil's. There are Tibullus and Ovid, too, the Canon answered—and he wandered to the table to refill his goblet—and Cicero is more difficult than any. Héloïse's hope was that he might not again drink too much wine, and to distract his thoughts from the flagons she came over with a passage that needed no explanation or comment.

CHAP. IV.

AS she sat in the company-room reading in her favourite seat by the window her thoughts were one day startled from her book by a chittering of agitated birds, and looking up she saw seven or eight swallows striving against the pane and so strangely that she could not but think that they were seeking her help. The birds did not leave the sill at her approach, but redoubled their pathetic cries, and not till the casement was ajar did they fly away, leaving behind the seventh or eighth, whichever it might be, an ailing bird that yielded himself to her, lifting his wings so that she might search his feathers and see what ailed him, some seven or eight great white lice; and when she had freed him from these pests, he seemed

to know that he was cleansed. She placed him upon the
sill, and after shrilling his gratitude, his wings took the
air, and a moment after she saw him hawking flies up
and down the river, according to his wont. Poor little
fellow, she said, already forgetful that he was sick, forgetful of me; and then, the swallow passing out of her
mind as she had passed out of his, she stood for a long
time looking at the landscape before her, wondering at the
leaves. One after another the leaves, faded, discoloured,
detached themselves from the stems, fluttered and fell
into the stream and were borne away. And turning her
eyes from the willows to the fields, she noticed how
quiet and reposeful they were, as if weary and glad to
dream a little while before the white oxen came forth
again to turn them into tilth, preparing them for the
sower who would come after the plough. The death of
the year, she said, just as Virgil described it a thousand
years gone by. A year dies every year and is born again,
and that for ever and ever. Her eyes followed the
clouds, bringing as they passed over the sun a little
dimness that she welcomed, and while admiring the fields
she asked herself how it was that she had never before
perceived how beautiful they were, though she had been
looking at them ever since she returned from Argenteuil,
the same fields under different aspects and signs, always
beautiful under dark skies or somnolent blue. It was
Virgil who opened her eyes and gave her sight to see
the world and remembrance of much that she had seen
and almost forgotten (she had seen without thinking),
and now recalling the great grey valley of the Seine, and
the river looping through it, with poplar-trees stark
against the sky, she fell to thinking that for six years
she had lived in Argenteuil without seeing anything but
wide spaces of earth and sky.

How beautiful, she said, is the dark cloud now at poise
over the next parish, drenching the ploughman there,
and in a few minutes it will drench that other in the
field yonder bending over the stilts as the white oxen
fare to the headland slowly step by step, so slowly that
it seems they will never reach it.   But they have reached
it and have stopped, good, patient beasts, she said, for
the ploughman to lift the share out of the furrow.   Again
they come down the field, accomplishing another furrow,
and again another, and so on till the hour comes for the
ploughman to unyoke and lead them to the byre.   The
same white oxen that we read of in Virgil are before me
now, the same oxen, their sides showing against the tilth;
and were I to go down to the river I would find among
the willows the swarm of bees about which he wrote,
murmuring in and out of a hollow tree.

If it had not been for Virgil I should only have known
the story of the world as told in relations of martyrdoms
and miracles, and have seen the world only in relics
of the saints.   But he unsealed my eyes, and by night and
day the skies and seas will be beautiful to me, and along
the coasts that the galleys drove against in their flight
from smoking Troy I shall see wreckage and Dido, the
unfortunate Queen whose lover the gods raped from her,
Æneas having been chosen by them for their fateful
purpose.   The smoke from the pyre trailing over the sea
in the wake of the departing galleys appeared to her,
and she fell to thinking that greater than the gift of
vision was Virgil's revelation of human love, love of
woman for man and man for woman; and the story with
all its sorrow seemed to her so beautiful that she would
have changed places with Dido or with Æneas, for on
leaving Dido his heart, too, was wrung, but he obeyed
the gods and founded Rome.   If it had not been for

Virgil, she repeated, all I should have known of love
was the fact that Sister Paula had had a baby and put it
out to nurse in the village—a mere physical experience
that befell her as it might any animal; on returning to
Paris I saw for the first time a man tipsy, another physical fact but no more, and the physical side of our nature
was known to me in the convent, but of the spiritual I
apprehended nothing, nothing till a heathen poet without
the knowledge of true religion, that has since been vouchsafed to us by Christ himself, the Son of the living God,
was put into my hands. And her thoughts running on
incontinently, she said to herself: the knowledge that
this heathen had is new to us and good for us, since he
reveals God's world to us, for if God made the world
beautiful it was because he wished us to see it beautiful;
and if the Christian writers were blind to the beauty of
the world it was because they were too busy considering
spiritual beliefs, and striving to purge faith from error.
But now that the faith is secure——

A cloud passed across the sun and the landscape darkened, but a moment after the sun shone forth and the
world seemed more beautiful than ever. By the spell
of contrast, she said; may we not say, therefore, that
beauty will return to us again, making the world seem
more beautiful than it was even in Virgilian days? Beauty
was Virgil's theme always, and he taught us by drawing
our attention to what is beautiful, and his art was to
make things beautiful in themselves more beautiful by
selection and exquisite refinements of language. Nothing
of the world's beauty seems to have escaped him, she
continued, picking up the book again; he raised all things
to a higher level, even the Gods, for the Gods of his
day were perhaps not as beautiful as he made them, nor
the men and women, though it would grieve me to find

myself thinking that they were less august than he
painted them to us. Even the insects he raises out of
their lowly instincts and includes them in divinity.

And giving heed to these marvels certain have taught
that bees have a share in the divine mind, and breathe
the airs of Heaven; for that God extends to all lands
and spaces of sea and depths of sky; from whom flocks
and herds and men and all the tribes of wild beasts fetch
at birth the fragile gift of separate life; yea, and to him
are afterwards returned, and, being dissolved here are
once again born, every one of them; nor is there room
for death, but living they take their station amid the
stars, and rise into the height of Heaven . . .

So real were her dreams and so thin the reality in
which she lived that she did not hear the door or see
Madelon on the threshold. Now what fine tale is my
Héloïse dreaming over her book in this lonely room?
Madelon asked—a room I never could abide. I shiver
in the morning when I come into it with my duster and I
am glad to get out of it back to my kitchen; but thou
canst not have enough of sitting here with a book on
thy knee all through the autumn afternoons, as if they
were not sad enough with the leaves going one by one
down the river. My troth! and talking to thyself, and
about what? Maybe, Madelon, thou wouldst like to
hazard a guess of where my thoughts were? Back in
Argenteuil among the nuns, Madelon answered. And
Héloïse replied that Madelon could not have made a
worse guess, for her thoughts were among some bees that
lived a thousand years ago in the days of the Romans.
Wishing the Romans back again, Madelon said, and all
for the sake of thy Latin language. But all that we
have to say can be said in the language we're speaking
(so say I to myself); the French language in France and

Latin if they like it over and beyond the mountains.
France for ourselves, so say I! But what about them
bees that lived a thousand years ago? They were much
the same as the bees that have their hive in the hollow
willow down yonder, I'll be bound they were; or is it
that thou hast been reading the contrary in the books
the Canon is always putting into thy hands, and which
make such pleasant reading for thee that the meal-times
are forgotten and the dinner kept waiting for the end of
a sentence? A funny lot we all are here below, say I, as
I bend over my pots and pans in the kitchen, loving and
hating each other not for ourselves but for what we
think about the Latin language or the Trinity. The
wrangles that I have heard in this room about the three-
ness and the oneness, coming to threats, almost to blows,
though the most of them are clerics, good wine-bibbers and
cake-gobblers, but with no palate for either, for at the
name of Roscelin they are all after him, ferrets after a
rat. Often did I say to the Canon: what is the good
of trying to please you all with my cakes, for once the
name Roscelin is spoken, or for the matter of that the
name of William de Champeaux will do as well, you
eat without knowing what you are eating, it might be
just dry bread and the best wine water from the Seine.
Stirs and quarrels up and down the room till midnight
and afterwards in the street, holding on to each other's
cloaks and parting worse friends than ever. We used to
have pleasant assemblies here till that Roscelin began
with his threeness and his oneness, setting everybody by
the ears. I liked well making the cakes and setting out
the glasses, and listening to the songs and the viols and
lutes that follow the singer. Yes, and a man that played
the vielle so well! Ah, I should like thee to have heard
him. My word! He could make his instrument speak.

But all that's over and done for, for to escape the three-ness and the oneness everybody remains by his own hearth.

Héloïse listened, amused by Madelon's relation of the misfortunes that fell upon the Canon's assemblies. Once a man gets into solitary habits, Madelon continued, it's hard to get him out of them. Now that I lay my head to thinking on it I wouldn't be sure that thou weren't left in the convent for that the Canon having gotten into lonely habits couldn't break himself. I know he was often minded to send for thee, but all that's past, it matters nothing now, since y'are the best friends in the world now, as anybody can see. It needs no telling and I am glad of it, but I have my doubts if thou'lt ever get back to Argenteuil, however thy heart may ache for the nuns; it will break the Canon's heart should thou wish to go back, though he'll never say nothing, no not he, but he'll miss thee, my word! for ever since thou beganst thy Latin chatter he's like a fish in a net drawn along; and as for those books there isn't another in the world but thyself he would let read them. I know him—perhaps the only one that does—and I take the measure of his love for thee by the books he lends thee; the one in thy hand he wouldn't see in another hand for—well, I can't tell how much would bribe him to let me as much as put it back in the cupboard; he'd be jealous were I to cast my eye over it, I do believe, though he knows that I can't read. But we being on the subject of reading, I may as well tell that thy reading in this room is well-nigh come to an end, for it must be plain to thee that there is only one pair of hands in this house, and a big house to keep clean, and I am very particular; the dragging up of wood—but what need to talk of the trouble of dragging up wood when there isn't wood to drag up. By troth

and faith, a fire in the kitchen is as much as we dare to
be having. I am sorry for that, Madelon, Héloïse answered, for it is pleasant to read by this window. Pleasant enough, said Madelon, when the leaves are on the
trees and the river flows warm through flowers and
reeds, but a shivering outlook in snow-time and the wolves
howling almost at our doors. Thou'lt be better downstairs, believe me, for I know what this room is like in
winter.

And Héloïse followed Madelon downstairs to the room
in which they had their meals. I don't know what there
is in this room to find fault with, Madelon continued.
With a fire here and a fire next door, thou'lt be able
to read at thine ease, warmer than a great many, for only
the nobles who live in great castles amid woods can have
fires in more rooms than one.

The sun is leaving us, it is true; these are the last days
of sunny weather, Héloïse answered, and beguiled by the
rays that fell through the round windows, they sat down
to talk, according to their wont, of past times, which was
easy for them to do, Madelon having had the suckling of
Héloïse till her milk dried, having tubbed and dressed
her in her infancy, and having been the one to take her
to Argenteuil (much against her will she had done this,
it will be remembered), and the only one from Paris to
see her during the next seven years, running backwards
and forwards on her short, quick legs, a basket on her
arm with always a cake in it, and in summer and autumn
fruits. The joy that these visits awakened could never
be forgotten and the thrill that the name used to bring
was still quick in her, as she did not fail to notice, carrying her back in spirit to childhood, when her uncle spoke
it suddenly as he came up the stairs; and her face lit up
at the use of the familiar second person singular of the

verb, which she would not, could not forgo. The stiff,
stupid You would spoil all, she said. And you, Madelon,
how are you? Madelon laughed, saying, we are accustomed to Thou and Thee, and sitting in the house alone,
the autumn sun diffusing a pleasant atmosphere of indo-
lence and warmth through the thick glass, Madelon
uttered her thoughts incontinently: I don't see thee, try
as I will, in a black habit, and a rosary hitched to thy
girdle; try as I will, I can't manage it. Canst see me
more easily walking about the pleasure grounds of a great
castle? Héloïse asked. Troth and faith, I can indeed;
and what would hinder me that saw thy mother before
thee in the grandest castle in Brittany? And Madelon's
rage at the injustice done to the young Comtesse boiled
over, and the story of her expulsion and disinheritance
was told over again, the story in its last ravellings gathering into Madelon's mind the thought that if the Comte
and Comtesse came to Paris they could not do else than
seek out their granddaughter. If that should fall out,
my stay in the rue des Chantres is ended, Héloïse said.
Madelon pondered on this question, getting almost a
little drowsy over it. If they don't come, others will, said
Madelon at last. But I am not beautiful enough for any
of them. Thou'rt well enough, Madelon answered, and
the straying talk of women idling the afternoon away
was soon back again whence it started, whether Héloïse
was going to a castle or a cloister. The Canon may live
yet for many years, but a man of sixty is not sure of his
life. None of us are sure of our lives, Héloïse answered,
and the words started a memory in Madelon of a young
man, a student, who used to come to the Canon's assemblies and died without any warning illness. Héloïse would
have liked to hear more of this young man, who played
the vielle and sang, but Madelon could do no more than

follow her own thoughts: The young man is dead and little use it will be for us to waste time over him. We have been very quiet of late, but if thou'rt to remain here the whole winter the Canon will have to do something for thee, and anxious enough he is to please thee; and thou must look to thy words, for thy learning is his brag, as the egg is the hen's; he do cackle over thee at the Cathedral, so it is said, and will be having an assembly for thee soon enough. The latter end of October is our usual time.

And early the next week, on a Monday or a Tuesday, Madelon bounced in on Héloïse, who was reading in the Canon's study in his absence, crying: now what did I tell thee? Before he left the house this morning he was asking me what day would be most convenient to invite some friends for music. Now which day did I think? All days are the same, says I: Tuesday, Wednesday, Thursday. Then Wednesday, says he, going out. And on Tuesday afternoon Héloïse and Madelon were busy making cakes and considering the wine that should be decanted for the feast.

Despite the great squandering of firewood there would have to be a fire upstairs, so Madelon said, the weather having turned suddenly colder; and for the appearance and the cheerfulness too, she added. He'll have all his own friends, patriarchs, of course, but he'll add some students for thy sake, for thou'lt like to talk to somebody of thine own age, which is but reasonable. Héloïse had never talked to a young man yet, but it seemed to her that an understanding of Virgil was far more important than age. So you all think when you come from the convent first; but Lord! thou'lt soon be looking round to see if they be looking after thee. And now I warn thee, talk of the Virgil and thine Ovid, but let not the names of

Roscelin and Champeaux or Anselm or Abélard pass thy
lips, for no sooner are these names mentioned than the
place is like a rick of straw with somebody dropping
lighted tinder about, for a word more or less will do it,
and in a minute the fire will be jumping hither and thither,
crackling, flaming, leaping; and if it doesn't blaze, smoking in sullen ill-humour, setting everybody coughing.
That's the way it is with us, she cried, and Héloïse
laughed at Madelon's farmyard imagery, and gave ear
to her warning, hearing from her that Virgil and Ovid
would come in handy, as good as a shower of rain to put
the fire out.   Now mind me, the moment thou hearest any
one of those names spoken, begin to ask him that speaks
about it about the bees that I heard thee talking about
to thyself the other day, and in a few minutes all danger
will be over.

  Héloïse bethought herself of some other notable passages besides the bees: a description of a storm that drives
the galley on to the shore and Æneas and the crew wading
through water filled with sand and encamping in a
cavern.   Æneas going forth in search of food meets a
herd of deer and shoots seven.   Such a story, Madelon
thought, might turn the thoughts of their guests from
Abélard and Champeaux.   And let thy thoughts be on
the cakes and wine and the songs they are going to sing,
reminding them that for eating and drinking and singing
they've come, and not at all for disputation.   Héloïse
promised, and her tongue was never off the wine and
cakes, as she passed them upon the guests, and so insistent was she that the dreaded names seemed to have been
forgotten by everybody.   Nor was the next assembly in
the rue des Chantres less agreeable.   It went by like
its predecessor, leaving behind a fading memory of cakes
and wine, delightful songs and lute-playing, and talks

of the Latin poets to which everybody contributed a few words, some too many. But the evening came when the guests talked without having anything to say that interested themselves or their neighbours, and rose to sing in the depressing feeling that themselves were not moved to sing much more than the audience to listen. The same guests, the same cakes, wine, music and talk, but how different, said Héloïse, and the Canon replied to her: It is always thus; one week we are up and the next week down, and the evening passes tediously. Let us hope that we shall be more lucky next week. Let us hope so, indeed, Héloïse answered, for I have no heart for a repetition of the last evening just gone by. How it stuck, how it clung! I thought we should never come to the end of it. Our poor guests, how dolefully they departed. Of that I'm not sure, the Canon answered: they enjoyed the wine and cakes. But no, uncle, the wine and cakes were the same but the enjoyment was meagre. One evening we're up, another we are down, the Canon repeated. We must hope for better luck next week, and let the wine and cakes be distributed more plentifully. Héloïse thought that she had pressed the flagons on everybody, but the next week she was still more insistent in her invitations, and her guests, catching her light-heartedness, began to drink, eat, talk, laugh and twang their lutes impatiently. This will be one of our best evenings, Héloïse said as she dashed into the kitchen, saying: More cakes and fruit are wanted. Wine we have enough for the present. She stayed to chatter with Madelon, and though she was but a few minutes away she was aware, as she came up the stairs, that something doleful had happened in her absence, for she heard neither laughter nor the sounds of lutes, but single voices, and very soon began to apprehend the cause. The

words that caught on her ear were: all energy at last
becomes identical with the ultimate substance, God, Socrates becoming God in little, and Judas himself identical
with both.

It was plain to all that the Nominalist was not fighting
fairly by thrusting theology into Dialectics, but since he
had chosen to do so he must take the consequences, and
everybody knew that the consequences were that the
Realist would do likewise. Ah, you are quick, pupil and
disciple of Pierre du Pallet—who is Pierre du Pallet?
Héloïse asked; Abélard, the Canon whispered—you are
quick to turn what I offered as an analogy into an argument of heresy against my person. I will meet you on
the same ground and with the same weapon. Will you
tell us if this concept, this image in the mind of man,
of God, of matter, for I know not where to seek it, be
a reality? I hold it as, in a manner, real. I want a
categorical answer. I must qualify—— I will have no
qualifications, a substance is or is not. Well, then, my
concept is a sign. A sign of what? A sound, a word, a
symbol, an echo of my ignorance. Nothing then! So
truth and virtue of humanity do not exist at all. You
suppose yourself to exist, but you have no means of
knowing God; therefore to you God does not exist except
as an echo of your ignorance! And what concerns you
most, the Church does not exist except as your concept
of certain individuals whom you cannot regard as a
unity, and who suppose themselves to believe in a Trinity
which exists only as a sound or symbol. I will not repeat
your words, pupil, disciple, whichever you are pleased to
call yourself, of Le sieur Pierre du Pallet, outside of this
house, for the consequences to you would be deadly; but
it is only too clear that you are a materialist, and as
such your fate must be settled by a Church Council,

unless you prefer the stake by judgment of a secular court.

The spiritual exaltation in the eyes of the rival philosophers that had lighted the way of the disputation was replaced suddenly by a fierce animal hatred, and they would have sprung at each other's throats if the attention of each had not been distracted from the other by a great turbulence that had just risen up in the street. The students have broken out again, the Canon cried, and every cheek paled and all ears were given to the riot. It grew fainter; and the philosophers, becoming certain that it was no more than a street broil, prepared to spring at each other, and would have done so if Héloïse had not thrown herself between them. Would you shame our house and be carried home, philosophers that you are, on stretchers like riotous students? She cut a fine figure standing between them, and although still frightened lest the riot should return, the guests broke into laughter, the philosophers included, and the danger within doors was averted. But without the din seemed to be returning from the river, wherein not a few young men have met their death, the Canon said, and then the riot seemed to subside, and the Canon continued: No more than a quarrel proceeding from wineshop to wineshop. Let us hope so, several voices muttered, and one began to ask another how they might manage to protect themselves on their way home, and if it would not be wise to return in company. The plight of those who had to cross the Little Bridge was the hardest, and several times it was asked if the crowd was scattering, and the guests, who had descended from Madelon's balcony to the ground floor, ran up to the balcony again and came back with the news that the night was falling fast. We cannot stay here all night, somebody said. The Canon protested, and somebody answered:

If we are not to remain here we had better seek our cloaks,
and while engaged on the donning of them they told
stories of the murders and robberies done by students
during the great outbreak of a month ago, when a battle,
begun in a wineshop in the angle of the rue Berneuse and
the rue Fosse aux Chiens, had spread all over the town.
On finding the house empty of all but the taverner's
daughter a student tried to rape her, and it was at the
moment when he had torn open her bodice that the
taverner entered. In the fight that followed up and down
the stairs the student took the thrust of a knife: and stag-
gering to the doorway he called for help, whereupon many
students forced their way into the house despite bars and
bolts, but not before the taverner escaped to the roof,
whence he called for help. Come all ye traders to my
help, he cried; and glad they were of the occasion to
wreak vengeance on the students.

The critical moment had come, one side or the other
had to win a victory, and the traders, determined that
the victory should be on their side, came out armed with
hatchets and knives and great earthenware jars, every
weapon they could lay hands on, and all night long the
war was raged through the rue Coupe-Guuele, rue du Gros-
Pet, rue de la Grande Truanderie, rue du Pet, rue Mederal,
rue du Cul-de-Pet, rue Pute-y-Muce, rue Coup-de-Baton,
rue Prise-Miche, rue de Trou-Punais, rue Tire-Pet, rue
du Petit-Pet, and through the narrow laneways, stews
and entanglements of these streets. It is said that three
hundred students were killed during the course of the
night, and their bodies thrown into the river, for they
had to be got rid of. The traders too must have lost
many, so fierce was the fighting, the Canon said, and after
speaking of the great number of wounded students, many
hundreds, the Canon's guests sallied forth hopefully, it

seeming to them unlikely that after so bad a defeat the
students would attempt to attack the hapless passenger,
an assumption that proved true for that evening at least.
Canon Fulbert's guests reached Notre-Dame without
meeting with any disagreeable adventure, nothing more
than the spectacle of a duel in progress, an excellent
swordsman defending himself with a cane against a
street bully.

And philosophers, lute-players and prelates watched
him striving to reach his opponent's eyes and mouth, where
the cane could wound. Now he will be killed for certain,
said Alberic, and he and Romuald were about to intervene
when with a simple *dégagement* a dangerous thrust was
parried and the cane passing over the assailant's guard
entered his open mouth, putting an end to the combat.
A fine swordsman, said Alberic, who would have put you
all to flight had he been armed. Whereupon the friends
of the wounded man cried: So thou wouldst take up the
debate with us? But seeing that Alberic and Romuald
had friends behind them they desisted, and Alberic and
Romuald returned to their friends, who rated them for
their foolhardiness, asking why they should come between
friends who had chosen to quarrel. Why, indeed, said
Romuald, since swordsmanship proceeds out of friendship, as the egg from the hen; we can't have one without
the other. Whereupon somebody said that it would be
well to hasten, for delay might cause them to fall in with
some prowling students who might claim their friendship. So they marched on, all in agreement that Paris
was at that moment much too friendly, and that it was
unwise for those living on either bank of the river to
remain on the city island after dusk. And before reaching the Little Bridge it was remembered that the evenings
would be shorter next week, that they were nearing the

end of the still autumn weather without doubt, though
it seemed hard to believe that in a few days loud winds
would be whirling round corners and the dry streets under
their feet would be turned once more into a very liquid
mud.   An aureoled moon, somebody said, is a certain
sign of a change in the weather.

CHAP. V.

I HOPE our guests will reach home safely, and she
stood looking up and down the street, still full of students.
A hazy moon is a sure sign of rain, said the Canon; we
shall have rain to-morrow or the next day, and high
winds, and no further venturing out to assemblies for
singing and lute-playing or theological discussion.   If it
hadn't been for thy courage ill blows would have been
exchanged and our philosophers carried home on stretchers, in thy words, like students after a broil in a wineshop.   No more assemblies this year? Héloïse said.   Ah!
so thou'rt craving after more lute-playing and singing,
and maybe the lute-players, too, have a place in thy
thoughts.   I was thinking, uncle, of the philosophers
rather than the lute-players.   For before coming to fisti-
cuffs they argued well, and I don't know now whether
Nominalism or Realism would have had the upper hand
if charges of heresy hadn't been made.   So, niece, thy
clever brain was able to follow the argument, a subtle
one; well-matched the sides were and equal the weapons;
and it is a pity that heresy cannot be barred and reason
given fair play, the last word, of course, being with
the Church.   At that moment the Canon turned into the
house, and sitting face to face the twain talked before
bedtime, Héloïse putting questions and learning from
her uncle that Roscelin, Canon of Compiègne, was the

first exponent of the doctrine of Nominalism, carrying it even to its extreme, not hesitating to say that the three persons of the Trinity were made from different substances, thereby falling into the heresy of Tritheism, the doctrine that there are three Gods.

The Canon would have liked to expatiate on the arguments put forward by Roscelin and his opponent William de Champeaux, but Héloïse, who had heard Plato and Aristotle spoken of, was eager to know how they came into the controversy, and she asked which was the Nominalist and which the Realist. The Canon shuffled, for his knowledge of Plato was not enough to make this plain to her. I have the *Timæus,* he said, and thou'lt find Socrates in it; but as he has no care for the science of nature he passes over the task of exposition to the Pythagorean philosopher. Of Socrates I have heard, Héloïse replied, but know very little about him, no more than that he was a great Dialectician. He was that indeed, Fulbert answered, but not after the manner of the two Dialecticians who were about to break each other's heads half-an-hour ago in the room above us. All we have of Plato in Latin is the *Timæus,* and it is pretty hard reading, I can tell thee; very unsuited for a girl's brain, but being given to learning as a girl never was before, take it. He put the book into her hands, which she opened at once. No, no, not now; leave it on thy desk and to-morrow morning thou canst take thy fill of it. But thou hast not given me Aristotle, uncle, and I would compare him with Plato.

A strange girl, indeed, he said, and going to his cupboard, he took out the *Categories* and handed them to her, saying: Now to bed; Madelon is in hers, and we should follow her example. To-morrow will be long enough to satisfy thy curiosity. At these words, uttered super-

ciliously, Héloïse sulked a little, not liking her desire of
learning to be sneered at; all the same she had no heart
for books at the moment, being tired, and went to her
bed wondering how much Nominalism and Realism she
would find in the Greeks. A wonderful people, she said,
and fell asleep full of projects for the study of the Greek
language. The arts and learning began and were completed by the Greeks. A wonderful people, she said
to herself during the night; for since their day the world
has done little else than to remember and forget. And
in the morning while lying awake thinking of the two
books that awaited her, her almost dream words returned
to her. With which shall I begin? she asked herself.
A suspicion that Plato was the Realist decided her choice,
and the day was spent in the pleasure of a new book
without it becoming apparent to her how Plato had come
to concern himself with the questions that now agitated
all men. She pursued her inquiry steadily, though disappointed to find little of the Dialectic, the new science,
or the old science that Plato had invented, or was it
Socrates—who was more or less Plato's invention—in
the *Timæus*. Instead of what she was looking for she
found an account of the world's soul, which was not God
but one of God's creatures, and the story that from out
the world's soul came the spirits that guide the planets.
And then, she said, turning the page, we seem to come
down to human souls. But what is this? God plunges
the soul into the flux of matter, which has a perturbing
influence; and the souls have to recover their original
nature, and when they have done this they return to the
stars, whence they came. But Plato could not have
meant all this literally, she said, and resolving not to be
turned aside from the book (which was, of course, one
of the world's books) by certain surface difficulties, she

plunged into the physics of the *Timæus* and read on, page after page, all that day and the next day and many days after, now and again laying the book aside to pick up the *Categories* of Aristotle and indulge herself in another bewilderment. But though he was easier to understand than Plato he did not please her so much, and she laid the *Categories* aside, saying: if Plato can be attractive in physics, how much more attractive must he be in the other books? Why haven't we got the *Banquet?* Ah! I must learn Greek; and she fell to thinking how long it would take her to learn to read Greek as easily as Latin. Two or three years, she said, and took up the *Categories* again, saying to herself: There's no use thinking about learning Greek; if I cannot understand these books in Latin how much less shall I understand them in Greek?

After diligent reading her curiosity was partly satisfied. There is, she said, one day, certainly a hint in Aristotle of the doctrine of the Nominalists. Here we have it: there are no primary substances but individuals.

She became so absorbed in the writings of these two great men that she hardly noticed the Canon in the evenings. Even when she laid her book aside, her thoughts were far away; and she did not seem to feel the cold, though the winter was now upon them, great violence of wind raging round the pointed towers and the peaked gables, storms of wind and rain, bleak, cold rain that only just escaped being snow. The Canon often asked himself of what she could be thinking as she sat looking into the smouldering log, the last one that they dared to throw into the grate that evening. He guessed her to be lost in Plato, so impassive was her face. No, she replied to his question: art thinking of Plato or Aristotle? no; I was not thinking of either. I was thinking, she said, of the wonderful Greek language, which, alas! we do not trouble to learn. Her casual sententiousness annoyed the Canon, but he restrained himself, saying to himself: Let her think of the wonderful Greek language, and begin it when she pleases. But how is all this to end? And forgetful of her, he fell to considering the mistake he had made, for he was now certain that he had not done well when he yielded to his conscience (or to some nervous scruple that he had mistaken for his conscience) and sent Madelon to Argenteuil with instructions that she was to bring Héloïse back with her. On a more senseless errand a woman was never sent, so it seemed to him in his present petulance, for if Héloïse were seriously minded to take the veil, it was folly to bring her to Paris; and if she were not seriously minded to take the veil, how could he have been beguiled into believing that she would return to Argenteuil at the end of a week's visit?

To be just, she had never asked to extend her visit. It was to please him that she consented to spend the autumn with him—his purpose being that she should read Virgil, and after Virgil Ovid, and after Ovid Tibullus. But now she was reading Plato and Aristotle, and with the same interest as she had read the poets. He did not know, and as likely as not she did not know herself, whether she preferred poetry to philosophy or philosophy to poetry; she was earnest and studious but without direction in her studies, and mere acquisition of knowledge for knowledge's sake is vanity. But this new craze would not last; the next one might be astronomy or—— He hoped it would not be astrology, for the Church looks with no kindly eye on that science. . . . If he had been true to his instinct and left her in the convent, only going to see her when she took the white veil, perhaps not then

—not till she took her final vows—her life would have been settled advantageously, for with her intelligence and gift for study she could not have failed to reach the position of abbess in some great community: Benedictines, Cistercians or Carmelites, it mattered not which. But the abbess he foresaw himself had killed. She would not return to the nuns. Her ambition would find satisfaction in the books that he had locked up so that she should not see them (for his instinct was right from the beginning); but alas! he had put Virgil's Æneid into her hands, and swayed by her eagerness and admiration of the hexameters he had said that she must not return yet awhile to Argenteuil, not before she had read all the Latin poets. Himself was the source and origin of all this vexation, and his thoughts taking a sudden turn, he remembered that she had never spoken of religion and had no care for stories of miracles, listening with unmoved face and catching at the first chance to speak of something else, wearing usually a smile on her lips when the talk was about relics; she had even laughed a little when one of his colleagues spoke of the Virgin's milk, a flask of which was now being brought to Europe, saying that she did not see how the milk could have been preserved through the centuries. The preservation was part of the miracle, and though it might be argued that miracles were becoming perhaps a little common, Héloïse's scorn of the story (if scorn was too strong a word, lack of reverence was not) showed him that his mistake in sending Madelon to fetch her from Argenteuil was not such a mistake as it seemed at first sight. For the further knowledge that he had acquired of her during this visit led him to doubt if there were the makings of a nun in her; she would have returned to him sooner or later, and if that were so, it was well she had not delayed longer in the convent, for she was a well-figured girl, pleasant to look upon: her shapely head framed in brown shining hair, her grey, spirit eyes and her alert voice were enough to win for her some great baron or count. Her intelligence and learning had already made her known to everybody in Paris, and would make her known to everybody who came to Paris at Easter. But here again Héloïse seemed to fail him, for men did not attract her; and he remembered that she spoke to one man as she did to the next one, to Alberic as she did to Romuald, and from Romuald he had seen her turn to one of his friends, a man as old as himself, with the same smile on her face, the same look in her eyes.

A strange, perplexing girl, he said; one who takes as much pleasure in talking to the oldest canon as she does in talking to the youngest man. Everybody likes her, everybody praises her, but nobody takes her into the corners of the room to talk apart with her, nor does she encourage anybody to follow her into corners for private little talks; her coldness chills; and looking still more deeply into her character he concluded that her vice was a certain aloofness, if aloofness may be called a vice. Well, there are plenty of the other sort about, so it may be well that there should be one like her. In this wise did the Canon think of his niece whilst he and she shivered together by the insufficient fire, and so did he often think as he left the house to go to the Cathedral; and if he met a colleague on his way thither the first words that were addressed to him were a question: how is Héloïse? Is she reading Aristotle or is she reading Plato, or has she gone back to Virgil? Everybody admires Héloïse, everybody likes her, everybody talks about her, and I am proud of her, he said. But when I am no longer by her, when she is alone in the world—— And

he fell to thinking of his years. And then, his thoughts
returning to Philippe, he said: I should not like to meet
him on the thither side and not be able to tell him that
she was well married or an abbess—if not already an
abbess, at least on her way to being one.

So whether going to the Cathedral or from the Cathedral, he was always thinking of Héloïse, making plans
for her, saying to himself: It does not follow, because
she did not like the few students I was able to invite
to my house, that she might not love a great noble, a
count, a baron; men and women usually love those within
their own circle. Héloïse is a Coetlogon on her mother's
side, and her grandparents may one day relent; if they
do, Héloïse may accept their patronage. Or she might
be influenced by the story—the story that I told her, fool
that I was. But we are guided by our instincts rather
than by what we hear, and of her instincts I know nothing, but Madelon, who has known Héloïse since she was
a little child, will be able to give me a rough and ready
but a true reading of her character and temperament.

The opportunity to take Madelon into his confidence
came a few days later, on the doorstep.

He blurted out a good many of his perplexities before
giving her time to close the door against the storm, and
the servant replied: She must have been very much on
your mind indeed, for you to begin telling the story in the
middle of the driving snow. A man of your age too!
Yes, it's very cold, he answered, and they went up to the
company-room, for if they talked in the parlour Héloïse,
who was in the study, would come out to meet them. But
in the company-room, the Canon said, she will not mind
us; she is too busy with her book. And walking up and
down, back and forth, to keep himself warm, he related all
his misgivings; he had done wrong in sending Madelon to

Argenteuil to fetch Héloïse. She would have become a nun for certain if she hadn't been brought to Paris. But no sooner was this opinion of Héloïse out of his mouth than he sought to qualify it, saying that as far as he could see she showed no religious inclinations, attending Mass on Sundays, of course, but well-nigh unwilling. And he continued to tell all his thoughts about her and about himself, till Madelon was past her patience. But what can I do? she asked. I can do nothing. A great deal, Madelon, he answered; if thou wilt but listen. But I have been listening, she replied, and the Canon, overcoming his rising irritation against his servant, begged her to tell him her reading of Héloïse's character. For I can make nothing of it, he said. Is she indifferent to men as she is to the Church? Will she marry, and if she won't what will befall her? I am thinking of my death, Madelon; and thou hast known her since she was a little child. Tell me. My brother Philippe put her in my charge. But I'm no wise woman, Canon, nor reader of the stars. Madelon, I will not be spoken to—— Checking himself again, he said: Madelon, thou hast an insight into her character, though nobody else has. And you would like to hear the truth from me? she answered. Well, it's easily told, for what is she but a child, seventeen—hardly that?—yet you expect her to know her own mind. Thinkest I am impatient, Madelon? Well, well! Impatient you were born and impatient you'll die. Impatient! Should we find a more impatient man if we were to travel the world over? I doubt it. Impatient for your dinner and impatient if anybody talks to you. Impatient in your stall in the Cathedral. Impatient—— Let us not waste time talking about the Cathedral. So thy hope is that when Héloïse has grown into womanhood she'll marry? You want to know how I understand her?

said Madelon. Well, she is just one of those women who
go through life without knowing how a man is made or
giving it a thought, if she doesn't find somebody who
comes with the right candle. Ah, should she meet the
right candle there'll be a blaze in the hemp stalks, I'll
warrant. So that is how thou seest her, and maybe thou'rt
right, the Canon muttered, half to himself. And having
got that much out of me, Madelon answered, no more
than anybody could see who had half-an-eye to see with,
we'll go downstairs, I to my kitchen and you to your
study, where you will find her reading.

As they came down the stairs Madelon spoke of a
wolf-hunt, saying that the hunters were waiting for the
full moon to beguile the pack into the city. Madelon
says there's going to be a wolf-hunt, the Canon said,
throwing open the study door. From whom didst get
the news? Héloïse asked. From whom indeed? Madelon
replied. Why, all the town is talking of it; nor are there
two in the town except your two selves who don't know
of it. And as uncle and niece begged of her to remove
their ignorance, she began to tell that the wolves had
been in the streets lately after nightfall, picking up what
they could get in the way of stray cats and dogs, and
emboldened by hunger, for the snow was falling fast, they
would soon come into the streets as they did in Brittany,
for had she not seen a child eaten by an old grey wolf
in her own village street? And lest the same disaster
should fall out in Paris, as well it might if the wolves
were not to be persecuted, the townsfolk were about to
begin to rid themselves of the large pack that came down
from the Orléans forest every night, a matter of fifty
miles. But what is fifty miles, she said, to a wolf? Just
no more than a little round to ourselves across the island
from bridge to bridge. The squealing of a pig tied to

a post by the Little Bridge will soon be heard, and the
wolf that hears it will let off a howl to his comrades,
a dozen or twenty, for no one knows the size of the pack,
and these will soon be growling and fighting over piggy.
Another will be tied within the island some yards behind
the bridge, and he too will be eaten; and three nights
from now, being full moon and the night almost as clear
as day, a dozen wolves or more will be seeking for food
beyond the bridge, and when they are well within the
city the bridges will be held by spearmen.   So let us
pray for a fine night, for clear moonlight means the
death of the pack.   It will be a clever wolf that will
escape with his life.   So said Madelon, and it was as if
God had answered their prayers, for on the night of
the full moon a blue stream of light shone right across
the island, and a dozen wolves were hunted through it,
shapely grey animals with bushy tails, pretty triangular
ears and long jaws filled with strangely devised teeth,
harmonising in their variety; exquisite instruments of
torture that would delight an executioner.   Again and
again the wolves escaped the spearmen in the street,
but all the doors were closed against them and large dogs
tracked them and drove them out of their hiding places,
and they were done to death in couples and singly, with
spears and great beams of wood sharpened and hardened
by fire, not dying, however, without a fight.   But the
wolf that stayed to bite was hewn down or pierced with
a sword, till at last the remnant began to see that only
by swimming the stream could they escape.   Some five or
six plunged in and swam valiantly, but archers were
placed along the left and the right banks behind the
poplar and the willow trees, and when a wolf reached
the middle of the stream an arrow struck him; he went
under the current swilled him away, and from their high

balcony Héloïse, the Canon and Madelon watched the shooting from the right bank, seeing one grey, courageous animal reach the bank despite the mortal arrow. He is the last one, Héloïse said, but at these words a beautiful young wolf galloped down their street and, catching sight of Héloïse on the balcony, he laid himself down against the door, and howled for it to be opened for him; and she might have risked being bitten, but before there was time to ask for the Canon's consent some hunters appeared in the street and the young wolf was slain in a corner, a big beam being driven through him.

There's no better covering than a wolf-skin to wrap round the knees, said one of the hunters. But I cannot sit reading with the skin of the animal about my knees that howled to me for help, Héloïse said. We thought, said the hunter, the skin came to you by right, the beast that wore it being killed at your door; and as Héloïse would not buy the wolf, he was slung over the beam and carried away for other knees.

CHAP. VI.

THE news of the hunt in the streets and markets next morning was that eleven wolves had been killed. The twelfth had escaped, and this was looked upon as part of the general good fortune, for he, so it was said, would tell his comrades of the danger of venturing into men's cities, especially those built on islands. It was hoped that the snow, which had begun to come down again, would not fetch more wolves out of their forests; it was hoped, too, that it would not be long upon the ground; a week was spoken of as likely, they being now in February. But almost while the folk were talking of the coming of spring, the blue sky darkened to a dun grey overhead; copper and sulphur it was along the horizon, betokening more snow. The wind rose and shrieked all night about the pointed towers and peaked gables; and in the morning snow was falling thickly, large flakes more wonderful than any leaf or flower or shell, for nothing compares with the large, white friable snow that passes into a drop of water almost as soon as it falls into the hand that catches it. But in eleven hundred and seventeen it lay on the frozen ground, deepening every hour, day after day, filling the roadway and the roofs, whitening the tops of the towers, bearing down the branches of the trees; a wonderful sight truly is a city seen through the white flutter, falling relentlessly, falling always, as if the sky sought to bury the world. Will the flakes never cease from falling? was the thought in everybody's mind, and looking out of their narrow windows, the folk saw little else but snow. It will snow all night, they said; and if it snows all to-morrow and the next night we shall not be able to open our doors. But at last the snow ceased to fall, and shovels were again heard clearing the streets, piling the snow up on either side of the roadway, the ditches rising to seven, eight, and even ten feet high.

It was often on the tongue that if a thaw came quickly water would ooze and trickle down the walls of the houses through the ceilings, bringing them down and littering the floors; and God began to seem ungrateful, in all eyes, for the armies that had been sent to Palestine to rescue the Sepulchre from the Infidel were in everybody's mind. Even the prelacy could not put their doubts aside, and so weary were all of the cold that it came to be said that the Seine might rise and drown them without anybody caring; better drowning than freezing; and the fear, too, was prevalent that great packs of wolves were assembling

in the Orléans forest, and would come one night across
the ice and devour the half-starved, who were without
power to fight them. Be this as it may, from near and
far the wolves howled their hunger over frozen fields,
and under all their blankets the shivering folk pictured
the animals lolloping through the streets, quarrelling
over the watchmen and then waiting for the doors to be
opened, or giving occasional chase to houseless cats and
dogs, and when these lacked following the ducks and
geese that had come up from the sea, and grabbing
starveling birds hardly able to fly. Very often a fox,
sneaking along the river-side in the hope of picking up a
rat or two, was picked up himself by the wolves and
eaten, despite cousinship. Hawks and hooded crows
were about, glad to get a bit of entrail or skin left behind
by the wolves, and as for the birds, Héloïse said, they
seem all to have come out of the woods and fields hoping
to find warmth and food in the city, for though there is
not much of either in Paris, still Paris must be warmer
than the country, and we always have a few crumbs for
them. Do they tell each other? she asked herself, as
she overlooked the feathered company gathered about
on Madelon's balcony, green and gold finches, sparrows,
robins, blackbirds and thrushes, bullfinches and even
wrens, and as she fed them she caught sight of all the
country beyond the river. Never did the drama of life
and death cease, taking unexpected turns. A great grey
bird came down the sky one day, the silver lining of
his wings showing as he wheeled, a heron in search of
an open pool, she said; and it was not long before she
saw the bird strike at something, but what the capture
might be the wriggle along the bank did not express.
Was it newt or frog? she asked, or a rat perchance?
And after swallowing whatever might have been his

breakfast, the bird disappeared into the sedges, raising from time to time a watchful, ecclesiastical head. He has found a pool where the current is likely to break up the ice to-morrow or the day after, she said; he would not have settled himself in the sedges, chosen that corner, if he did not sense a thaw. Ah, a fox is lurking, and will get the heron and the rat together. But the watchful bird rose, escaping capture, leaving behind a hungry fox who watched the grey wings aloft, carrying the bird, it seemed, no faster than himself could run. If I had made my rush a little sooner I might have got him, the fox is saying to himself, Héloïse said, as she entered the house, with the intention of seeking more bread in the kitchen; for there is no end to my beggars, she added. On her way thither she met Madelon returning from the market with a long tale to tell that no food had come into Paris that morning, carts having been delayed on their way by the snow, which had become like ice. The horses slipped and slithered, she said, unable to get their loads along, and the city farriers are gone to reshoe the horses, but the frosting will soon wear down. And then the farriers will have to reshoe the horses, Héloïse replied; a remark that Madelon seemed to resent, for she retired growling.

Nobody stirred out of doors who could remain within, but walls are poor shelter from great masses of snow piled along the street, grimy heaps that might be dust-heaps but for patches of white here and there; snow soon loses its beauty in the city. The sky darkened again and the yellow rim over the horizon told of more snow. As soon as it ceased to fall men were at work raising the ditches higher. It began to be felt that none could redeem the city but God. To win him over, Masses were announced, and for these the Canon had to struggle up the street, he and Héloïse supporting each other, and, losing their shoes from time to time in the snow, they spoke, whilst they sought them, of the cities of the North, whose fate it was to lie three or four months of the year under snow.

But the North has sledges, the Canon said, and great stoves in the houses; we are unprepared against the snow and must pray for a thaw. The noise of stamping feet almost silenced the celebrant, and the preacher could only beg the folk to put their trust in God, and to his exhortations the folk answered inly: what have we done to deserve this plague? We are not Egyptians who keep the Lord's people in captivity. Have we not sent the flower of France to Palestine? Of what good to be good if a winter like this is our one reward? God is laughing at us. Such was the talk in the rue des Chantres as the folk went back and forth from the Cathedral through the thin wintry day, a small passage of daylight between the long nights.

It is in our legs that we suffer, Fulbert said; one can keep the body warm but not the legs. And Héloïse thought of the wolf-skin she had refused as they sat watching the spluttering log, not daring to ask Madelon for another, knowing well she would say: if you ask for any more logs it will be the worse for you; you'll be without dinner in three weeks, for there is no telling that the snow won't be with us till then.

The last time they asked for a log she told them that she had seen snow lying on the ground in Brittany for months at a time, and that whilst the snow lasted no logs could come up from the forest. Only in our beds are we warm, Héloïse said, speaking at the end of a long silence; but we cannot remain in bed all day and all night. She had a little pan that she kept within her muff, for her finger-tips burned so bitterly that she could not fix her attention on her book. The Canon had long ago ceased to read, and sat stamping his feet on the cold hearth in which there were but some glimmering ashes, careless whether Héloïse was reading Plato or Aristotle, or had returned from philosophy to poetry; nor had he any longer thought of her future, whether she should return to the cloister or marry one of the great nobles that came up from the provinces for the Easter ceremonies at the Cathedral. And on his giving utterance one day to the hope that if she did marry she would live in a well-wooded country, she asked him if he would like to see her a comtesse or an abbess, and they talked for a while on the married and the celibate life, without much interest in these questions, a burning log having become more important.

It may be that a change is come; let us go and see, said the Canon. The stars were shining, alas! and they went to their beds disconsolate, thinking of a completely frozen river, for if this last calamity were to fall out then indeed they might say their prayers and prepare for paradise. Or hell, Héloïse said, and the Canon had no heart to reprove her for her levity.

But the frost they detected in the air did not last. The wind changed, clouds began to gather, and once more they were living in a moist atmosphere, but the cold was not less than before, for the streets were full of snow. Dirty, ignominious, earth-disgraced snow, the Canon said, and leaving the rest of his thoughts to be inferred from the context, that the fallen snow and the fallen soul were comparable, he started to wade through mud and water to the Cathedral, stopping on his threshold to remind Héloïse that news had not come from Palestine for many

weeks. Have the Crusaders been defeated? he asked. Is
the Sepulchre again in the hands of the Saracens?

The rain poured and the wind howled. Now and then
the sky blackened a little, giving token of another downpour, and an icy flood carried by a whirling wind swept
about the streets. We are back in the original marsh,
the people said; the earth is without green and the sky
without blue. Not a streak of blue for many months.
A late spring, said another, and his words were understood as ironical. God indeed seemed angry with his
people, for at the beginning of March snow began to fall
again and an old willow, the one, Héloïse said, in which
the bees had made their nests, crashed into the storm and
was carried away by the swirling water. Madelon, who
thought more of honey than of the bees, said: we have
lost many pounds of honey. Not many, Héloïse answered; for the bees perhaps died this winter for lack
of honey; we may have taken too much from them. Of
that I know naught, Madelon said; they are gone and
the tree with them. But Madelon, said Héloïse, are we
going to get any spring this year? It doesn't look much
like it at present, Madelon answered, the snow still on the
ground and we in March. And Héloïse, who had not
seen many springs, fell to thinking that the prophecy
that the world would end in the year one thousand was
about to be fulfilled. The prophets had miscalculated the
date of the end by a hundred years, that was all. The
beginning of the end is at hand, she said; and next morning she awoke to find that she was mistaken, the sky was
blue, the air warm, and before evening the passengers
were walking in the middle of the street to avoid the
drip, talking about the rising river and saying that boats
would soon be plying about the Cathedral. But the river
sank despite the melting snows, and every morning **an**

almost summer sun was busy drying up the streets, turning the marshes into fields again, the genial warmth and
gaiety of the sky permitting Héloïse to sit in the company-room without a fire, a rug about her knees, reading
in the window, hearing (in her mind's ear, of course)
the great minstrel Orpheus singing as the galley pranced
over the curling waves, through the Hellespont, passing
island after island, the Chorus telling new stories of
adventure, enchantment and prophecy, that new worlds
shall be discovered in the age to come, that the imprisoning ocean shall be thrown open till there shall be no
land alone, no Ultima Thule. After many months of
absence from the play, she returned to it to learn that
Jason, having lived with Medea for two years, wearied
of her enough to marry Creusa, the daughter of Creon,
King of Corinth. The poet's reason for including the
murder of the children in the story eluded Héloïse, making her so unhappy that the thrill of happiness was
extraordinarily keen when she perceived in a sudden
inspiration that the murder of the children was the act
of a barbarian girl and not of the sorceress. For Medea's
nature was a double one: two souls in one body, each
striving for mastery. A true woman and a type of humanity, for every human being contains two different
souls, neither of which ever succeeds in overcoming the
other. But was she aware, Héloïse asked herself, that
there were a barbarian girl and a great sorceress within
her? And casting a glance inward she asked herself for
the first time—she had never put the question to herself
before, certainly not so plainly—if she had a destiny,
glad or sad, no matter which, but a destiny—and waited
for an answer that did not come. Her life, as she apprehended it, looking back, seemed strangely trivial and
inconsequential. I seem to have been walking in my

sleep till now, almost unaware of what might betide, but now I feel like rousing. And she began to examine and weigh words that she had let go by without consideration. The dead, she said, have a hold upon us that the living haven't; my father rules from his grave in Palestine. And in one intense moment of vision she saw into life as it is offered to women, the obliteration of themselves in marriage or the obliteration of themselves in convent rules, and understood that she must marry or return to Argenteuil.

Her uncle had sent for her under compulsion, urged by her father's ghost, and she had come to Paris to spend a week, not longer; but her uncle had detained her so that she might read Virgil. She had read Virgil and many other poets, but reading Latin was not enough. A time comes when a woman must choose, and the choice is stinted, convent or marriage, it's always that for a woman. But the pain of choosing is great, she said; the power of choice not being within us; and the happy woman is she who doesn't choose but allows time to choose for her. But time is laggard. A few years will decide better than I which is my natural bourne, the cloister or the castle. Why press me to choose? But nobody is pressing me; and she began to ask herself what might be the cause of her disquiet. Like Medea, she said, two destinies are struggling for mastery; and feeling that she could not sit thinking of herself any longer she began to ask herself if a walk in the woods and the gathering of violets, which would be sure to be springing up almost everywhere, would reveal to her some truth about herself, or if she would gain knowledge of herself by going to the Cathedral and addressing a prayer to the Virgin. And being unable to choose between violets and prayer, she left fate to decide this not very important question. The river drew her that day as it did every day; and over-looking it she watched the ducks swimming in it, saying to herself: Virgil does not speak of the beauty of ducks swimming in a river, the softness of their voices and their round, black eyes so intelligent, but I should not have known how beautiful they are when swimming in a river if I had not read Virgil, and might well have lived my life out from birth to death without knowing that ducks swam with their pert tails turned up to the sky. It is strange that he should have no words about water-lilies, yet he taught me to see their great leathery leaves. He loved the earth, for man lives by the earth as well as on the earth; and her thoughts going back to the fields that repaid the peasant for his labour, she figured him returning in the dusk.

When the scales make daylight and sleep equal in hours, she said, and just halve the glow between light and shadow, set four bulls at work, O man; sow the barley fields right into the showery skirts of frost-bound winter. No less it is time to cover in the earth the flax plant and the corn poppy and to urge on the belated ploughs while the dry earth allows it.

But one cannot read verses such as these and forget the violet-scented vale, and the priest, accompanied by a sleek Tuscan boy blowing an ivory flute, leading a goat to an altar under God's own sky, she said; but it was in the autumn always that thanksgiving was made for the fruits of the fields, for it was then that the orchards and vine-yards gave up their fruits. It is true, she continued, that the spring shower is as needful as the sun and there should have been thanksgiving for it, and unable to recall any she wondered whether, if she fared far enough, she would come upon some bluebell wood where the ancient rites were practised.

CHAP. VII.

ON reaching the Great Bridge she stopped like one upon whom a spell was laid, and she could not do else than abandon the ramble in the woods, for it came to her memory that the King's Gardens were open to the public on Thursday, and that students assembled there for discussion. Soon the swallows will be here, she said, building under the eaves, and she repeated Virgil's lines all the way up the rue des Chantres, passing the Cathedral without seeing it, her feet leading her instinctively to the Little Bridge that connected the city island with the left bank. Clerks and students were coming over it. For what are you coming hither? she asked, and heard the news that Abélard's enemies thought that they had found at last a champion whom they could trust to withstand Abélard. But the one they have found, the scholar said, is but a barking dog that should be driven off with the stick of truth. All the same I'd like to hear his story, said Héloïse, and the student began:

Abélard's opponent is Gosvin, a young man from Joslen's school at Douai, and one full of pluck and resource in argument, whom Joslen, his master, tried all he could to dissuade from his resolve to go to Paris and challenge Abélard in disputation, telling him that Abélard was even more formidable in criticism than in discussion, not so much a doctor as a wit; that he never gave in, never acquiesced in the truth unless it was in his favour; that he wielded the hammer of Hercules, and never let go, and that he, Gosvin, would do better to unravel his sophisms and avoid his errors than to expose himself to laughter. But as he could not be dissuaded his friends and comrades accompanied their David, cheering him most of the way hither; and now all Douai is praying for him, so it is said. Abélard knows nothing of it. Gosvin has a few friends, and as soon as the master begins his lessons Gosvin is to rise up. You'll hear it all in an hour's time in the cloister. From another she learnt that Gosvin was a stripling of six and twenty, slight as a child, with pink and white complexion. And Abélard? she asked. As the student was about to answer her, he was accosted by another student, and Héloïse gave ear to him, thinking he was about to speak of Abélard. But it was of the fine weather they spoke, and not many words were exchanged when a phrase about the cloudless sky provoked the sally: a sky that you do not often see here, but which we see so often in Italy that we weary of it. How proud the Italians are of their sky, cried another. Is not then the sun the same everywhere? Héloïse asked, and it was this simple question that raised the discussion which she had heard her uncle say, the evening the philosophers almost came to blows, was one of daily hap in the Cathedral Gardens. The same sun? a student asked. Have a care. Did not the master tell us that qualities are real and that the species are as real? Of course, cried another student, things are not words, and whoever denies it falls into Roscelin's heresy.

A contentious statement this was, one that soon called forth a challenger who said: If the qualities exist beyond the things with which we associate them, the colour of the flowers exists apart from the flowers; and if the Italian sky is of one colour and the French sky of another, there are two skies. If one sky is cool and grey and the other blue and burning, it seems hard to deny that there are several qualities of sun—two suns. But we know that there is but one sun, cried several voices, and the students agreed that the question was one that should be put to the master. But another student held that the question was too simple to trouble the master with, and in answer to many he said: There is an excellent white wine in thy country, Alberic, and there is an excellent red wine on thy hillsides at Beaune. But what is wine? A species, and liquids are the genus. Now the species is a real thing. It is the vininess that makes the thing, the wine, just as humanity makes the man. But white wine and red wine both are species of the same genus, liquid, and they both are the same in the possession of vininess; therefore, red wine and white wine are the same. But we can go farther. The genus is also a real thing. The genus liquid exists in water, just as it does in wine, and the genus is the truth. It is the essence, and therefore wine is the same as water. I hope you will understand that wine and water are interchangeable. I suppose it is all right, and I'll try to swallow this conclusion, though I choke. Another example: Pacquette is blonde; Madelon is dark. Both are of the species—girl. They have it . . . the essence . . . that . . . how shall I say it . . . *puella virgo* . . . I give it up. For who shall say that they possess that which——

Of a sudden the voices ceased, and, turning her head, Héloïse saw a short man, of square build, who, although well advanced in the thirties, still conveyed an impression of youthfulness; for though squarely built his figure was well knit, his eyes were bright, and his skin fresh and not of an unpleasing hue, brown and ruddy. The day being warm, he walked carrying his hat in his hand, looking round him pleased at the attendance, and it was this look of self-satisfaction that stirred a feeling of dislike in Héloïse. He seemed to her complacent and vain; and

she did not like his round head, his black hair, his slightly
prominent eyes: Solemn eyes, she said to herself, and I
like merry eyes; the only feature that forced an acknowledgment from her was his forehead, which was large and
finely turned. But her admiration of it passed away
quickly in her dislike of his blunt, fleshy nose. His name
had often been mentioned in her presence, she was even
familiar with it, and had she thought about him at all
she would have imagined a thin, finely cut profile, sensi-
tive nose and pointed chin. She could not imagine Aristotle or Plato—Plato still less than Aristotle—or Seneca,
or Virgil, or Ovid, or Tibullus (but these last were poets),
converging to the type that Abélard represented so promi-
nently. She had seen his broad, almost clerical, face
before, dimly, it is true, but she had seen it in certain
prelates, and the thought rose up in her mind that that
philosophy wore an altogether different appearance. But
as soon as he spoke her feelings about him changed as
the world changes when the cloud passes and the sun
comes out. The voice had much to do with the transformation, but not all; it gave beauty to his very slightest
utterance; and the phrases that caught upon her ear were
well worded. He speaks good Latin, she said to herself,
and the words had hardly passed through her mind when
another thought whispered to her: Were Plato and
Aristotle dandies? Half-an-hour must have been spent
in the donning of the laces at his cuffs and another in
choosing the buckles of his shoes. But her criticism of his
apparel was quickly swept away again by the sound of
the smooth, rich, baritone voice, and this time she perceived that the voice was accompanied by an exquisite
courtesy, and that the manner in which he walked addressing those who gathered about him to admire and to
listen was kindly, although it was plain that though

familiarity from him would be an honour he would resent
it quickly in another.

The students gave way before him; he smiled upon
all, waved his square hand, stopping before one who,
on the approach of the master, strove to obliterate a circle
that he had drawn on the gravel with his stick. On seeing
the circle and divining the use of it, Abélard stepped forward from his admirers and held a little court before
proceeding into the cloister to hold his greater court.
A circle, he said, is a figure in which all the lines drawn
from the centre to the circumference are equal; and of
the lines there may be any number. But some of you
would say that I can add another hundred lines and
another two hundred lines, but a moment comes when no
more lines can be added, and this puts into the arguer's
mouth the question: Does the circle exist? Hence all
the difficulties that we know of have arisen, for the circle
does not exist in substance. But it exists in the mind,
and the mind is something, therefore the circle exists.
On these words, amid many acclamations Abélard resumed his resolute gait, exchanging words with those
whom he knew, smiling encouragingly, inviting all to
follow him to the cloister.

Héloïse fell into the crowd of pupils and disciples that
followed him into the cloister—herself the newest—and
from thence into a sort of classroom, a vaulted hall with
many benches in front of the pupils and one long bench
fixed to the oak-panelled wall. The pupils took their
places on the distant benches, the disciples on the benches
grouped about the pulpit; Héloïse sought an obscure
corner, and her eyes followed Abélard as he went up the
five steps that led to the pulpit, and saw him spread
his notes on the desk in front of him. But no sooner had
he done this than a stir, almost a quarrel, began in the

hall, certain pushing their way in and others opposing them. And among these intruders she caught sight of Gosvin, recognising him by the description she had had of him from the students in the Gardens. Now what is the meaning of all this? Abélard asked, and he was answered by Gosvin. I have come from Douai to Paris to thine own school, the little man answered, to get an answer from thee at the request of the students. It would be better for thee to learn to hold thy tongue and not interrupt my lesson, Abélard replied. But I have come all the way to challenge thee to discussion. From whose school? Abélard asked. From the school of Anselm of Laon, Gosvin replied. Hold hard, cried one of the disciples, rising suddenly to his feet. Who is this ill-conditioned fellow who comes from Douai thouing and theeing the master? Who indeed is he? cried several voices, and in a moment a dozen were ready to fling the little impertinent without the doors, and would have done it if Abélard had not interposed. My lesson ended, I will call on the youngest among us to answer you. Douai shall thou and thee Paris while Paris employs the more formal you. At these words Abélard's disciples and pupils released Gosvin. It may be that the youngest is able to answer my arguments as well as the master, but Douai has sent me to meet Abélard in disputation. The disciples rose from their desks, some five or six, and whispered that Gosvin was of good repute in disputation, and urged Abélard to hear him lest a bad impression might be created and their enemies return to Douai with stories. Speak, Abélard said, turning to Gosvin, and Gosvin, unabashed, began:

I am here to overcome, to put to flight, those who hold the false doctrine that there are no substances but individuals. Wilt hear me? he asked. And Abélard answered: have I not said that I will hear you, but be brief, for the question is of little interest here, it having been unriddled and judged long ago; but speak, my boy; only one condition do I make, that you will leave the hall as soon as you have gotten your answer. Now speak.

I will put my argument simply and into the space of a few lines, saying that if there are only individuals then there are Peter, Paul, John and so on, but no humanity. Horses, too, have names, so have dogs, albeit there is no equinity or caninity; and the relation between any man and any horse and any dog is the same as between any man and man and horse and horse and dog and dog. But this being thy doctrine, we in Douai would hear how comes it that we speak of the community of mankind.

The question that you have put to me is even simpler than I had expected, Abélard answered, and it almost shames me to answer it, but since I have promised an answer, hear it. Humanity, equinity and caninity, we say, do not exist as things separable from men, horses and dogs, but we do not deny that men resemble one another, that horses resemble one another and dogs resemble one another. The names of the species indicate the resemblance, which is greater than the resemblance of all to one another as animals, and there you have the reality of species and genus indicated by the names men, horses, dogs, animals.

No sooner had Abélard ceased speaking than Gosvin began again, but before he had uttered many words Abélard, with stern face, answered: Thou hast my answer, interrupt my lesson no longer, else I shall have to ask my pupils to remove thee among some cinders on a shovel. On these words the hustling began, and the little man was pushed to and fro, almost carried out of the hall, crying back all the while: But I haven't yet ended, I haven't ended, while heedless of the outcry, Abélard applied himself to his notes just as if the scene had already faded from his mind, ready to begin his lecture as soon as the disciples returned.

The two poles of man's moral existence, he said, are faith and reason. But it is not our object to-day to inquire which is the more important. We wish rather to affirm and show that both are equal and that the work begun by faith can be continued by reason; that, in fact, reason was given to us to continue it. Faith and reason are the theme of to-day's lecture, and the relations which each bears to the other; but before proceeding into discrimination I would call your thoughts to the consideration that faith and reason projected themselves into literature, taking a final form in the same century, as far as can be known about the sixth century before Our Lord Jesus Christ was born in Bethlehem. It was fifteen hundred years before this great event, the greatest that ever happened in the history of the world, that the Bible began to come into literary existence, nearly a thousand years before the Babylonian captivity the story of man's birth and fall was communicated by God to his Chosen People in Palestine, a stiff-necked, rebellious people, as himself has called them, accepting the revelation without enough apprehension of the honour that was done to them, disobeying the law that was given unto them for their preservation at all times, until God in his anger resolved to destroy the world, but was moved to spare the world and to accept the atonement proposed by his Son, Our Lord Jesus Christ.

The second communication of God's will was received by the Apostles, Matthew, Mark, Luke and John, from Jesus Christ himself.

I must ask pardon for calling to your thoughts truths
so well known to you all, but it seems to me that for a
plenary understanding of to-day's lecture it was necessary
to remind you that the Bible, unlike Homer, is entirely
dissociated from man's imagination; the Old and the
New Testaments are both messages from God to Man.
In saying this I am on sure ground, none will dispute it;
none except the Infidel from whom our armies have succeeded in rescuing the Holy Sepulchre. None will dispute save the Infidel that the Bible, being inspired by
God, must be accepted by man through God's own gift,
faith. We accept the Bible without discussion. It is our
duty, of course, to interpret the Bible; it is the duty of
the Church, for God has given us the Church, as well as
the Bible. I need not labour the point any further, and
will pass on to a matter less trite and commonplace than
to say that the Bible is a work of Divine inspiration, to a
matter that has not yet been considered, brought into
relief, by anybody that I know of: that while the Bible
was coming into existence, at the same time a great poet,
the greatest the world has ever known, was brooding and
writing the Iliad and the Odyssey. And these poems,
though they came less directly from God than the Bible,
are also a gift from God in something more than is
implied by the trite phrase: all things come from God.
Inspiration has never been denied to the Iliad and the
Odyssey. Homer was inspired; he received his gift from
God, and though the inspiration was less direct than the
inspiration that was vouchsafed to Moses, still it must
be held that he was inspired. I do not know if the point
has ever been disputed. Virgil, too, was inspired, and
perhaps his inspiration was even more direct than
Homer's, for did he not predict the coming of Our Lord?
It is a remarkable fact—remarkable—I choose this word

with care—remarkable that the great work of faith and
the great work of reason should have been written in the
same period, for Homer lived perhaps a thousand years
before the birth of Our Lord, about the time of David or
Solomon, who continued the Bible.

A student raised his hand. May I put a question,
master? The master, with a slight contraction of the
brow, resigned himself to the question, and it was debated
for some minutes whether Homer's poems should not be
considered as arising out of a new sense come to man,
the sense of beauty. Are not the poems concerned with
beauty rather than with reason? The interrupter seemed
to have brought a truth to light, but the master explained
that the sense of beauty implied reason, for beauty means
to discriminate, and to discriminate we must have reason;
the animals that have not reason do not discriminate, but
are guided by their instincts. The interrupter acquiesced,
unwillingly, it seemed to Héloïse, and she hated him, for
her whole being was drawn to the idea that Abélard was
about to make known, drawn as the needle is to the lode-
stone, wholly without thought, all other thoughts and
desires being absorbed in one desire, the desire of the
story on the lips of the Prophet; for he was that in her
eyes already. This much, however, I will concede to
Raymond, Abélard continued, looking towards the student, who blushed with pleasure at feeling the master's
eyes upon him, and as the word concede implied that in
the master's opinion his interruption was not wholly
valueless he became at once a centre of admiration. This
much I will concede, Abélard said, to Raymond, that
Homer's poems were not the dawn of reason: the dawn of
reason arose some hundreds of years later in the East.
Homer's poems were but a beacon fire, or shall we call
them the cry of the watchman: The dawn is nigh! for

it was four hundred years later, Abélard repeated, emphasising the point, which he seemed to regard as of primary importance, that man leaped, as it were, into a new existence, about six hundred years before the coming of Christ, that man broke at least one of the links that attached him to the animal, and rose to higher state than before: Buddha appeared in India, Confucius in China, a little later Plato and Aristotle in Greece. All these were inspired, and all these prepared the world to receive the great revelation that was to come to the Apostles from Jesus Christ himself in Palestine eleven hundred and seventeen years ago.

The throne is in heaven and invisible, but the stairway leading to the throne is under our feet; we can look back and count the stairs, each one of which is a step in the ascension of man. Each generation mounts a stair, and when a generation mounts several there is a halt for man to draw breath and prepare himself for the next ascension. Eleven hundred and seventeen years ago man reached a great stair-head, Christianity; and ever since we have been calling to the laggard nations to follow us. They have not followed as quickly as we would wish, and to bring them up to where we now stand a new revelation was needed. It has been vouchsafed to us. One hundred and seventeen years ago it was thought that the old world was ended; and men gave their wealth to the Church, certain that the last day was at hand. Nor was their mistake as great as it has been since supposed. If the foretelling had been: the old world by faith alone is ended, the prophets would have foretold no more than the truth, for it has come to pass within the last century that a new revelation has been given to us, and by it all the world may be won to Christianity.

As Abélard spoke these words Héloïse remembered the

words of the chorus in Seneca's *Medea*: new worlds shall be discovered in the age to come, the imprisoning ocean shall be thrown open till there shall be no land alone, no ultima Thule. And she longed to rise to her feet and speak them, for they would bring wings to the master's argument, a flying feather, at least. So did she feel as she sat entranced, questioning herself; carried, in truth, out of an old world into a new one. In her trance, for it was one, she accepted the intellectual and the physical as one, though a few moments before she distinguished between them. Nor was this strange, for the man was not the same; all the defects of parade and artificiality had disappeared, and the faith he was preaching, that reason had come to man's aid and was about to remould the world, shone out of his pale blue exalted eyes—all she saw of him clearly were his eyes and she heard only his smooth, rich voice; and his arguments mattered little or nothing to her now. So deep was the spell put upon her that if he had told her to mount the tower of the Cathedral and cast herself over she would have done it.

He had passed into the second part of his lecture, into analysis and discernment, and the disciples were putting questions; she heard him answer every one with ease and was carried out of herself beyond control; drawn along in sensations of fear and happiness, she knew not which, nor what would befall her, till Abélard began to gather his notes from his desk, and while doing so he continued to address his favourite pupils and disciples. She strove to resist the impulse urging her, but her strength broke and snapped like a viol string, and pressing through the crowd, lost to reason, she threw herself on her knees, and catching his hands as he came down from the pulpit, she kissed them. Women did not come to his lectures, and his pupils regarded the interruption as unseemly—if not

unseemly at least an uncomely incident—and pressed
forward, thinking that the master must not be subjected
to violent demonstrations twice on the same afternoon.
But Abélard turned them back, and raising Héloïse from
her knees he led her out of the cloister into the quadrangle. His arm was about her, his voice whispered in
her ear.

What happened afterwards she never succeeded in remembering exactly, but supposed that she must have
followed the familiar streets instinctively without knowing
she was following them. It could not have been else,
for when she awoke finally she stood on the steps of her
uncle's house ashamed, not knowing how it had all come
about.

CHAP. VIII.

IT is her step, Fulbert said, as he sat reading, and laying down his book, he waited. But hearing her talking
in the front hall with Madelon, he grew impatient. Come,
he cried, and tell me thy roamings in the woods. What,
no violets! I have not been in the woods to-day, uncle.
And she told how at the Great Bridge she was moved to
go to the Cathedral to say a prayer to the Virgin for her
guidance. An excellent thought! the Canon exclaimed,
and was about to add that he wished such thoughts were
more frequent in her, but he checked himself in time;
and it was as well that he did, for Héloïse had to confess
that her pious project was swept out of her mind by the
groups of students in the King's Gardens. Waiting for
Abélard, the Canon interposed, with some, to be sure,
waiting for Gosvin and looking forward to his triumph
in disputation, a young man of genius whom Douai sends
to Paris in the hope that his dialectic may be enough to

stop the spread of Nominalism. To bid the tide retire,
Héloïse said, with a quiet smile. So thou regardest Abélard's genius as a tide that cannot be stayed. Gosvin's
bidding will not stay the tide of Abélard's success, she
replied. Instead of seeking violets in the woods thou
wast in the cloister, niece, augmenting by one the swelling crowd of Abélard's admirers. Yes, I was in the
cloister, uncle. And I gather from thy words and tone
that he triumphed over Gosvin. Héloïse raised her eyes
contemptuously and asked the Canon in a quiet, even
voice, which irritated him, if Abélard were greater than
Plato and Aristotle, to which the Canon replied that none
was and none ever would be greater than Plato and
Aristotle; but being of tractable humour that morning and
disposed to worship the rising sun, he said that Abélard's
genius was an honour to France, and that if he could
steer clear of heresy he would rank sooner or later as the
descendant of Plato and Aristotle. He comes from thy
country, niece, Nantes or near by. An argumentative
fellow truly, the son of Bérenger, a soldier attached to
the court of Hoel IV., Duke of Brittany, and the story
runs that he gave up all claim to the family estate so
that he might be free to wander the world over, ravelling
and unravelling thoughts and entangling opponents in
webs of arguments. Many are the stories told about him,
and they agree in this, that he has never yet been worsted
in an intellectual encounter. But how is this, niece?
I never knew thee give a thought to a living man before.
How is it that he has captured thine imagination? Did
you think it difficult to capture it, uncle? Yours as well
as mine would have been captured too had you been in
the cloister to-day. And knowing you as I do, I wonder
with what words you would have praised him. I was
detained in the Cathedral, the Canon answered, through

the fault—— But there's no need why I should trouble
thee with the story; far better that I should hear how
Abélard overthrew Gosvin in disputation. It was soon
over, Héloïse answered, and after keeping the Canon
waiting a long time, she spoke aloud, but to herself
mainly: Nobody was ever more wonderful. So he de-
molished Gosvin at once? the Canon interjected. Gosvin!
she cried. Yet he is a man of good repute in argument,
else he would not have been chosen as champion, the
Canon said, and now fully awake, Héloïse began to tell
that his aggression was as stupid as it was impertinent.
By what right did he interrupt the master's lesson? she
asked. All the same, he was treated none too fairly, being
only given an opportunity of saying a few words. Abélard replied briefly, and deeming the argument at an end,
muttered, as he turned to his notes, that if Gosvin did not
leave at once he would send for a shovel and cinders.
The Canon laughed outright; such ferocities of language,
he said, were characteristic of Abélard. But the provoca-
tion put upon Abélard, she averred, was very great, and
I am not in agreement with you, uncle, that ferocities are
characteristic of him, for I heard him speak with courtesy
to his disciples in the Gardens and controvert with gentleness, stopping to explain by means of a circle his
doctrine of Conceptualism. But the Canon gave little
heed to her eulogy, remarking casually that Abélard was
a master of honeyed words as well as bitter. Enough,
however, of Abélard for the present; tell me his lesson.
I am not Abélard and cannot relate his lesson. I do not
ask thee to relate the lecture but to tell the subject of it.
The subject was Faith and Reason, she answered. One
that he would treat well, the Canon said, and he begged
his niece to relate as much of the lesson as she could
remember. But he could not persuade her out of her

thoughts, and when he pressed her she replied: I would tell it if I could, but cannot. At last she broke the pause: But do you tell me his story. And if I do? he asked. If you do I will try to remember his lesson, she replied.

At the time of which I am about to speak I was not Canon of Notre-Dame, but I remember hearing that William de Champeaux was never tired of saying that he had never had a pupil like Abélard, and his praise ran on the lines that Abélard could develop an argument in several directions, drawing from it unsuspected thoughts and ideas. But the lad had no intention of repeating and reshaping his master's thoughts, and Champeaux, it is said, had to yield to him in argument more than once, which made an enemy of his master and many of his master's disciples. But enemies mattered little to him, for he could learn anything he pleased in half the time that anybody else could, and his daring was so great that men gave way before him as men will do before victory, accepting him for the sake of his success, bowing before him as before a conqueror. At that time he was a mere stripling, and anxious that his friends' hopes of him should come to pass, he began to look round him for a school in which he should be master. And Melun, an important town near Fontainebleau, seeming to him suitable, he settled there. At once his school became famous, and it was at Melun that his talent began to take wing; England, Germany, Italy, sent students, and encouraged by the good fortune which he now believed was his for ever, Abélard left Melun for Corbeil. The choice was a lucky one, maybe a wise one. However this may be, Corbeil became soon after. like Melun, a royal seat, and at Corbeil he was nearer Paris, ready at any moment to carry the citadel by assault. Which he did, Héloïse interjected. Yes; but no sooner had he succeeded in establishing a school at Corbeil than his health yielded to the strain he had put upon it and he was obliged to give up everything and to go away for a long rest. He travelled, it is said, in Germany and England; some hold that it was in England that he met Roscelin, but it is not known for certain, for he never speaks of these years, and the secrecy he keeps regarding them has set many tongues wagging. A wonderful man, uncle. But go on with your story, for it is as wonderful as—— Go on with your story, uncle. Well, niece, he reappeared after some four or five years. But if thou wouldst understand his reappearance I must tell what befell William de Champeaux in the meanwhile. Leave Champeaux out of it, uncle; tell me about Abélard. The story of one cannot be told without the other, the Canon answered testily. I must tell the story in my own way. Champeaux, fallen into years, was living in as much seclusion as a man of great reputation may; but he was persuaded to open a school again at St. Victor, and one day, while lecturing to his pupils and disciples, he caught sight of Abélard among them. His heart misgave him, and it is said that he found difficulty in continuing his lesson till Abélard came forward to reassure him, saying: I have come to ask permission to attend your lessons, master. Champeaux could not exclude him from his school; to have done so would have been a confession that he was not able to meet him in argument; and it seems to me that the story I am telling of his invasion of Champeaux's school shows the spiritual adventurer who left his home in Brittany to meet men in disputation and overthrow them, the pitiless logician who cares for nothing but his art. But his turn will come, as it comes to all who are carried away by pride and believe their destinies are written in the signs of the zodiac.

At first he was full of deference, but it was only a mock, for Champeaux's doctrine was the very opposite of Roscelin's, and Abélard began to press him back with arguments clear and striking, worsting him in his own school and obliging him to retire from the position he had taken up.

After this second victory, Abélard's position seemed more than ever secure; his doctrine acquired greater force and influence, and many of those who attacked him before passed over to his side, won by his personality and eloquence. He conquered where nobody else dared; his enemies were afraid to meet him; he was so skilful in argument that he could attack both sides equally well; Realist and Nominalist went down before him, and he came to be spoken of as the new Socrates. But this was unendurable, and William de Champeaux assembled all his partisans and friends, all the congregation of St. Victor, and challenged him to a decisive argument, one that must bring ruin to one or the other. Abélard was victorious? Héloïse asked. Yes; but in the middle of his triumph, or perhaps I should say at the moment when his triumph was complete, another idea seems to have come into his head and he left public life without telling anybody he was going. This second withdrawal was well calculated, a matter of some three or four months, a period long enough for the people to feel how much his presence and teaching meant to them. In three or four months he was back again, before the wonderment ceased. He entered Paris as a conqueror, triumph after triumph drawing crowds from all countries; Germany, England, Italy, came to listen to Abélard, the renowned philosopher of Europe.

The Canon stopped speaking so that Héloïse might ask him some questions that would lead to a further un-

winding of a story which had begun to seem to him better
worth telling than he thought before he began it.   But
Héloïse said nothing, and after waiting for a question
from her, he said: Where are thy thoughts?   My thoughts,
uncle, were—— I do not know exactly where they were.
I suppose I must have been thinking.   Can one think
without words?   Ah, now, I remember; I was asking
myself if Abélard's story would have revealed to me
the man whom I saw and heard in the cloister——   If
thou hadst heard his story from me before seeing him?
Yes, uncle; and her face still deep in a cloud of meditation, she confessed that it was not until she heard him
in the cloister that she began to see that what she saw
and heard were not two different things but one thing,
for he would not be himself without—— Without what,
niece? the Canon asked, for he was amused by Héloïse's
embarrassment, and to continue it, he added: his beauty?
The sneer threw Héloïse off her guard, and she answered
that nobody could call Abélard an ugly man.   A stocky
little fellow, the Canon persisted.   And he would have
said more of the same kind if Héloïse's face had not
warned him to proceed no further with his teasing.   He
spoke instead of Abélard's forehead, which he admitted
to be of the Socratic type in its amplitude; but he averred
that the likeness between the two men ceased at the forehead, for whereas Socrates was of the ascetic temperament, Abélard was by his face notably a free liver, a disparagement that seemed to Héloïse like a challenge.   She
asked the Canon to mention a feature that would testify
to the truth of this, and the spirit of battle being upon
him he could not keep back the words: his singing of
French songs.   You never spoke to me before of Abélard
as one divided between free living and philosophy.   Nor
is it many minutes since you were speaking of him as the

intellectual descendant of Aristotle and Plato; your present sneers of him cannot be else than an attempt to anger
me, and we would do better, mayhap, to talk of matters
on which we are agreed. The Canon did not answer her,
but sat perplexed, anxious at least to tell her that this
unseemly quarrel was accidental. He began to explain
that in speaking of Abélard as stocky he had been led
away by his love of banter. Héloïse's face stopped him
in the middle of a sentence, and instead of finishing it he
went to his cupboard and returned with two books; he
handed her Virgil and began to read Tibullus, and this
act was so graceful and conciliatory that Héloïse could
barely restrain a smile when their eyes met.

The storm was over, but a storm leaves disorder behind
it, and her uncle's disparagement of Abélard made it
impossible for her to continue sitting opposite to him,
though she knew that his sneers and sarcasms were intended to provoke her or to put her enthusiasm for the
lecture (which he judged to be excessive) to a test. He
was forgiven, but his presence was an irritation, and she
sat thinking how she might leave the room without rousing her uncle's suspicions that she was angry; and to
save him from all misapprehension she continued to read
the *Eclogues* a while longer, till at last, unable to bear
the strain, she rose to her feet abruptly and bade him
good-night, saying that she felt tired and was going to
bed. A very long and dragging hour it has been, but it
is over at last, she said, on her way to her room, and as
she could think better lying than sitting, she undressed,
turned over in her bed, folded her arms, and began to
ask herself why she had omitted to tell her uncle what
had befallen her in the Cathedral. The words were often
on her lips, but they were checked and passed over, which
was unfortunate, for it was nearly certain he would hear

the story from somebody present, Alberic or Romuald;
and besides these there were others who were on friendly
terms with him and came to the house in the rue des
Chantres. As soon as he heard of her behaviour he would
come to her and say: What is this story I hear about
thee, bursting through the disciples at the end of the
lecture and throwing thyself at his feet? What answer
would she make? At last it became clear to her that she
must confide the whole matter to her uncle when he
came downstairs next morning. But she was down before
him, and after waiting some while, she and Madelon
started forth for the market, their baskets on their arms,
thinking that the Canon would be up to meet them when
they returned. But though they were an hour away, the
Canon was still abed when they returned, having drunk
more wine than was good for him after we bade each other
good-night, Héloïse said to Madelon, who answered that
on these occasions the Canon was unfit for the transaction
of any business. He will sign any papers that are put
before him, and it is my duty to deny him to callers;
we shan't see much of him before three o'clock. Her
words hit the mark; it was a little after three before the
Canon left the house, without Héloïse hearing him, and
when an hour later she asked Madelon for news of her
uncle, Madelon answered: he has gone to the Cathedral;
he left here about an hour ago, and thou must have
been deep in thy book not to have heard him, for he
banged the door behind him. There is often much noise
in the street, Héloïse answered, and she returned to the
company-room, thinking to continue her reading till her
uncle returned, for her mind was still fixed on confiding
her trouble to him. And if she got tired of reading she
would go to the woods and come back with the violets
that she did not gather yesterday. He will smell them

from the doorway, and will be pleased to find them in his study, she said.

And her thoughts passing from violets, she began once more to consider the story she had to tell her uncle. At what point would she begin to tell it? She would have to tell him the whole of it, so she would begin by telling that as she was about to cross the Great Bridge something stopped her from crossing it. He would ask her what she meant by something, and she only knew that she was turned from her first purpose (which was to go in the woods and gather violets) by a thought that she needed the Virgin's intercession. She was on her way to the Cathedral to say a prayer, but was turned from this second purpose by the sight of the students in the King's Gardens, where Alberic and Romuald were indulging in mental gymnastics, laughing alternately at Realism and Nominalism; and it was in the midst of their jocular disputation that Abélard crossed the Gardens, surrounded by pupils and disciples, on his way to the cloister. All this she had told her uncle, and about Gosvin; and of the wonderful lecture on Faith and Reason she had given such an account as she was able. Her story would therefore concentrate on the moment when she was compelled to press through the crowd and throw herself at his feet. Alas, her uncle would think she was telling him a fable, a dream that she had dreamed overnight and mistook for reality. She would not blame him, for her conduct was so unlike herself that she did not recognise herself in it, nor would anyone who knew her recognise her in it. The nuns, were they told the story, would deny it, and who knew her better than the nuns? Not even Madelon. Madelon wouldn't believe it any more than the nuns would, nor could she blame them, for she didn't believe it herself--yet it was true. How little one knows of oneself! She fell to wondering if the impulse that had compelled her in the Cathedral would arise again; not the same impulse, but similar impulses. Was she subject to these? And was the one that had risen yesterday but the first of a long series?

Overcome, almost afraid, she sat viewing her future life through her imagination, and so immersed was she in the possibilities a single thought had evoked, that she did not hear the door open, and was startled almost out of her wits by Madelon's voice: Now whatever is the girl thinking about? Did I frighten thee, Héloïse? Well, these frights are soon over, and as soon as thou hast recovered thy wits tell me the story thou hast been reading. It's no story, Madelon; I was only thinking. And it not being Madelon's way to press for an answer, she said: A letter has just come for thee, and I have brought it up. Héloïse thought she detected a faint irony in Madelon's voice. A letter for me? she said; from whom can it be? I can tell nothing about it, Madelon answered; a boy brought it and went away quickly. Brought it and went away quickly, Héloïse repeated. The letter could not have come from any but Abélard, and the thought brought a change of expression into her face, which was unfortunate, for Madelon's eyes were upon her. Did the boy come from Argenteuil? Wouldst thou have me stand in front of thee guessing whence a letter comes, and it in thy hand, silly? And the answer put the thought into Héloïse's mind that she had not spoken wisely in mentioning Argenteuil. Her first mistake was followed by a second, for she did not dare to read the letter under Madelon's inquisitive eyes, but threw it on the table beside her, saying: the letter can wait; I am busy reading, Madelon. But she would not betray me, Héloïse said to herself, so why did I not trust her? And opening her letter as soon as Madelon left the room, she read the brief note that Abélard had sent her, saying: I must write to thank you, Héloïse, for your quick outburst of admiration for my lecture, and I shall be waiting for you in the Cathedral after vespers. That was all. Waiting in the Cathedral after vespers for me, she repeated. Héloïse—who can have given him my name? Alberic or Romuald? It matters little which, she said. What was important was that he knew her name and had written to her. His letter was proof that he did not look upon her as a little fool, so she had been frightened by nothing. He had written her a letter, a letter asking her to meet him in the Cathedral? And she sat lost in an amazed delight at the honour that had befallen her. But why did he want to see her? The reason was not far to seek; he had said that he would like her to attend his lectures, and to make sure of her attendance he sent for her; he wished her to sit under him in the cloister and to take notes like the other pupils, and to put questions to him like the others, though she was only seventeen and had come from the convent of Argenteuil not more than six months ago. But would her uncle allow her to attend Abélard's lectures? He would be only too glad, he was proud of her learning, but if he had not drunk so much wine last night and had left his bed earlier, she would have confided the story of her conduct to him, and he would have remained in the house talking to her, forgetful of his business in the Cathedral, till Abélard's letter came, which she would have had to show him, and he would have said: let us go together to see Abélard. Instead of the great pleasure that awaited her, meeting Abélard alone, hearing him talking to her, she would have sat apart hearing Abélard talking to her uncle, a thing that would be no pleasure to her whatsoever, nor to Abélard; he would have been

annoyed with her for showing her letter (for if Abélard
had wanted to see the Canon he would have written to
him); he would have thought her a little fool, and she
would not have been able to explain. He might never
have written again, never wished to see me, so what luck
it is for all of us that uncle drank that wine, she said.
Uncle had spoken about the benefit I could get by going
to the cloister to attend the lectures; true, he was talking
of Champeaux, but I couldn't have learnt from Champeaux, I know I couldn't; Abélard would like to teach
me and I could learn from Abélard.

Her thought of him brought him before her eyes, and
his image set her thinking of the little quarrel overnight
between herself and her uncle regarding his appearance.
He was short, it is true, but strong and well knit, with
fine shoulders. A noble and kindly brow bespoke his vast
intelligence and placed him above all men and made all
men jealous of him. She had heard him spoken of as
proud; she knew many who were proud without just
cause, but he was proud—could it be else, since he was
acknowledged by all the world as the greatest philosopher
of his time, perhaps of all time? She had heard it said
that he could not brook an interruption, but she had seen
other people fly into a rage about trivial things. Mother
Ysabeau, for instance, when a novice came in to ask her
a question, interrupting the addition of a column of
figures. It was said that he resented contradiction, as
well he might, for he knew that all he said was true and
could be proved; nor could she blame him for the words
he had uttered against Gosvin, offensive though they were.
It was part of his genius, and if we are to have genius we
must put up with the inconveniences of genius, a thing
that the world will never do; it wants geniuses but would
like them just like other people; how stupid the world is,

it never can understand. And she stood like one at bay,
hating the world for its inability to appreciate Abélard,
working herself up into a rage, saying: never is he praised
for his kindness, his tolerance; yet these qualities were
manifest no later than yesterday, when a student interrupted him in the middle of his lecture to ask him if the
Iliad were not more beautiful than reasonable, by no
means a stupid question; and that was why Abélard had
been at pains to answer the student, to lay aside his own
thoughts and apply himself to discovering an answer,
which of course he did. And how well he explained that
it was reason that gave us beauty; saying that the animals
may have preferences, but can have no thought for
beauty, for they have not the power to compare one thing
with another. And he discovered this wonderful answer
in the middle of his lecture, returning to his lecture, easily
picking up the thread just where he had left it. How
wonderful!

She awoke suddenly though she had not been asleep,
and her first thought on returning to herself (she seemed
to have been absent for a long time, for how long she
did not know—a few seconds or a few minutes) was to
rue the time she had spent over the Latin poets; how much
better it would have been if she had given half the time
to the Greek philosophers. Plato was always in his
mouth; he reverenced Aristotle, but Plato was almost a
God in his eyes; and having acquired the right to ransack
her uncle's library as she pleased, she opened a closet and
sought for the *Timæus,* and spent a couple of hours poring over it; but her mind was so distraught by the prospect of meeting Abélard in a few hours' time in the
Cathedral that she failed to fix her attention for long
on any page of it. Aristotle is easier, she said, and returning the *Timæus* to its place, she took down the

Categories, hoping that he would fall in with her mood better than Plato. But her attention wandered from Aristotle as it had from Plato, and she was soon thinking of another philosopher, one of whom she had heard Sister Josiane speak in the convent (Sister Josiane rarely spoke of anybody else), an Irishman who had come to France three centuries before; a petulant, irritable man of violent temper, afterwards killed by his pupils in England, who could bear his despotism no longer. Sister Josiane pressed this man's writing upon all and sundry, and if she had hearkened to the Sister she would have been better able to meet Abélard in the Cathedral and talk to him befittingly, but—— Her thoughts seemed to fall into nothing, and she sat for a long while unaware of any thought, in a lethargy, a stupor, from which she awoke surprised to find herself in the company-room.

CHAP. IX.

SHE had not told Madelon from whom her letter came; she had refused to read it in front of her, afraid of her searching eyes, but Madelon never stopped till she knew everything; patient as a cat she watched and waited till she knew, though she never made any use of her knowledge. She can't bear, Héloïse continued, to be ignorant of anything that is going on in the house, that is all, and uncle is often afraid to speak, walls having ears and speech too, for Madelon—— How else is it that she knows next day what was said overnight in the study? . . . I'd like to get out of the house without her knowing it. And choosing the moment when she thought she might leave without encountering Madelon in the passage, and with all the streets well in her mind that she must take to avoid meeting the Canon on his way home from the

Cathedral, Héloïse hurried on, a little vexed and anxious, for why, she said, did he give me a tryst so late in the evening? And why did he choose the Cathedral? It will be as black as night, maybe. But I shall miss him if I stand thinking; and she hurried on through the by-streets, arriving at the Cathedral without being stopped by anybody she knew.

It's blacker even than I thought for, she said, as she pushed through the swing doors; so black it was that she barely escaped falling over some penitents kneeling within the shadows of the first pillars, and as she advanced into the Cathedral she came upon other groups of penitents, all so immersed in God that they lay indifferent whether the passer-by lost her feet or kept them; and indifferent to them as they to her, the girl sought her lover through the gloom of the pillars, peering and stopping to listen but not daring to call his name aloud. At last a voice spoke her name, setting her heart beating violently, for though she could not see the face she knew the voice was Abélard's: It was good of you to come. Good of me? she repeated; but I wanted to come. If there was only a little light. And still picking their way through penitents, they moved up the church, guided by a rim of daylight high up in the roof. I was so glad to get your letter, she said. Tell me why you were glad to get my letter, he asked. You must know very well, she answered, for it is not difficult to guess; because I was ashamed of what I had done and afraid that you would think me a little fool. But I could not help myself, for what you said sounded to me like a prophecy, and it is one. Neither you nor your disciples laughed at me, did you, when you returned to the lecture hall from the cloister where you left me? Laughed! he said, and the accent of indignation that he put upon the word convinced her even more than

his letter that she had done no more than to obey a fortunate impulse. You were so kind, so thoughtful, and
you understood where many another would have failed
to understand; but of course you understand, I am talking nonsense; you understand everything, even Héloïse,
which is but natural, since you understand Plato and
Aristotle. And then, encouraged by his eyes, which she
could just see in the darkness, she began to tell him that
as soon as she reached home the Canon asked her how
it was she had brought no violets home from the woods:
And I answered him that I hadn't been to the woods but
to the Cathedral; and after telling him about your lesson
and giving as good an account of it as I was able (a very
poor account of it, it is true, for it was all in a tangle in
my head and I could not unravel it yesterday, not even
as well as I could to-day), I put questions to him about
you, and he told me all your story; how you had given
up your lands to your brothers and sisters so that you
might be free to wander the world over teaching; and the
story seeming to me like some Old Testament story I
was carried away by it, almost as I was by your own
words. But did you tell him, Abélard asked, that you
pressed through the pupils and disciples as I came down
from the pulpit, and——? No, she said; I did not tell
him that I threw myself at your feet and kissed your
hands, but afterwards I saw that I had done wrong in
keeping back anything; I suppose I was ashamed to tell
it; but I am ashamed no longer, I glory in it; for if one
is not to give honour to the greatest philosopher in the
world, perhaps the greatest of all time, to whom? But,
she continued, after a pause, it fell out that I couldn't
tell him, for to-day—— We shall be able to talk better
in a side chapel, Abélard said, interrupting her, for penitents were moving about them, and though Héloïse spoke

in a very low voice he was afraid that some part of their talk might reach other ears than his. Penitents, he said, are apt to forget their sins when there is anything to overhear; and taking her by the arm, he led her through the church. Not this way, she said; there is a side chapel where we shall be quite alone and where there is a little light; and as she was leading him to it she tried to continue her story, but he said: wait, for I shall be able to listen to you better in the side chapel. As soon as they were in it, he said: You were telling me that you were unable to tell your uncle—— That I threw myself at your feet? Yes, she said; I intended to tell him this morning, but he was still in bed; and every morning I go to the market with Madelon, our servant—— And when you returned, Abélard interjected, the Canon had left for the Cathedral? No; he did not leave till the afternoon, and I was reading in the company-room, waiting for him, but he left the house without my hearing him. But you told him on returning from my lecture that you had seen me? Yes, she answered; there was no reason why I shouldn't tell him I had been to the cloister. No, there was no reason, Abélard said. But if you would not like me to tell him that you wrote to me and asked me to meet you in the Cathedral—— I shall meet the Canon to-morrow or the next day, and think that my account—— Would be better than mine, she interjected. Of course it would be. But how fortunate it was that I did not hear him leave the house, for if I had, I should have had to show him your letter and he would have stopped and talked to me, and perhaps would have come with me; and he and you would have talked together, and I should have been left out, listening to my uncle, who is often very talkative. You read Latin, he said, every evening together. Now, who could have told you

that? Alberic or Romuald, of course, who often come
to my uncle's house in the rue des Chantres. And they
told me, too, he said, that you came last autumn from the
Benedictine convent at Argenteuil, the favourite pupil
of the nuns there, and that you are already known in
Paris as *la très sage Héloïse*. The nuns have praised
me to my uncle, and my uncle is proud of my learning,
such as it is, but what is it compared to yours? Nothing
at all. But I do love the Latin language, and am wondering why we are not talking it instead of the jargon, and
why you asked me to meet you in the Cathedral?

The Cathedral is very dark, he answered; and I have
many enemies. Is that why we are talking jargon? she
asked; because none would believe the story, if it were
put about, that the great philosopher Abélard met the
learned Héloïse in the Cathedral and held converse in
jargon. But you must not speak of the French language
as jargon, he answered: it was not until the last century
that the language of the people, spoken only in the fields
and in the market-places and on the high roads, but never
written in, found its way into literature. Have you not
heard of the *Chanson de Roland?* And a language that
has an epic poem written in it cannot be spoken of as
jargon. Have you not heard of the troubadours and
trouvères? Héloïse answered that she had heard of the
trouvères and the troubadours, but knew nothing of their
songs, and Abélard continued to tell her of the progress
of the French language: spoken to-day, he said, in all
the castles of the nobles. But you speak it in the rue
des Chantres. I speak it to Madelon, and Romuald and
Alberic speak it when they come to the rue des Chantres,
in the corners. But it is frowned upon by the canons
who come to your house from Notre-Dame, Abélard replied. I forgot just now when I said that I had never

heard a song in French; some of the students sing in
French—— But these songs are frowned upon? Abélard
interjected. Yes, just so, she answered. The Church
would have Latin spoken by everybody except the working folk, he replied; for the Church wishes the world
to remain in ignorance, reserving learning to itself, as its
exclusive possession; a mistaken view, for in spite of the
Church the jargon, as the ecclesiastics are apt to call it,
has become the language of music, and poetry and music
and the arts, I have often thought, are as powerful as
dialectics. We have therefore art and reason on our side;
and the Church will not prevail against us in the end,
though the end be far distant. But why, then, asked
Héloïse, do you not lecture in French? I should be
understood, he answered, only by a handful, for the
French spoken in one district is not exactly the same as
in another; the language is in the process of formation,
and Latin will dominate the lecture-room for many a year
to come. But the language of the future is the French
language; even the ecclesiastics are obliged to speak it
when they call assemblies to urge the people to enlist in
Raymond's army, and the welcome given to Pope Urban
was really given to the French language. I will never
speak of the jargon again, but always of the French
language, Héloïse said, half to herself, half to Abélard.
An awkward silence fell between them, and at every
moment it became more acute and intense, till it seemed
impossible to break it. You asked me to attend your
lectures, Héloïse said at last. And you will come, he
interjected, his speech returning to him suddenly. She
asked him when he would lecture again, and he answered:
not till the end of the week. I am lecturing to-morrow
and the next day at Ste. Geneviève; but I am afraid I
shall never be able to please you again as I did yesterday.

Why do you say that? You will. Each time I shall be
delighted more than the last, for I shall understand you
better, she replied.

He would have liked to keep her thoughts on himself,
and to speak to her about herself, but his vanity intervened; and wishing to hear what part of his lecture
appealed to her more than any other part, he said: you,
who were so deeply moved by my lecture on Faith and
Reason, may be able to tell me what part of it you
liked best; general statements are good; one should begin
by liking the whole, but the Nominalists, and we are all
Nominalists to-day, believe that it is only through the
parts that we have knowledge of the whole.

You would not have me, a schoolgirl from Argenteuil,
advance my reason against yours, master? Not against,
he replied; but without repudiating any part you can
tell which struck your imagination. Tell me, for to hear
will be a help to me. I liked it all, she answered, but
the piercing was when you said: it has come to pass
that within the last century a new science has been given
to us whereby the whole world may be won to Christianity,
for then I could barely restrain myself from calling out
to you the words of the Chorus in Seneca's *Medea*: new
worlds shall be discovered in the age to come, the imprisoning ocean shall be thrown open till there shall be no
land alone, no ultima Thule. I remember the play, he
replied, though it is many years since I read it. She
gathered from his tone that he did not like the play or
had forgotten it partially, and she did not feel certain
that she had done well to mention it. After thinking a
while, he said, Jason goes in search of the Golden Fleece
and brings back Medea. In a galley, she cried, with
Orpheus singing at the prow. A wonderful story, but not
more wonderful than your own, which I heard last night

from my uncle, all of it except the years when, after
confounding Champeaux, you fell ill and went away nobody knows whither. Did your uncle not hazard a guess?
Abélard asked, and Héloïse answered that her uncle
spoke of England and Germany; England especially,
where he said you met Roscelin. And in which country
do you think I spent those years? I like to think, she
said, that you went in search of the Golden Fleece and
found a Medea to help you, for without Medea Jason
would not have captured the Fleece from the dragon that
was set to watch over it; it was Medea's mother, the
great sorceress, who gave the poison that Jason threw
into the dragon's jaws. So you think that a man cannot
conquer unless he has a woman to help him? Abélard
asked, and Héloïse, feeling that the question was directed
against her, was loath to answer; but her courage came
to the rescue, and she replied that it was so in Jason's
story and likewise in St. Paul's; for it might have fared
ill with Paul if he had not met Eunice at Derbe, she said,
who, with her mother, carried him and Barnabas to their
house after the populace stoned the Apostles, and kept
them there for many months. And did not Eunice, she
asked, go to hear Paul preach and was converted by him?
And did not Paul circumcise Timothy, lest an uncircum-
cised man should give offence to the Jews, who were in
great numbers? And you will not deny, Abélard, that
Eunice gave her son Timothy to Paul to accompany him
on all his wanderings, even to Rome; nor was Eunice
the only woman in Paul's life, for when he was in great
straits for money, did not Lydia, the dyer of purple in
Philippi, come to hear him and was converted as Eunice
was, and like Eunice, did she not take him to her house?
And so it seems to me strange, Abélard, that in all your
wanderings you met neither a Eunice nor a Lydia. For

you not to have met either puts the doubt on my mind that the women of those days were greater than the women of these, for I can imagine no greater glory for a woman than to be a man's partner in a high enterprise, such as yours is; to carry the faith of Christianity over the world by means of reason, which has not yet been put to the service of Christianity; for that, in my simple way, is how I understand your lesson.

You speak well, Héloïse, very well indeed for a school-girl from Argenteuil, and do credit to the nuns that taught you and to the uncle with whom you live; you apprehend my lesson better than any other and are from this day my favourite pupil. Other examples of men who owe their fortunes to women might be given. It is true that Æneas left Dido behind to go away to Italy to accomplish the will of the Gods. And you, Abélard, she said, were like Æneas, who left your Medea on the shores of England maybe? There was no Medea, he answered; I fought my battle alone. And it was on his lips to tell that his battle was only just begun and that a woman might come to his aid to win it, but it seemed to him out of keeping to speak words which would certainly be misunderstood; and his mien becoming graver, he said: I wish I had thought of Seneca's words, they would have given additional point to my lecture; for Tiphys was a prophet though there be no new worlds for our ships to discover. The world within us has been enlarged, horizons have been thrown back; and when you return to my lessons you will understand that I always try to exhibit the genius of the Latin poets, for it is part of my teaching that wisdom was not invented yesterday. All my quotations from Seneca and Lucan are made with a view to showing that antiquity was aware that righteousness springs from within and not from without. The

spring never runs dry—not altogether. It flows in him
who pleads that faith may not divorce reason, as it did
in Seneca when he taught that a right action should be
performed independently of any desire to please the
Gods. And you will remember that Cato declined to con-
sult the Oracles when he went to Africa to defend the
republic against Cæsar, saying that he knew what was
right and that advice from an Oracle was not needed.
The spring was in humanity always; stones were thrown
into the spring-head and the spring was closed for a
time, but never for long. The history of mankind might
be reckoned by the opening and closing of the spring.
A thousand years ago Our Lord Jesus released the spring
again, and new life was given to the world by it, and
at the end of another thousand years the spring is again
open. All may drink and be refreshed, and all may hope,
for the science of dialectics has been given back to us,
the science of reason, he said; and out of this science
he began to build a world of dreams, in which faith and
reason would walk hand in hand, a wedded couple, two
mighty forces that together would rescue the world from
evil. Which, dear child, would disappear were we not
loath to use our reason; why we should be afraid of reason
it is hard to say, for it is the quality above all others
that divides humanity from animality.

Héloïse listened, ravished by the voice that came to
her out of the darkness, by the sound of the voice, by
the ideas, or by both, she did not know, for she heard
him as one hears in a dream; and the awakening was painful, though his words—that he could not talk to her any
longer without seeing her—were a compliment to her.
Let us go into the cloister where we can see each other;
nobody comes to the cloister at this hour. And it was hand
in hand that they picked their way once more through

the groups of penitents, finding their way almost instinctively to the cloister where their eyes could distinguish
the cherry bloom and the figure of Ste. Geneviève showing
through the dusk of the quadrangle, and when she looked
up in his face he was pleased to see in her a woman that
appealed to his passion as much as to his reason. For
though by no means beautiful, he said to himself, she
is better, for she is to my taste, and forgetful of Faith
and Reason, he thought how her figure might be: delicate
and subtly made, he said to himself, without harsh angles;
and he was near to taking her in his arms, so ardently did
her ruddy complexion and her brown silky hair appeal to
his senses; and he admired the thick braids wound above
the nape. A neck, he said, that carries the head as a stem
carries its flower. And she too was satisfied with what
her gaze gave back to her, for she read a fixity of purpose
and an idea in his brow, and she could not doubt but
that he bore the mark of a high destiny.

So you spend your evenings with your uncle reading
Seneca? he said, and she answered: I read Seneca in
the morning when he goes to the Cathedral; in the evening
I read Tibullus, for my uncle took Cicero from me; he
wanted to read the *Academics* again. So you read Cicero,
Abélard replied. I have only read the *Academics,* she
interjected, and that being a work that Abélard did not
know even as well as he knew the *Medea,* he asked her to
tell him the plan of the work; and when he had gathered
from her that the plan of the *Academics* was to set one
inference against another, he said: a most earnest work
it must be from your description of it, one to which I
must give my attention at once. His mien becoming
graver at that moment, she inquired: of what are you
thinking, master? A thought has just come to me, he
replied, that a book might be written in which the infer-

ences of the Fathers might be set one against the other, as Cicero set the inferences of the philosophers. I shall read the *Academics* before I see you again, and do you look into them too, if you can get the book from your uncle. But shall I see you again, or will you forget me? she asked, looking up into his face. A man does not forget a girl—but I must not pay you compliments, else you will say that I am laughing at you. Within the next few days you shall hear from me.

Within the next few days I shall hear from him, Héloïse repeated, as she picked her way through the rue des Chantres, thinking of the *Academics*. Where is the Canon? she asked Madelon, who opened the door. Asleep in the company-room, Madelon answered. And where hast thou been? Héloïse did not find a prompt answer, and Madelon returned to her kitchen saying: there is a lover or a liker about. And next morning she marvelled greatly at the assiduity with which Héloïse sat poring over her book, for as soon as the Canon left the house she was immersed in Cicero, forgetful of all things except to obtain Abélard's approval, committing some pages to memory, and going to meet him in the Cathedral on the third day, certain that she would be able to answer all his questions. She expected certain questions, and was eager to speak her answers to them, but Abélard seemed to have forgotten Cicero and was much concerned to know why she had not been to the cloister to hear his lesson yesterday. I am not ashamed, she answered, of what I did, but much as I would have liked going to hear you, shyness prevented me; I was afraid of the eyes of Alberic and Romuald and others. Do you know, it is a pity that I yielded to that impulse. It's always a pity, he answered, to take the world into our confidence, but if it hadn't been for that impulse we might never have known each other.   But we should, living in Paris together, she answered; we could not have gone missing each other for long, unless indeed you left Paris again to hide yourself from everybody.   My dear Héloïse, he said suddenly, this is the last time we shall meet in the Cathedral.   You speak, she cried, as if you were bringing me welcome news.   I hope that my news will seem welcome when you have heard it, he answered; and he told her that he had heard from a common friend that the Canon desired to make his acquaintance.   Nothing will give me greater pleasure, was my message to the Canon; and on the following day it was our lot to come upon each other on the steps of the Cathedral.   If our friend were here now he might make us known to each other, I said, addressing him, at which we laughed heartily and fell into pleasant talk.   A pleasant man is Canon Fulbert.   There is no need for dismay, Héloïse, but for rejoicing rather.   At parting I happened to speak of the difficulty of preparing my lessons, so noisy was my lodging.   Whereupon the Canon, who, by repute, loves money dearly, told me that a great part of his house was unoccupied.   Come and see it, he said, and if it pleases you to share it with us—— We shall see each other every day, she cried.   We shall assuredly; and I shall be your private tutor, for I mentioned that much time remained on my hands after preparing my lessons, leading him to ask me to give you some of my spare time; at which request I made pause.   But will you, master? He wishes for your advancement in learning as much as he does for the money I shall pay him, and lest I should prejudice my good fortune (for a pupil like you is indeed a great good fortune), we must part now.   It would not be well that we should be seen together.   Do not speak to your uncle of these two visits.   But I have told him of the lecture, master. Did I do wrong? No; for it is well to be truthful about what cannot be withheld from our enemies, and mine are many, and my reasons for giving you a tryst here would be difficult to explain away; so you will not speak of these meetings to anybody. We shall meet as strangers to-morrow—— Not as strangers, Héloïse, for we have never been strangers. It seems, he said, that I have had you in my mind always. And I have always been striving after you, master, unwittingly striving.

After parting with her, Abélard called Héloïse back to ask her if she had a story to tell that would explain her absence. She had none in mind, but did not think she would be asked questions. Madelon will not betray us, she answered, and returned in the hope that no questions would be put to her. The Canon is very angry, were Madelon's words, whispered quickly in her ear as she crossed the threshold. Go to him at once and tell him a good story of the fields and posies. Then Madelon knows, Héloïse said to herself, as she crossed the living-room. At her footsteps the Canon flung open his door, and unable to restrain his words he walked about the room, his large nose more than usually prominent, saying that he had not foreseen such folly as her venturing out in the evening, exposing herself to all dangers. But of the dangers you speak, uncle, I have no knowledge. On these words he cut her short, asking her where she had been; and hardly waiting for an answer, he stormed on again, and it would have been better, perhaps, if she had not attempted to tell him she had walked under the willow-trees to hear the nightingale singing, for it was there that many robberies had been committed. But, uncle, why so much ado? So much ado! he cried, and possessed of a sudden idea, he turned: Go at once to thy

bed, child, and without any supper. May I not take the
Academics of Cicero with me? No, he answered; an
unmerited return is thy disobedience. But you never
told me, uncle—— Little thou knowest of the means I
have been seeking for the completion of thine education.
And Héloïse, shocked at his anger and at the deception
she had been led into, went to her room ashamed at what
had befallen her, finding excuses for her uncle's anger
but none for herself, till Madelon told her next morning
that the Canon had locked up all the manuscripts before
going to the Cathedral.

She began to feel that though she had done wrong
her uncle was not free from blame. So I cannot even
be trusted with a book, she said; willing to admit that
her uncle was within his rights to send her supperless to
bed for having left the house in the evening, but what she
could not admit was his taking her books from her; for
what reason? That she had left the house in the evening
without asking leave was no reason. But after all, it
didn't matter; Abélard was coming to live with them and
then he couldn't forbid her his books. The Canon is on
the stairs, Madelon cried, and Héloïse's face lighted up,
for another step caught her ears. It is Abélard's, she
said to herself. Pierre Abélard, this is my niece, of whom
you have heard, the learned Héloïse of the convent of
Argenteuil, the best Latin scholar they have ever had,
which I will guarantee her to be. She reads and writes
Latin and speaks it as well as any of us in the Cathedral.
Now, my dear child, let us forget last night. Héloïse
did not answer, and turning again to Abélard, he said:
At nine o'clock she was under the willows listening to
the nightingale, a place where footpads and dangerous
characters loiter, and now she is sour because I sent
her to bed supperless. Héloïse, it was for thy good

that I spoke angrily to thee. My words are often harsher than my heart. Now wilt thou hear the good news that I have brought? Hearken: Abélard, the great Pierre Abélard, the renowned philosopher, has done us the honour to accept a lodging with us, and he hopes that this quiet house, for we are quiet here, will enable him to finish a work which will be of great value to the world, and it is for thee to profit by this great chance of getting instruction from him. It is indeed, Abélard, a great good fortune to myself and to my niece that you are able and willing to come and live with us.

It is I who am obliged to you, Canon Fulbert, and not you to me, Abélard answered, for hardly an hour of my life was my own in the house in which I lived, so besieged was it with pupils and disciples coming to me from all parts. But here I shall be free of trouble, and there will be time for me to put such poor knowledge as is mine at your niece's disposal. Any help that I can be to your niece in her studies shall be given willingly. I have heard her well spoken of and it was a pleasure to me to see her in the cloister. She has told you of my lesson, no doubt? She mentioned it, Canon Fulbert answered, saying that everybody thought it was one of your greatest. It was interrupted by Gosvin of Douai, an impertinent fellow, Abélard replied, for the question he put to me was not worthy of a scholar. We have here a fair library of the Latin writers, Fulbert said, and taking his keys from his bag he went to the closet and showed his books to Abélard one by one, begging of him to handle them, saying: here is the *Æneid* that Héloïse has just finished reading, and the *Georgics* are here. Seneca is her last love, and before long she will be speaking of *Medea* to you. I give her into your charge, Pierre Abélard, a girl with much love of her books; an insurgent spirit, too, if last night be characteristic of her. We shall find that out. I give her into your charge and confer on you the right to punish her for her transgressions.

CHAP. X.

IT was during the third lesson that she sat, her eyes wide open, listening, now more than ever intent, for she had dared to confess her doubt to Abélard regarding the importance of the questions now agitating all minds: Nominalism and Realism; and having already learnt much in the preceding lessons, she was not without some knowledge of the answer he would make. He would say that the intellectual quarrel known as Nominalism and Realism led men towards the science of words, the greatest of all, for it was through words that men communicated their ideas one to the other, rising by means of words out of the almost animal to the reasonable state. But he never said anything twice in the same way; and, his eyes and voice compelling the belief of reciprocation in all that might befall them, the silence seemed to swoon about them. It was broken by the sound of lute strings in the street, and giving ear to the song she heard a bass voice troll out a slow, solemn plain-song. He sings too loud, Abélard cried; he overpowers the accompaniment. And flinging the window open, he thrust his head out. How intently he listens, she said to herself, and began to wonder how he could lay aside an important argument so easily for a song.

After some eight bars, on the completion of the theme, the singer, the bass repeated it, answered by another voice starting a fourth higher with a whimsical set of variations, a rollicking reproof, so to speak, as if the baritone judged his comrade to be overstating his case. I told

thee so long ago, but thou wouldst not listen, he seemed
to be saying. Anon, a third voice starting again a fourth
higher joined in, and the tenor's phrase seemed to be intended to bring about a reconciliation between the bass
and the baritone. Life is never so bad or so good as we
think for, seemed to be the burden of his charming rigmarole, which he continued heedless of the lamentable tale
that the bass continued to relate, deaf to objurgations and
reproofs from the baritone. The piece of music ended
here, and Héloïse and Abélard expected the minstrels to
begin another. But as if relying upon the popularity of
the piece they had just sung, or because it was especially
asked for, it was sung again after a short interlude in
which many other instruments joined with the lutes, an
unhappy accident, however, marring the second performance of it, the baritone delaying to intervene with
his counsel—an accident that was rectified by Abélard,
who sang a new set of variations from the window.
Héloïse was afraid that his entry into the concert might
provoke a quarrel, but it was accepted cheerfully, and the
minstrels sang other pieces, Abélard joining in several
and winning applause from the crowd and the musicians
themselves, who generously cheered the stranger while
picking up the money that he threw to them.

Have I then for a master a great singer as well as a
great philosopher? Héloïse asked. And somewhat heed-
lessly Abélard answered her that it was many a year since
he joined in troubadour minstrelsy. But a craft is never
put aside altogether, it's always on the watch for us, he
said; and looking round the room, and spying a lute hanging on the wall, he went to it. It lacks some strings, but
Fulbert must have some if he be a lutanist. Do not leave
me, Abélard, to seek them, but tell me how it was that
you could devise variations on a theme heard for the first

time. Not a difficult thing, he replied, for the words and
the music of the song are mine; and if my song pleased
thee, let me sing thee another. But to sing I must have
a lute. No, do not go, she cried, and her senses inflaming
suddenly, her lips sought his, but the sound of footsteps
parted their mouths in the middle of a violent kiss, and
they fell perforce to a pretence of study, sitting without
raising their eyes from their books, listening. Dost love
me, Héloïse? Raising her face from her book, she answered: thou knowest well enough that I do, for thou
knowest my heart better than I know it myself; and her
truthful eyes set wide in her face were fixed upon him in
an innocent yet searching gaze. O Pierre, I am very
happy. If thou lovest me, I am happy; kiss me again
and as before. Others have loved thee—it could not be
else—many. But thou wilt love me and forget them?
Yes, I will love thee, Héloïse, he cried. Wilt thou forget
all and shall I have all thy love? My love is thine, he
answered, present and future. Whereupon she lay upon
his shoulder, her eyes half closed, saying: My uncle told
me of the surrender of thy lands to thy kindred so that
thou mightest be free to wander over France teaching the
people. Is it a true story? It is a true story, Héloïse,
he answered. I am glad, she murmured, for I would
have thee as thou'rt in my mind, one that was called to a
task. I always knew that my bent was philosophy——
he began, but at that moment footsteps were heard again
about the stair-head, and the lovers were at pains to gain
their several seats in time to escape the notice of their
visitor, who might be the Canon or Madelon. It was the
Canon, and he almost stumbled into the room, talking
thickly of minstrelsy in the streets disturbing scholarship.
A thing which must not fall out again, for your lessons
are—— He stopped speaking and stood rooted, gazing at

them, till they began to fear that their guilt was showing in their faces. Your lessons are, Master Abélard, priceless things in all Fransh; that is how I think; and your pupil, Master Abélard, how does she think? Proving herself to be worthy of your attention, is not that so? If not, Master Abélard, you must punish her. A little touch of the birch on our hinder parts . . . good for all of us, especially the young. A thing they know well in convents is the value of—a touch of birch about the buttocksh. Ishn't tha' sho, Master Abélard? Am I not right? Maybe the taste of it lingers in my niece's mind or elsewhere, and maybe not, for good accounts of her always came from the convent; and good pupil wants no birching. But good pupil and good master need a tankard of good wine. The right of every Frenshman is good wine; and we are all Frensh here, thanks be to God, except Madelon, who is a Breton, but a good Breton; you hear me, don't you? A good Breton. The Canon stood by the great table, a flagon in one hand, surveying the distance between him and the table at which Héloïse and Abélard were sitting in the window, doubtful of his legs, for they were drunkener than his head; so unloading the Canon of the flagon and of the tankards, Abélard took him by the arm and helped him to a seat by them, saying that the honour he craved was to pour out wine for a canon of Notre-Dame Cathedral. It is a greater honour, Fulbert replied, for canon to drink with philosopher than for . . . for . . . philosopher to drink with canon; to be sure it is, for there are more canons than philosophers; but there's more difference between one canon and another than there is between philosophers, so it is hard to say—— You 'gree with me, don't you? And understand me to say that there's many feet between Abélard and any other philosopher, Champeaux, Roshlin—mice,

say I, mice, mice! Mice get in everywhere, Philosopher
Abélard, but great men have to climb up steeple on to
vane, up yonder with Plato and Arishtotle, and to
drink—— An honour, my word! to drink with philosopher bigger than any Plato—a Realisht he was, or Arishtotle, who was Nominalisht more or less. Am I not right,
Philosopher Abélard; am I not right, niece! A lucky girl
thou'rt to have the greatest philosopher in the world to
teach thee. A lucky girl, a lucky girl, Master Abélard.
Let us drink to the health of ph'loshophers. She tells me
you spoke of Buddha and Con . . . Con . . . Confucius,
and afterwards of Plato and Aristotle, ending of course,
for where should we end but at the end of the spire, the
shummit, the top of all . . . And on these words the
Canon's head fell across the table.

Had it not been for that last tankard we might have
guided him to his room, Héloïse said, and bending down,
she spoke into her uncle's ear. Abélard lifted him a little,
but he fell back, and there seemed to be no hope of pushing or carrying him across the room. I will fetch my
cloak, Héloïse said, and place it for a pillow under
his head. May I go with thee? Abélard asked. No;
stay with my uncle. It might be well to wake up Madelon, she said, in a loud voice, adding in a whisper: He
often rouses out of a stupor and gazes round the room
wide awake. At these words Abélard's face darkened.
Have a care, Héloïse whispered to him as she escaped
from him, for he may be watching us; and when she returned with her cloak she begged Abélard to lift the
Canon from the table so that she might place it under his
head. Abélard, I beseech you! she cried. May I not kiss
thee before we part? he asked. Wouldst thou be parted
from me for ever? she replied, but his passion inflamed her
and she gave him her mouth. But the nectar of thy

tongue——— he cried. Nectar! the Canon said, lifting his head from Héloïse's cloak; a fig for all the nectar in Olympus. Give me wine. He gazed round, seeing nothing, and the lovers ran to their different beds. But he may be roused, Abélard muttered, returning. As well try to lift a mountain, he said, and allowed the Canon to fall back over the table. Not a particle of hope, he sighed, and returned to his bed to fall asleep suddenly. How was it that sleep came so quickly? he asked himself, when his eyes opened. And what awakened me? The birds on the sill, the dog in the street? And considering the question, he lay between sleeping and waking till he remembered that the drunken often rouse at dawn and stagger to their beds. If he has roused a bit, I may be able to lead him to his bed But no such luck awaited his eyes; the Canon lay where they had left him, snoring among the tankards. Abélard bethought himself of a wet towel, but it failed to rouse Fulbert for more than a few seconds, and he returned to his bed, to awaken later to the sound of lute strings. And after listening, he said: Somebody is stringing, or striving to string, a lute, and as he opened his door the Canon came into sight sitting on a stool, one leg tucked under him, the lute on his knee, seemingly too drunk to find the right pegs, and as he turned wrong ones a string snapped. The devil has got hold of the world by the leg or by the cat's gut, he muttered, and was about to throw the lute aside when Abélard came forward to point out that the gut was not so much to blame as the Canon seemed to think, for it had had the grace to break close to the bridge. If you will allow me, sir, and taking the lute out of the Canon's hands, he retied the string and began to tune it, singing the required note, finding it first in his mind, afterwards on the string. A fine ear, the Canon said, it

is that remembers the pitch all this while away from
music. But who broke the strings? They were but five
when I awoke, so I went to my drawer where I keep
them, and broke one myself; quite true, Master Abélard,
that I broke the string, but the other strings? Maybe
I broke them too, he muttered, as he refilled his tankard.
The poison of yesterday is the remedy of to-day, he said,
and seemed annoyed when Abélard began to plead that
he must finish his dressing. But who will tune the lute?
Abélard heard the Canon ask, and a minute after he
heard another string snap. I hope he hasn't broken the
lute, he said, as he pulled on his hose; for it is a beautiful
instrument. And so heedful of it was he that he started
from the room to see. The Canon was gone, and picking
up the lute that had been recklessly thrown aside, he
examined it. He has broken all the strings but two, he
said, laying it down, but the lute is safe: delicate as an
egg-shell, he said, as he hung it up. And meeting with
Madelon at the foot of the stairs, he learnt from her
that the Canon was lying down after drinking much cold
water. Maybe there is as much water in his belly as wine,
she said, and busied herself setting food before Abélard,
who ate in silence, exchanging no words with her till he
rose from the table saying: When my pupil Héloïse comes
from her room, tell her that I have gone down to the river
for meditation. I will tell her, Madelon answered, but
am I to say that she is to join you, master? Yes, he
answered; and with the intention of preparing a discourse, he bethought himself of the warmth and sweetness
of the morning: Enlivened, he said, with a gentle breeze
laden with a faint fragrance of daffodils; and pacing a
pathway chequered with the pattern of budding branches,
he tried to pick out a subject from among the many he
had stored away in his mind. But the almost inaudible

gurgle of the river distracted his thoughts from his
search of a subject to Héloïse herself, who was truly a
wonderful child, a surprising being, more surprising now
than the day she threw herself at his feet, and more
surprising last night than she was when she kissed his
hands in public; those kisses revealed an exalted soul,
but last night's kisses an almost barbaric passion quite
unforeseen, and he pondered on the sting of lips so
innocently red. An innocent kiss, in spite of its sting, he
said; for Nature spoke through her lips, and with, he
reflected, a very delightful accent.

It was pleasant to sit recalling her pale brown curling
hair, wound so gracefully into a knot above the nape, the
pale grey eyes that seemed out of keeping with the rest
of her personality; and he fell to thinking that to find
so much passion in a child was strange, almost unnatural,
and then his thoughts took a different turn, and passing
from her mind to her body, he remembered how shapely
she was (or seemed to be) under her gown. Her breasts
would have been in his hands last night had it not been
for that drunken uncle, and his thoughts going still
deeper, he said: More child than woman, more woman than
child. Which is it? he asked himself; and his imagination taking fire, he began to dream of the perfect shapes
he would one day find under her nightgown, and then to
think how a mere accident may rob a man of his pleasure.
But the memory of her kiss reassured him, and he applied himself once more to the task of trying to discover a
subject for discourse in the Cathedral that afternoon.
But his thoughts were soon back rifling her body, and
the words that they would exchange as they lay side by
side, the ecstasy and the turmoil of the senses, the ebbing
of desire and the recovery of it again. . . .

But why does she not come, he said, to meet me, in-

stead of leaving me to lose my day in arid meditation?
And singing a southern ditty, he returned to the rue des
Chantres, arriving in time to hear Madelon bringing the
dinner from the kitchen, and the Canon talking of the
great discourse that they would hear during the afternoon in the cloister. The different dishes were pressed
upon Abélard, and he was asked if he had met an inspiration under the willows. The murmur of the Seine irritates
instead of soothing, and my discourse to-day will be a
failure, Abélard answered. The Canon refused to believe
that such a thing could happen. All the same, Abélard's
presentiments of a failure in the cloister were fulfilled,
the Nominalists agreeing among themselves that the day
was not one for a public argument between Abélard and
Champeaux, nor Abélard and Anselm. Nor even between
Abélard and Gosvin, cried a severer critic, as he left the
Cathedral. These criticisms would not have added anything to Abélard's perceptions of his failure if they had
reached his ears. No, do not flatter me; to-day I was
stirring up old memories, skimming the froth as it came
to the surface—— And he broke away almost abruptly,
leaving his friends wondering, asking each other what
offence they had been guilty of, never guessing that his
head was filled with songs and lute accompaniments and
that he must talk with his ancient comrades if only for
an hour, and breathe again the air of a tavern in the rue
le Pet du Diable. Likely enough, I shall find those of
yester night, he said, as he pushed open the door, singing
one of his own songs. But who is he that sings without
a lute? An old comrade, he answered, and he claimed
their company, telling that when they last sang in the
rue des Chantres he had joined in from a window, singing
a new set of variations over his own theme. So they
drank and sang together and told each other stories till

the day waned, until it came upon one of the lutanists
to say: Why not sing thy song again under the window
of thy lady-love? But now I am a philosopher, Abélard
answered, and the lutanists said: We will give thee a cloak
and a lute and thou wilt sing this time the melody itself
and we the variations. Abélard replied: Be it so, and disguised as a gleeman, he repaired with them to Canon Fulbert's house, where his singing and lute-playing soon
gathered a multitude ready to pay for their pleasure and,
inadvertently, to keep the Canon waiting for his supper.

This is the end of taking in lodgers, to be kept waiting
for supper half-an-hour beyond the time, the Canon
fumed, unable to give ear to the music. Uncle, Abélard
is among the crowd perhaps, listening to the singing, and
will return as soon as it is ended; nor must we believe
that the pie is spoilt because Madelon fusses. But my
belly, the Canon said, does not fuss without reason; and
that man keeps it waiting. The bells have rung the
seventh hour and will ring the half-hour presently; yet
he keeps me waiting. Whosoever takes in a lodger regrets
it. He puts me past my patience. But a lodger to whom
students from all countries come should enable you to
extend your patience. It does not, Héloïse, and if Abélard
again keeps me waiting for my supper—— You will
take him to the door, uncle, Héloïse interrupted, and tell
him never to return again, and be sorry for your impatience afterwards. Now listen, the Canon said, are those
street singers here again? And going to the window,
uncle and niece listened to the song the bass had sung
yester evening under the window, now sung by the baritone. Abélard's voice, Héloïse said to herself, and her
heart was delightfully flattered that Abélard should come
and sing under the window disguised as a gleeman. He
has borrowed a hat and cloak. and is singing for me.

A beautiful voice, said the Canon, which I should enjoy
more if Abélard were not driving my belly to the uttermost of its strength; a rich baritone, soft as velvet, and
not raised beyond the range of the voice.   I hate a baritone that sings beyond his range.   Hush, uncle, for I
would listen to the end of the piece.   And I would listen
too, the Canon replied, were I not thinking of the excellent hard-boiled eggs that crust contains, and the wine
whose fragrance is so mocking to the nose—— O uncle,
let me listen.

A fine piece of singing it is, but were it ten times
better than it is it could not keep me one moment longer
from that pie.   Come, Héloïse, let us to it.   As soon as
his back was turned Héloïse beckoned to Abélard in the
street below, and as if he understood her he threw his
disguise to the minstrel from whom it was borrowed, and
two or three minutes after he was with them, telling the
Canon that his appreciation of the minstrels kept him.
They sang well, did they not?   Very well indeed, the
Canon answered; that baritone, I could have listened to
him for an hour had it not been for the pie in front of
you, master, for though the singing was good, the pie
is better; and now let me fill your glass with wine; we
will drink to Madelon's pie and to the minstrel's song,
for that too is worthy of a toast; but not another word
to me; speak to Héloïse if she will listen, for she is your
pupil.   I am not, and can think only of ridding myself
of the hunger that I have borne too long.   Another jug of
wine will do neither of us any harm, and there is still
another helping for you in the dish, Abélard.   Madelon,
the Canon called, another tankard of wine.   Ah, the wine
is good and smooth on the palate, as good as I have
drunken this many a year, and were the minstrels within
call I would have them up here to meat and drink, for

that piece of music was a fine piece, well turned in its
every period.   And the baritone—— Yes, the baritone,
Abélard answered, has a fine voice: he can troll it out,
and if I could remember the melody—— Can't you recall
it, Pierre Abélard?   Your ear is a keen one, for after
hearing a tune once you know it in all its turns and twists.
I think that with time I might recall the whole of the piece
and give it to you, Reverend Canon, written correctly.   I
know we have here a great philosopher, the Canon said,
and as it would seem he is doubled with a musician, thy
fortune, Héloïse, is made, for every girl should know
music, and who could teach music better than he who can
hear a concert in the street and keep it in his mind,
melody and variations?   Would you have me join music
to my usual instruction, Reverend Canon, of her who is
your niece and my pupil?   That is a question I must turn
over in my head before I can give you an answer, for
her thoughts are on the Latin poets and it might not be
well to distract her from these by adding music to your
instruction.   It shall be as you wish, Reverend Canon,
Abélard answered, and he pressed more wine on the
Canon, hoping that wine and beefsteak, aided and abetted
by pigeon-breast and hard-boiled eggs, would induce
sleep.

To be kept another night from Héloïse might rob him
of all reason, and half-an-hour later, in spite of her
prayer for patience, he might have fallen on his knees
before her, deeming the Canon to be already asleep.   Thou
knowest not my uncle, she whispered, drawing him to
the window, which was as far as she could take him from
the Canon's chair.   He may be shamming sleep.   Thou
knowest not my uncle.   He is sly, and were he to suspect
us we should be separated for ever.   Have a care for
my sake, for the hour will not be long in passing, and

as soon as he wakes he will have no thought but for his pillow. That hour will be an eternity to me, Abélard replied, and that thou canst bear it without too much suffering casts doubt on thy passion; a poor thing it must be It cannot be that thou art aching as I am, Héloïse, he pleaded. But she held her finger up for a sign; she besought silence with her eyes, and pushing him from her, she forced him to read, if not to read, to pretend to read, till with a great cry the Canon rose out of his chair and, without bidding either of them good-night, stumbled from the room. Now we can love each other, Abélard cried. My lover, have patience, for there is a dread in me that my uncle will return. And ere long, as if possessed by evil thoughts, the Canon returned to the room, pleading the need of a book to put him to sleep. It cannot be that he will come back again, Abélard said. It may be that he'll read himself to sleep, she answered, but her eyes said to him that she would not endanger their nuptials with an unseemly interruption; and to help him to further patience she asked him to tell her why he came with the minstrels disguised as one of them, a question that recaptured his kindly humour, and he began twanging the lute while telling her. We have awakened the Canon, he said, laying the lute aside. But it was not Abélard's incontinent strumming that had awakened him; a little insomnia was upon him and he had returned to ask Abélard if he might share the lesson, a request to which Abélard was obliged to accede. Have you, Reverend Canon, any knowledge of the instrument? The Canon answered that he had often tried to learn the lute, but had failed, a failure that was not difficult to understand, for his admission was that he had always found a great diffi- culty in tuning the instrument. Abélard denied the im- perfection of the Canon's ear, and condoned his mistakes

when to deny them was impossible. The presence of
Héloïse sitting opposite gave him courage to bear with
his tormentor; and a full hour had to wear itself away
before the Canon's eyes were again loaded with sleep.
You must be weary too, he said; so to your rooms, he
continued, and they parted, the lovers to lie in their beds
angry and disheartened by the evil luck that had befallen
them.

And then it seemed to Abélard as if he must escape
from the house, and he weighed his career against his love
of Héloïse, knowing all the while that he must abide with
her. Come what might, he must abide. But to be near
her yet without her seemed more than he could bear, and
he bethought himself of the Seine as a means of escape
from the sleepless Canon, who continued to wander about
the house. Every half-hour his feet were on the stairs.
Does he suspect us? Abélard asked himself, and next
morning he affected more rage than was in his heart
against the Canon, and she answered him: Thou knowest
what my uncle is, so why rage like this and make me
unhappy? Thinkest that I did not rue thine absence
from my couch as much as thou? Didst burn for me,
Héloïse? he said, and the lovers came to their peace in a
kiss—to a momentary peace, for the kiss inflamed Abélard,
and he fell to telling how he barely kept himself to his
bed, whilst thou, he said, lay indifferent, forgetful of me,
perchance. Worse than forgetful of me, for thou wert
forgetful of love itself or else would have been by my
side, let come what might. Was I then so indifferent to
love when I was with thee? she asked; so indifferent that
I deserve reproaches? And hast thou forgotten that it
was the first time I was in a man's arms? I should not
reproach thee for indifference, Héloïse; thou wert all
thou shouldst have been and more, and that is why a

night of abstinence was hard to bear. Sleep was very
far from me, and all night I lay thinking of thee. Was
that, she asked, so unnatural that thou comest with a
complaint on thy lips? Lovers, Héloïse, should think
always of each other, and in the courts of love that I
visited when I wrote songs for the Comte de Rodebœuf,
Queen Elinor decreed that a true lover is enthralled with
a perpetual image of his lady-love; it never departs from
the mind. She has ruled it thus. Nor wast thou absent
for a single moment of the long night, in all becoming
lights and shades and in all attitudes exciting to the
senses. Didst sleep, then? Héloïse asked. Sleep! not a
wink, he answered. The best moment was when between
sleeping and waking, thou camest to me with a lamp in thy
hand. But, Abélard, I could not come, for Madelon and
my uncle talked away the morning on the stairs outside
my room, relating of their different sicknesses or else of
the rising prices in the market. I could not come to
thee, and thou canst not doubt that I am telling thee the
truth. I waited, hoping that my uncle and Madelon
would part, would stop their chatter and lie down together
or separate. I cared not which, for I was thinking of
thee. But at last their chatter lulled me to sleep, and I
slept so deeply that if thou hadst come I should have
needed shaking before I could welcome thee for a kiss.
I should have wished thee to come with a lamp, Héloïse,
in thy hand, and all the light of it flowing down thy
naked body, for so thou wouldst seem in my eyes more
beautiful than in any vain garment. It was thus that I
thought of thee all the long hot night through; the door
opening and a white arm holding a lamp high. For should
it come to pass that we, Héloïse, spend a night or part
of a night together it must not be without a lamp. Would
it please thee, Abélard, to see me naked? It would be a

gracious deed, Héloïse, for thee to come with a lamp to
my couch, for this would tell me how vainly I have pictured thee, yet it seemed that thou wert fair enough in
my imagination. My hands remember thy small breasts as
mere handfuls, and thy face foretells me now the great
summer whiteness of thy body. But my summer is not
yet come, Abélard, she said; I am but the month of April.
Call me not the month of March, for this is a cold month,
and I am not cold. A fair month indeed, he answered, is
the month of April, one not to be despised, though the
month of May is a better month, and the month of June
is—— Well, June is a month for the Gods. But thy
June, Héloïse, is many months distant, and waiting for it
shall be my joy. Wilt grow tired of waiting? she asked.
Tired of waiting? How little thou knowest yet about
love. A true love never tires or wanes, Héloïse, but is
with us always, like our blood, like our breath. I shall
never weary of that brow nor those grey, wistful eyes. I
thought last night to teach thee love; wouldst learn from
me, Héloïse? I would, and from none other, she said.
And wilt come as I picture thee, holding a lamp high, for
I would see all thy roundness in the fair glow? But,
Abélard, is there naught in me but a body that will waste
in thine imagination each time of seeing it? There is
much, Héloïse, besides thy body. Thy mind is as agreeable to me; we have spent delightful hours together reading the Latin poets hour after hour without weariness by
that window. Abélard, thou hast never wearied of my
chatter, though I often feared thou wouldst. But now
I hear no word about Virgil, Ovid, Tibullus and Cicero,
only supplications to see me naked. Dost think of me
differently now? Not so differently, Héloïse, that I have
forgotten thy soul. But can we think of the soul and
body at the same time? When thou comest to me, the

lamp held high, to learn all the sports of love from me, thou wilt not think of my soul—not then—but of thy pleasure, as I shall think of mine. Yet let it not be said that the soul and the intellect of the woman is forgotten by the man, though he cannot love body and soul at the same time. Each is loved in turn; without love of the body the love of the soul is a poor thing without purpose when the twain are side by side on a couch, nor valid even when thou sittest apart from me in a window-seat; for we cannot think in the presence of the loved one, and still less can we dream; we prepare whilst on the couch or in the window-seat for the hours that are to come when our love lady is not by us. So it is only, Héloïse said, when her body is not by him that the lover admires the woman's mind. But wouldst thou have it otherwise, that he should dream of her body when she is absent and of her mind when she is by him? Abélard, I make no complaint, I am happy in the knowledge that I shall see thee when I return from market, whither I go now with my basket. And do thou profit of this interval to prepare thy lesson, for to-day thou art to lecture in the Cloister. To-day is not the day that I can take my thoughts off thee, he cried, nor would I take my thoughts from thee if I could. Ask me not, therefore, to prepare a lesson, for I cannot. Nor wouldst thou ask it of me if thou knewest the years of life that I have sacrificed to learning; and now that life comes to me in Héloïse's sweet shape, am I not to take what the Gods have put within my reach? Put thoughts of love by, she said, for an hour. That thing I cannot do, he answered. Go to thy market and leave me to write songs and to play the lute, and return to hear thyself praised, for there is a song singing in my head that I would write for thee. Since it must be that we separate for a little, let the interval be one of commemoration.

CHAP. XI.

WHAT! she cried, on her return, no song for me to hear? And he confessed to being mistaken in his inspiration; words and music had gone awry. I will not believe it, and she asked him to sing to her. The phrase is well enough, he said, but I am too restless to write song or lecture; come, sit upon my knee. She was barely seated thereon when the sound of footsteps alarmed them and Héloïse with much ado skipped to her seat in time. It was Madelon, and as soon as her question had been answered Héloïse said: I suspect her; we shall have to be careful. But as Abélard could not be contented unless he was fondling her, perforce to put herself out of his mind she could not do else than to ask him to tell her the story that was on his lips yesterday.

The Canon has told my story, a tiresome one until I met thee, Héloïse, nor is there any danger of his returning; so come and sit upon my knee again. Do not ask me to risk much for very little, she answered, and a long argument began between them whether the pleasure was greater to Abélard to have Héloïse upon his knee or to Héloïse to be sitting there. As hard a matter, she answered, as Nominalism and Realism. Which knee is Nominalism and which is Realism, and where does Conceptualism, thy theory, lie? she asked, springing away from him, for footsteps seemed once more to be moving by the stair-top; and deceived thereby and drawn by some flattery, he yielded himself to her question whither he had gone when he left Melun in search of rest. Whither I went when my health broke down from long study? It is said that I travelled in Germany and in England—— And that thy humour is various, she interjected, which is not surprising, for there is a philosopher and a poet in thee, and both seeking for rivalry. Yes, he replied, and a wanderer, too, as the Canon has related. My lands in Brittany were surrendered to my brothers and sisters so that I might be free to throw myself into philosophy and wander, as thou hast heard, seeking disputations and controversy with all and sundry, thereby gathering much renown and maybe some glory. And thou hast heard from the Canon of the overthrow of Guillaume de Champeaux and of Anselm, too, who in the imagination of the Canon is a man of great genius, but a mistake I would hold this to be, saying rather that Anselm is gifted with a great flow of eloquent phrases, never at a loss in the Assembly Hall; but it is worth no man's while to go to him with a question, for instead of having the question answered and his trouble allayed, he will come back with twenty more doubts, all more irritating than the first. Thou hast heard from the Canon how I taught in Paris after Champeaux's retirement, whom I so worsted in argument that he could no longer find pupils who would listen to him, and of my own school at Ste. Geneviève; thou hast heard, too, of my school at Melun, and how I was told that rest was needed, which was true, for of the sweets of rest I had not tasted for many a year; and that when I was ill and unable to give myself to study, the memory of my already ancient wanderings stirred up a great yearning in me to follow the roads once more: April was coming in; blue and white, according to her wont. One evening I heard the thrush singing under a rising moon, and next morning he sang from an elm bough. There was money in my purse, gaiety in my heart, and a lute on my back, and lodgings I found at nightfall; some were pleasant, none too vile, for all the world was abroad: gleemen, acrobats, pedlars, wayfarers, all like myself, were walking ahead seeking their fortunes. My health returned to me at every mile, for it was April. All the world was dancing and singing; the lambs frolicked up the banks and even the heavy sheep skipped when the lambs returned to them; the rooks tumbled over each other in the soft air, and I said: All is that ever was, even I. But I could no longer teach by the roadside; I was no longer a peripatetic philosopher, and might well have returned to Brittany to my father and mother, and to the old Manor House and lands belonging to it, had it not been that Brittany was a long way off and my strength not great enough for the journey. Moreover, lute-playing is not favoured in Brittany as it is in the peasant Norman land whither I wandered, exchanging one band of minstrels for another, till the day came when I wearied of three gangrel churls whom I had fallen in with on their way to a fair—men with little knowledge of music, more apt with dogs that they could train to walk on their hind legs, to jump through hoops, to steal and put the blame upon the cat, and many other diversions of the same kind. One of them could play the vielle and another a pair of regals, and with them was a gleemaiden who danced with two great mastiffs, their forepaws on her shoulders. Héloïse asked how she was dressed, and Abélard told her that the gleemaiden was gowned according to custom in azure blue with silver spangles on her skirt.

As I have said, these minstrels were on their way to a fair, and not caring to accompany them thither, and not wishing to lower them in their own self-esteem, for to do so is a dangerous thing and might have earned me an evil blow, I feigned to have a return of my illness, and lay down under an oak-tree and bade them good-bye, wishing them, of course, every luck at the fair. They

were loath to lose me, for my lute-playing helped them to
gather money, but as they could not carry me on their
backs, and were without money to buy a horse for me
to ride, they departed, and it was with a great uplifting
of the spirit that I watched them stumble out of the wood.
I must have fallen asleep shortly afterwards and slept
maybe for a couple of hours, for the prime of the
morning was over when I woke, and looking up I saw a
finely accoutred horse bending over me, but he started
away from me when I sought to catch his bridle. A horse,
I said to myself, belonging to some great noble who will
come in search of him; and with some notion at the back
of my mind that an acquaintance of this sort would suit
my present circumstance, I set myself to capture the
horse, which I failed to do till I bethought myself of
the plan of filling my hat with pebbles and shaking them,
and he, thinking that I was about to bring him corn,
let me take him; and I had barely tethered him to a
tree when a fine gentleman came riding by, no less a
person than the Comte de Rodebœuf mounted on one of
his servants' horses, who, on seeing his horse tethered,
said: Thou shalt be rewarded for thy capture of my
horse, to which I answered: I am a gentleman like thyself, and for the slight service that I have rendered thee
I need but the story how it fell out for thy horse to
escape, whereupon he told me that his horse had stepped
into a rabbit burrow and thrown him. Thy horse came
sniffing me while I lay asleep, poking me up as if he
missed a master. On that our talk languished. But it
broke out again on seeing a lute by me; a gentleman like
myself thou art certainly, said Rodebœuf, from thy speech
I can tell that, and the lute tells thou'rt a musician
like myself. So if it be not unpleasing to thee we will
sing a song together, for the air is pleasant in this

wood. After hearing me sing, he said: we must not part like this. My castle is near by and it is open to thee as long as it pleases thee to remain with me. A fine voice is thine and I have little doubt thou'rt skilled in composition. But didst return, Abélard, with the Comte de Rodebœuf? Not till many months after, Abélard answered, for the Comte de Rodebœuf is a great trouvère, and spring being by again he had just left his castle to visit his neighbours to help them with lute-playing and song to forget the tedium of the winter months they had come through.

So I entered into his service as head gleeman. We journeyed on, I by the Comte's side, the gleemen singing in front and behind us, attracting the folk working in the fields, who came to the hedges to listen to us as we passed twanging our lutes, for our thoughts were set on the songs we would sing at the castle of Raymond of Castel-Rousillon some miles distant. We exchanged friendly greetings with the folk as we journeyed through the still sweet daytime, taking heed of all the sights and sounds of April. A very pleasant ride it was, so pleasant that thou wouldst have stopped often to snuff the fragrances that the breeze carried across the glades and the scent of the wallflowers when we passed under castle walls. A spring morning unfolding blue and white among lovely haze, with birds singing in every covert, is easier to remember than a spring evening, but one evening is still clear in memory, so quietly did it pass into night without vulgar lights shining through the park trees, only the drone of frogs in the rushy ponds and ditches as we approached the great gateway of Raymond's castle, in front of which we blew our horns. At their blast, the sleepy rooks rose out of the branches, and they were still clamorous in the air when the Comte's retainers

began to run from the doorways and the projecting corners of the castle. The Comte de Rodebœuf was assisted
from his horse and relieved of his armour. A cloak
edged with fur was thrown about him, and we entered the
castle and gave display of our art in the minstrel gallery,
the Comte Raymond de Castel-Rousillon and his wife
Margherita sitting at the end of the hall with the Comte
de Rodebœuf. My name was no longer Pierre Abélard,
but Lucien de Marolle, and the song that had been turning
in my mind during the ride thither will be found written
in the book kept for the recording of the songs composed
in honour of the castle. About this castle there was a
green sward spread with embroidered tapestries, and the
ladies sat thereon and we sang to them from time to
time, Margherita listening so eagerly to the Comte de
Rodebœuf, who asked me to accompany him, that I knew
she loved him and valued his praises more than any other
thing. I learned too that the Comte Raymond de Castel-
Rousillon was unsuspicious of his wife's infidelity. But art
thou sure, Abélard, of his wife's infidelity? One is never
sure of such things. But it seems as if it could not be
otherwise. Be this as it may, the Comte de Rodebœuf
was greatly pleased with me for the song that I wrote
praising his lady's beauty and for the care I took to
cast no eye upon her that might tempt her thoughts from
him.

One day we were up betimes, and in the same pleasant
sunshine we started forth to journey to another castle
where a court of love and a great tournament was to be
held. A court of love, Héloïse, is a court in which all the
quarrels of lovers and the rights of lovers and the wrongs
of lovers are weighed and adjusted by great ladies assembled for the purpose. And the castle to which we were
going was the Castle of Autoford. The Comte thereof

was expecting the most celebrated troubadours, gleemen and knights-errant to rejoice in the recovery of Geoffrey of Camborne from his exceeding jealousy, a jealousy that had preyed upon him, leaving him no peace, a jealousy so cruel that he could not abide any man inside his castle —all were suspected of having designs upon his wife; and if the visitor stayed on for a while, the Comte would call to his servant to prepare his bath, saying that he bathed before dinner, and if the guest did not accept the intimation and hurry away, Geoffrey would ask him to stay for dinner, having care that the food set before him would be so bad that he would never return again. At last the Comte's jealousy turned to a sort of madness, for 'tis certainly madness to keep a woman locked up in a tower with two maids to wait upon her, to forget all cleanliness of habit and go to her in rags and with a beard matted like a sheaf of oats badly tied together. Yet this was the wont of Geoffrey, and the unfortunate Flamietta, his wife, about whom all the country-side was speaking, telling stories of her, saying that her despair was so great that she had confessed to her maidservants Alice and Margherita that she thought it was God's great favour that she had not borne a child, for a child might have awakened love again; and that it was better that love should cease in her, she being without courage, without hope. At which telling her two maids, Alice and Margherita, wept, for they were attached to their mistress. No greater misfortune can befall me now, she said to them, than that one of you should leave me; at which they protested that neither had thought to do such a thing, that lovers did not tempt them, and that they would sooner die unloved than be separated from their beloved mistress.

Flamietta looked into their eyes and doubted them, as

well she might, for Alice was at that moment planning to leave her, but she had no heart to tell her mistress of her design. But day by day her need of love became more pressing, till at last she came to the Comtesse Flamietta with the truth on her tongue, that she could no longer keep her thoughts from her betrothed, nor could he keep his from her: they must die or enjoy one another. Whereupon the unhappy Flamietta fell to weeping, saying that her heart had told her that the thing she dreaded was about to befall her. But Alice bent over her mistress, saying that she must not grieve so. For another servant will come, she said, who will serve you better than I. Give me service that thou hast not been able to give? What means this talk? It is as I say, mistress, Alice answered, and she spoke of a maidservant of the castle who had come into the service of the Lord of Camborne: so that she might see your beauty, madam, as it passes by on the terrace. But I never pass on the terrace, cried Flamietta. I am locked in this tower and see nobody except a man whose habit is unclean and whose beard is like grass in autumn. What story dost thou tell me? Alice was loath to answer. But Margherita came by and said: What Alice tells you, madam, is the truth; the new maidservant will bring to you a great joy. Bring a great joy to me? Flamietta repeated, vaguely disturbed in a reason that had nearly left her. But no entreaty enforced by tears could wean Alice from her design, and Flamietta cried out: Thou goest to happiness leaving me in grief. The last words that Flamietta heard as she lay sobbing her grief away were: The new maid will be a better help to you, madam, than I can be—words that she could put no meaning upon. Nor did she try to understand what had befallen her when she heard the word alas! on the new maidservant's lips. Is my lot so pitiful that even

my servant maid pities me? She must not tie the latchet
of my shoe again, she said to Margherita as soon as the
new maid was out of hearing. And it was then that
Margherita confided the truth into her mistress's ear,
saying: this servant maid who has just tied the latchet
of your shoe, lady, is no servant maid at all, but Gérard
de Montador, who by virtue of his youth and beauty is
enabled to deceive all in this impersonation. The story
of the Comte's cruelty to you, madam, has gone abroad,
and is told everywhere, and has reached his ears in many
stories that stirred his heart, and there being no other
way to see you but to offer himself as maidservant in the
castle in the hope that one day one of thy personal
attendants might be dismissed, he engaged himself to
the cook as scullery-maid. As no one was dismissed, he
bribed Alice? Flamietta said. Yes, returned Margherita,
and with a large sum of money that will enable her to
make another man happy. So all is for your good, madam,
if you will but believe. But it is a fairy tale thou'rt
telling me, Margherita, for which thou deservest punishment, and if my lord should know—— Hush, my lady,
it is no untruthful story that I am telling you, but the
very truth, as indeed it will be easy for you to ascertain
this very night, for Matilda sleeps in my room and you
have but to call her. But a man who can disguise himself
as a girl is not worthy to be called to a woman's bed. On
that matter I can tell you nothing, only you can test him
fairly. At which Flamietta's face flushed, and then turned
white, for she was sorely perplexed whether to believe
Margherita and call Matilda to her bed or to tell the
whole tale to the Comte and have the girl removed from
her service. And two or three days passed in the perplexity thereof, for Matilda's conduct was always what
a girl's should be, and the only difference in it from that

of any other girl's was her sadness, for each time she
came near her mistress she sighed. Only once did their
eyes meet, and the glance awakened in Flamietta a desire
to make an end of the matter for good or for evil by
calling out in the night-time, saying that the crashing
of the thunder frightened her. But the summer may
pass without a storm. There are always noises in the
turret, she said, and to-night the turret may be more dis-
quieting than usual, and she fell to listening to the wind,
which soon after began to rise. Every howl was welcomed by Flamietta as if it were a song. I am frightened.
What sounds are these? I am frightened. Margherita,
come to me. Myself, mistress, am too frightened by the
noises to leave my bed, but I am sending Matilda, who
is more courageous than I am. A dreadful moment it
was for Flamietta while Matilda crossed the room. Margherita tells me that you are frightened, madam. In a
quiver Flamietta answered: Yes, Matilda; I am frightened
by the wind in the tower. But hast thou no fear? None,
mistress, when I am by you. Nor have I, Flamietta said,
now that thou'rt here, but I quake as I lie alone, hearing
strange sounds about me. Shall I sit by you, madam,
till sleep comes? But it will be cold sitting by me.
Would you have me for a bed companion? Matilda asked.
For answer Flamietta lifted the bedclothes and Matilda
entered the bed, and when they were close together side
by side and fear had passed away from Flamietta she
began to ask Matilda why she sighed so often and why
the word alas! was often on her lips. To these questions
Matilda answered that she was mortally in love and was
without hope or strength or will. Margherita tells me
a strange story that all this great love is given to me,
and thou art not a woman, but I know not whether to
believe it. Thou dost not answer, Matilda, Flamietta

said, breaking a long pause. But lying beside each other
words are not needed, the servant said. I am frightened,
put thy arms about me, which Matilda did, and they lay
still, only conscious of the other's breath. So it is true,
Flamietta cried suddenly, but at that moment there was
a great scuffling of daws in the chimney and Flamietta
believed for a while that the Comte was at the door. But
thou must have loved me very much to have accepted this
disguise for my sake. But when I saw your beauty,
lady, passing me on the terrace, I was recompensed. But
was my beauty enough? A vain question indeed to ask
me, since I am with you and have proven my love. Thou
wouldst not withhold anything from me? Indeed thou
hast earned all I have to give thee, Gérard. Whereupon
sighs took the place of words, and for many nights afterwards the lovers enjoyed one another, for it so happened
that the Comte was ill and kept to his chamber. On his
return to his wife, Flamietta hated him more than she had
done before, for he put the sweet presence of Gérard out
of her reach, and while he was pressing her from behind
the thought came to her that Gérard might be enjoying
sweet felicity in Margherita's arms. Flamietta trusted
her maidservant, but Margherita must not be tried past
her strength, and how was she to resist Gérard should
he be moved to pass from his bed to hers, and the thought
that Gérard should taste with another the joy he had
tasted with her helped to apprehend the torture that
Gérard had suffered for her sake, becoming a kitchen
wench. Moreover out of her jealousy came the knowledge
of Geoffrey's long agony. But her mood of pity was
soon over, and the pillow was wet with her tears so
frequently that the Comte began to believe that his wife
had no heart to love any man. I am different now, she
said, from what I was; have pity on me. And feeling

that he was secure from all rivalry, he said to her one day: I see that such indifference to love has come upon thee that thou canst keep thyself strict as a virgin, and she answered him: I think that I can keep myself strict from wicked pleasures, words that caused Gérard, who was standing by with his mistress's slippers in his hand, to drop one of them, a slight act indeed in itself, not meriting Geoffrey's censure that she was an unmannerly wench to stand by while—so great was the Comte's rage that he was not at pains to finish his sentence, but Gérard heard him say as he was thrown from the room—while I am talking with my wife. I did not notice her presence, the Comte said, when he returned to Flamietta; an untaught girl, no proper servant for thee. Flamietta mentioned that the girl understood little of what was being said and that it was not the Comte's words that caused her to drop the slipper but fingers that could not be relied upon. Thou must have another maidservant, the Comte answered, to which Flamietta answered that though the girl dropped things occasionally she was devoted to her, especially in times of storm; when the wind sent the mortar clattering down the chimney and strange noises were heard in the turret Matilda's presence pacified and soothed her with good sense. The old green light of jealousy came into the Comte's eyes, and Flamietta turned aside, saying to herself: Jealousy leaves us no repose of mind. It was then the thought came to her that the Comte might order Gérard a whipping, which would reveal all and bring him his death, but being devoured at the same time with the thought that every night he might be lying in sweet felicity in Margherita's arms she came to an understanding the next day with Gérard that he must not waste his life in a girl's habit for love of her, but must earn his love in a knightly combat. I shall weep for thee, Gérard, in secret. And I shall sing thy beauty where'er I go, Gérard answered.

And the next day, when the Comte asked: Where is Matilda? Flamietta called her soul into her eyes and said: My dear husband, hast thou forgotten that she displeased thee yesterday by standing by whilst thou wast talking to me? She is gone? cried the Comte. In obedience to thy wishes, Flamietta answered, by these words plucking the last sting of jealousy out of the Comte's heart, and well-nigh freeing herself from all suspicion of loitering passion by speaking of love with contempt whenever it came to be spoken of, almost daring to aver that she had never found pleasure in the naked battle. Are we not happier now that it is over? she asked him, adding that much else was in the world to admire, her voice sinking into carelessness as she spoke of chivalry and knight-errantry, for she did not wish it to be known to the Comte that tidings had reached her that a young knight, Gérard de Montador, was now winning great renown in all the lists in Provence. But of him the Comte did not fail to receive tidings, and not many weeks after he told her that no knight had been found to withstand Gérard in the field of chivalry and romance, for Gérard was as skilful with words as he was with the lance and sword. Wilt tell me, dear Geoffrey, if we shall see this renowned knight? she said; for one day I would see him and a noble rival coming to the clash.

The Comte bore her wish in mind, and was glad when a letter came to him from Comte Raymond of Chaudlieu telling that a young knight, Gérard de Montador, was coming from Provence to his castle and would give examples of his prowess in singing and in tilting. A great assembly was expected, but it would not be complete without the presence of Comte Geoffrey de Camborne, bringing with him his wife Flamietta. It is known far and widely that we have been at variance, Geoffrey said, and this occasion is felicitous to show that I no longer am afraid to trust her. Flamietta's instinct put appropriate answer into her mouth. I would be seen with thee in public, she said, for thou hast become the man again whom I wedded. Thy beard is trimmed and thou wearest raiment in keeping with thy nobility. And both happy in different anticipations, the twain drove in their great coach to the castle of Chaudlieu, where Flamietta met Gérard, who, with no sign of recognition in his face or in his manner towards her, asked if he might wear her badge on his arm in the lists. And Flamietta, with an equal witlessness, turned to her husband: Gérard de Montador would wear my badge on his arm. To which the Comte answered that he, too, would be honoured if Gérard de Montador wore his wife's badge in the lists, for he had heard of the young knight's prowess and knew that there was no danger of his being overthrown.

And Flamietta's beauty drew the knights about her. All were her suitors, and Geoffrey's trust in his wife was praised in all the groups. It was remarked that never had a greater change come upon a man, and that much honour was due to Flamietta for the transformation of an unkempt madman into a courtly gentleman. Wherever she went Flamietta was followed by a crowd of knights; and Geoffrey and Gérard, as they walked together, were spoken of as souls created for one another, who had wandered for long apart and met at last. Gérard bore Flamietta's badge through the tournament without failure, and when the poems written by the knights in honour of the ladies whose badges they had worn were read, many were admired, but the poem that excelled all the others in intricacy of metre and richness of rhyme was written by

Gérard de Montador. It touched all hearts, and none was so deeply moved as Geoffrey, who thanked Gérard for having celebrated his wife in such noble words.

Geoffrey, Gérard and Flamietta returned together, the Comte on horseback, Gérard and Flamietta in the coach —Geoffrey would hear of no other departure, and we all marvelled, Abélard said, as we saw them go away together, in our cynical humour believing that the friendship that had ripened so suddenly would drop as suddenly from its stalk. But did it? Héloïse asked. No; the three lived together happily ever afterwards, Abélard answered, and the quarrels rising, for quarrels rise among those who love each other, were settled amicably with skill and tact by Geoffrey; and his fame of peacemaker was extended from his own household to other households, till a proverb rose up in the country that bad beginnings made good ends. But how did it become known that Gérard de Montador had served once in Geoffrey's kitchen so that he might see Flamietta's beauty as it passed on the terrace? Alice, the maidservant, told the story, Abélard answered. And after the tournament at the castle of Chaudlieu, whither wentest thou, Abélard?

We wandered from castle to castle, meeting the same knights and ladies, hearing the same stories, singing the same songs, some new ones, of course; but the new ones had begun to seem to me like the old ones, and the Comte de Rodebœuf, a friend at first, began to seem like an enemy. He was not changed towards me, nor was I changed towards him, but my heart was not in all this singing and psaltery, and when the summer was at wane at the end of September, and our wandering not yet at an end, though the woods were red, my heart misgave me; but Rodebœuf would not hear of my departure, and being weak I followed him to his castle, arriving thither among autumn rains and a whirl of leaves. And the winter went by stringing lutes and playing them, writing songs and wondering which Margherita would like, Mathieu's or mine, for he often sang mine to her when he liked mine better than his own. But though he liked mine better, he was sad when Margherita preferred them; she had a fine ear, and my musical turns of phrase were often less trite. We were always going back and forth, they coming to our castle and we going to theirs. It may have been that if Rodebœuf had left me more time for my own thoughts I might have forgotten philosophy and given my life to lute-playing and singing. A man's fate hangs on a little thread. Margherita de Castel-Rousillon was Rodebœuf's mistress? Héloïse interrupted. Yes, Abélard answered, and he was about to begin a story about her when Héloïse said: how quiet, how still the house seems. It would seem that we are alone in it, Abélard answered. We are indeed, Héloïse replied. Half-an-hour ago Madelon shut the door behind her, and my uncle is at vespers. At these words a strange disquiet fell upon them, and they stood looking at each other, each with a choking in the throat.

CHAP. XII.

AS they crossed the company-room towards the window Héloïse put her hand into his arm, and they stopped at the stair-top to listen. No one is in the house, he said; and that he might regale his eyes upon her womanly shapes afresh he asked her to loosen her girdle, and she, being without thought but obedience to him, did so, saying: Do not look too closely at me, lest thou weary of seeing me. At which he laughed, and fell to talking of the beauty of many parts of her, till, overcome by a sudden reverence, he seized her hand and kissed it. Sing to me, she said, giving him the lute, and he sang his translation of one of the beautiful *albes* (dawn songs) of Provence, that one in which the lovers lie together in an orchard, the woman bemoaning the passing of the night, for the day will take her friend from her; her hope is that the watcher will perceive his mistake, and that the dawn is still afar; but she knows that this is not so, and cries: Ah God, ah God, the dawn! it comes so soon. In each stanza a new phase of the night's passing is narrated. The ousels singing in the meadows remind her again of the watcher and force from her the passionate cry: Ah God, ah God, the dawn! it comes so soon. The air rises cool through the orchard ways, she drinks it, but it is not as sweet to her as her lover's breath that only can assuage her thirst, and once more the cry breaks from her lips: Ah God, ah God, the dawn! it comes so soon. The lover answers that his lady is fair and gentle and has won many hearts, but to one only is she true, to his heart, which now cries out the wild cry: Ah God, ah God, the dawn! it comes so soon.

The perfection of the poem, its words, its tune and the singing of it raised Héloïse's truthful eyes, and she fixed them on her lover, who, singing softly in her ear, his breath fanning her cheek, moving the soft down on her neck, repeated the first stanza:

> In the orchard and beneath a hawthorn-tree
> The twain lie hand on hand and knee to knee
> Until the watchman cries, and planets flee,
> Ah God! ah God! the dawn! it comes so soon.

The troubadours have written many beautiful verses, he said, but none more perfect than this song. The orchards, she answered, were coming into flower when we met, beloved. The orchards are still in flower, and tomorrow we might be lying under the summer skies hand on hand and knee to knee, seeing the stars through the leaves and feeling the breeze grow colder as the night passes into dusk. Every morning the ousels are singing in the hawthorns, but we are not about to hear them. The season is passing; soon the ousels will cease to sing and we shall hearken to the cuckoo. Ah God, ah God, the season goes too soon. But the season is still with us. Abélard. if I had not met thee should I have lived out my youth and virginity and gone down into old age without knowing love? If thou hadst not come, should I have loved another? Thine eyes tell me that thou thinkest another would have satisfied me if I had not seen thee, yet it seems to me that thou wast always part of me, and if chance had not given thee to me all others would have seemed worthless. Abélard, thou art a great philosopher, yet these things thou durst not make plain. It cannot be that I could have loved another as I love thee, but thou hast loved often and loved much before thou sawest me. I love thee, Héloïse, and we must take the love that God gives us. If a boy loves a married woman he learns from her much that she would not have been able to teach him if she had not learnt from others, and he should be thankful to his predecessors—— But I needed no teaching, Héloïse interrupted, for I knew love from the moment I saw thee. Thy name affrighted me when I first heard it, stirring a sense of fear in me. I remember it all now. But no, it was not fear, Abélard, but the ringing of my heart telling the destiny that awaited me. Is it true that I should have lived all my life without knowing what love is if I had not met thee? I wonder. Love is the singing string in a woman's life. Hear it, Abélard, she said, taking the lute from him; that is my string; life would be like the lute without it. Should I have dreamed a love and been faithful to my dream, Abélard? Has such a thing never fallen out that a man should hide himself away from reality, almost spurn it, so that he might bring himself closer to his dream? Such a lover may have been, Héloïse, for love takes strange turns, weaving strange stories, making fools of men and heroes, too. But of such a lover I know naught, Abélard answered. Ah, there was one Godfrey Rudel, a true knight and a good singer of songs, sought after by ladies, but who denied himself to all for the sake of his dream. Did women seek him for his beauty, his art, or for his renown? Héloïse asked. And Abélard replied that Rudel was not ill-favoured, tall and slim, and walking with a stoop, deep in his dream, seeing his princess far away more clearly than the women about him. To win her love, he said, I must go to her pure; she would divine an impurity were I guilty of one, and would deem me unworthy of her love, as indeed I should be. With such answers he strove against those who would rob him of his purity, thereby humiliating the lustful and the capricious by his faith that her name would be made known to him in good time. And how came the announcement to him, tell me? Héloïse said. Through a bard from a far country, singing in a court of love of Idena of Rathmoule, who waited for her lover far in Ireland. At these words: Idena of Rathmoule, a light of dawn came into his face; he withdrew from the hall, and soon it began to be whispered throughout the assembly that tidings had come to Godfrey of his princess far away.

My good friends, I have sung my last song here, he said, when he returned; if I sing again it will be elsewhere. All asked: but wilt thou not return? No, he

answered, his voice touching a sort of ecstasy, I go to
my fate. But why should not thy lady return with thee?
he was asked. To this question he gave no answer, and
walked henceforth by the harper's side, hearing from him
that Idena of Rathmoule lived in a castle by a lake in
a forest, and that she always said that a song would come
to her from over sea. Godfrey asked if Idena was wedded,
and if there were singers in her own country to proclaim
her beauty. The harper could make no answer, or would
make none, but his silence made no change in Godfrey,
who said to his friends: The time has come for me to bid
you farewell. It was then that his friends saw that his
eyes were hollow, without light, and they muttered: She
has cast a spell upon him from afar, a sorceress she is
who desires his death, not his life, whom he will not live
to see. But though he melted on the voyage almost out
of human shape, he reached the distant island alive, and
on reaching it the harper was sent forthright to the lady's
castle to tell her that a knight from the far land of
Provence had heard her name from O'Moran, the harper,
and recognising her as his fate he had come to her without
knowledge of how she would receive him, certain, however, that he was obeying the will of God. The lady
stood elated by her luck, saying: God is good; He has
sent me my dream lover; and at once the preparations for
meeting him were begun. But these took a long time,
Godfrey waiting anxious but growing feebler as the days
went by, till at last it came to be doubted by himself and
his physicians if he would live long enough to see Idena
with his bodily eyes. But it was granted to him to see
her as plainly with these eyes as he had seen her with
the eyes of his soul. So thou hast come to me, he said,
from thy western castle, beautiful as in the dream. And
thou art the Godfrey I saw in my dream, she answered,

for the dying Godfrey was hidden from her. Reality
and dream had turned to one, and on being told that
Godfrey was near to death, she fell upon her knees and
prayed that his life might be spared. But there are
bonds that cannot be loosened, and Godfrey's turn had
come. All life now, she said, has ended for me; and going
to a nunnery, she lived in prayer and abstinence, dreaming always of their meeting in eternity, till she fell sick
in her turn, and physicians assembled about her bed. To
their grave words of admonition, she answered: Why all
this sadness, for am I not going to him who is waiting
for me? Of all my life this is the most joyful moment.
Till the very last she continued to give instructions regarding the great tomb which the masons were still building for them. Abélard ceased speaking, and it was
Héloïse who broke the pause that followed the narrative
of the life and death of two great lovers: canst tell me
if our destiny is as beautiful and as sad as theirs? Thou
canst not tell, Abélard, though thou art a great philosopher. We are but blind mice, and philosophy does not
help us in the straits of our lives. Thou dost not know
whether if Godfrey had foreseen his death he would have
sought it in Ireland or lived his life shabbily amid the
vines and olives of Provence. Godfrey, said Abélard,
would not have lived his life shabbily, for that is the sin
against the Holy Ghost. Come what might, I should have
gone to thee, Héloïse, and on these words a great silence
fell between them, and when the silence became strained
he broke the pause, saying that he did not know why
they were not out and enjoying the sun. Héloïse answered: we are not sitting under the willows, lest we
should be seen by the folk coming and going over the
Great Bridge; I have often longed to walk with thee.
And these words awakened the thought, never very far

away from Abélard's consideration, that sooner or later he would have to leave Fulbert's house to take Orders.

To break this second silence, more irritating than the first, he spoke of the river so idly lapping itself to the sea, but in no hurry to reach it. A wise river truly, for the season is pleasant here, the air full of circling swallows A happy month indeed they have had above the river. A long way above it, Héloïse said, for the swallows do not come down to the river till rain is nigh—— And we have not had a shower for nearly two months, Abélard interrupted. Two months of summer-time wearies us, for we are northern folk, and too much sun makes us unhappy. Our taste is for a few lovely days, and then one or two drenching rains to brighten the foliage and kill the flies. But we need not, said Abélard, fear the folk coming and going over the left bridge; the bridge is empty now. Moreover, why should we not walk together under the willows by the river's edge? Let us go, she said; but bring thy lute with thee, Abélard, for I would have thee sing some more *albes*. But why sing *albes* in the evening? Abélard asked. I'll bring the lute and will sing a sirvente. and they descended the stairs into the street, talking of Bertram, one of the great singers of Provence, and she heard Abélard say that he would sing one of Bertram's beautiful sirventes to her, telling how France is to-day a land of song; how everywhere voices are singing praise of young leaves and flowers, singing like the birds, without thought that the world has risen out of winter, singing happily without knowledge. Then the cause of thy laying the lute aside, Héloïse answered, was the knowledge that there are many singers and but one philosopher. Abélard's eyes smiled in recognition of the compliment, and he said: Our winter was truly a long one, five hundred years, but man has begun to use his reason again and

religion must conform to man's new condition, and it is
because religion must be serious (by serious I mean reasonable) that I laid aside the lute. But will the Church
allow religion to be reasonable? she asked. It was to
save the Church, he answered, that I sacrificed art for
philosophy. Sacrificed art for philosophy, she repeated;
alas, was the sacrifice necessary? Will the world be as
beautiful again as it was in Virgil's time? It was in
many ways more beautiful than ever it will be again, he
answered, but we cannot go back, even if we would.
Jesus was born and taught in Galilee. I know not how it
is, Héloïse answered, but I never could take any interest
in religion. Never take any interest in religion? he repeated, deeply concerned, for her words seemed to Abélard an avowal of her whole nature. And they did not
speak again for a long time, and when they rose to their
feet the stars were springing in the sky, and they wandered home feeling that the hour of love was approaching
for them both. But suddenly, on their way home, Héloïse
broke the silence: Abélard, I have forgotten to point out
to thee the kingfisher's nest; it is on the bank below us.

CHAP. XIII.

ABÉLARD, she said, one day, though she struggled
against the words that overflowed her lips in spite of herself, Abélard, is it not true that the time has come to return
to thy good friend philosophy? A question that at once
set him telling her that his present bout of singing and
lute-playing was in accordance with the general humour
of the world; and failing to satisfy her that even the
exception to the rule must return to the rule for fortifica-
tion against eccentricity, he reminded her that for years
his life was given over to work and nothing but work.

Thou art my recompense for those patient years, he said
Héloïse found it hard not to accept this plea, but her
heart misgave her. Abélard, she said, thou art the great
philosopher the world has been waiting for; I would not
rob the world of thy gift, even for my own pleasure and
thine. Wouldst drive me away from thee into the schools
again? No, Abélard, I would not, she answered; but it
cannot be harmful to remind thee of thine own words.
Hast thou not said many times that there is no advancement for a layman, and the meaning of this is that thy
career is in the Church. Wouldst thou then have me
leave thee, Héloïse? Leave me? Héloïse answered. I
would not have thee leave me, but I would have thee a
great man. But, Héloïse, thy love for me is not because
I am a great philosopher? Answer me, Héloïse: if I had
been a mere minstrel wouldst thou not have loved me?
Abélard, a riddle thou art putting to me, for can I think
of thee save as a great philosopher? Was it not as a
philosopher that I first saw thee? Was it not as a philosopher that I learnt to love thee? But, Héloïse, I should
have loved thee as a peasant girl. I know naught of man's
love of woman, only how thou didst love me, Héloïse
replied. How did I begin to love thee, Héloïse, and what
prompted my love? I would hear the truth, for I have
no knowledge of it. I only know that I love Héloïse.
Thine eyes took pleasure in me, though I am not as beautiful as many another; still I was made for thine eyes.
So it is only through the eye that I love thee, Héloïse,
and all thy learning counts for no part of my love?
Abélard, thou art pleased that I can talk to thee about
thy lectures and appreciate them, and I am glad that my
Latin is learned enough to put thy manuscripts into closer
accord with the ancient language. Am I saying too much,
Abélard? Not enough, Héloïse; thy help is valuable;

together we write Latin better than we write it singly.
I fetch thee ideas and thou'rt apt with a turn of phrase
more like Cicero and Seneca than any that I can devise
without much thought.   Always kindly towards me, she
answered, and disposed to speak well of the humble help
that I bring, if I bring any.   But, Héloïse, he said, let
us not forget the subject of this talk, that outside of the
priesthood there is no advancement for a layman.   Which
wouldst thou prefer, for me to be renowned among men
or to be thy faithful lover always?   I would prefer thee
to be great, for then I could watch and rejoice in thy
triumphs.   Thou art my triumph, which is not unnatural
since I am a woman, a satellite.   It is hard for me to
believe that thou wouldst sacrifice thy love for a vanity,
he answered.   There would be no sacrifice, since my desire
is to hear thee well spoken of in the world, she said.   And
would that be enough? Abélard asked; to live contented
apart, hearing of my triumphs?   And if there were no
triumphs, wouldst thou cease to love me?   Abélard, I
cannot think of thee apart from triumphs.   Thou hast
given more thought to thy love than I have given to mine,
he replied.   The words: There is no advancement for a
layman outside of the Church, may have been spoken by
me, but if so they were spoken without application of
them to myself.   They were treasured up in my mind, and
used to mould thy love of me, to shape it to an idea, that
the man must be glorious for a woman to love him.   But
love is an end in itself and not a means to an end.   I
know not why I loved, nor how I loved, but abandoned
myself to it, content that much might be well lost if one
thing were won, thereby gaining reproof from thee, who
sayest that my present lessons are but repetitions of
former lessons.   Thou makest the most of the argument,
for argument is thy business and thy genius, Héloïse

answered, but my heart tells me that I am right, that I
am the lover and not thou. With the skill of the great
dialectician thou wouldst have it that thy honour and
glory are but the selfish ends that I seek. So our life
may be argued about, for it is or may well be but a passing phase of another life. Every moment of our lives,
Abélard answered, is but a passing phase. We do but
cheat each other, Héloïse returned; and as is common to
a man, thou must needs lay the burden on me, for thou
knowest well in thy heart, as I know in mine, that in
giving thee to the priesthood I only give part of thee.
Our separation need not be for long; a year at most.
Wilt thou wait here for me in content, counting the days
till I return to thee? And how soon after my ordination
may I return to thee? Why not at once, Abélard? At
once, Héloïse? Are priests not as other men? she said.
Nature made man for woman and woman for man; Nature
abides, dogmas and doctrines come and go. Thy words
come to thee easily, Héloïse, as easily as tinkling from
the bell. It is hard for me to associate thy words with
thee, for what art thou but a child? But thou art always
thyself, just as the bell is itself always. None taught
thee to think. Thy thoughts do not rise out of books,
but are natural to thee, and that is why they seem so
wonderful to me, who have learnt to think out of books.
A courageous nature is thine without alloy, speaking always out of itself. Héloïse, I shall always love thee, for
thou art myself, an Abélard that might have been. Only
in philosophy are we divided, for thou hast little taste
for philosophy, yet thou wouldst have me a philosopher.
To be a philosopher thou must needs be a priest, she replied. A priest, he answered; the words sound like a
knell in my ear. I ask thee, she said, to be a priest,
Abélard, so that I may retain my love always, for it is all

that I have in the world. Let it be so, Héloïse; a priest I will be, and will begin to-morrow to inquire out how my ordination shall be accomplished. To-morrow! Héloïse cried. See, thou art frightened already, he answered. Nay, I am not frightened, but I would not have thee leave me till thou hast been my lover wholly to the very end. I will come to thy couch to-night, Abélard, she said; and two hours later he was waiting for her, and she came into his room and lay down beside him, her face telling him that she had been weeping and had washed her tears away. They began afresh, and she clasped him voluptuously yet in sorrow, saying: Dear, I am to lose thee, and so refuse all partial love from thee. But if thou shouldst find thyself in child? If that should be my fortune, she answered, I will bear it without complaint, for he will be thy child, and the suffering he will bring me of the flesh, and the shame, will help me to endure the sorrow of our separation. And this night, this night, thou shalt not break away from me, and thy seed shall flourish in me if God wills it so. I will have thee, Abélard, wholly, altogether, for I was born for thee and thou for me, with God's forbearance and perchance his blessing. Before I yield myself I must have thy promise that our love shall be complete. Let me find God's blessing in it, he said. She gave her mouth, and they lay a long while in each other's arms, to lie again and again possessed of love of one another. Only now do we belong to each other, she said, all that went before was nothing. We have answered Nature's bidding, he answered her, and it is as thou sayest, there is but one mutuality in Nature's law, and as thou sayest, all that went before was nothing. But now that what had to be has been, we must be careful of our secret, for enemies are about, and until the

Canon leaves the house we may not kiss. But we may sit together, she said, with books before us.

And so the books were always open, and their eyes bent upon them when Fulbert came into the room. The sight of so much learning pleased him, and he would leave the room abruptly, afraid to stay longer, his presence proving an interruption to their studies. But once Fulbert returning suddenly to say something he had forgotten, Abélard seized the birch that hung upon the wall, saying: That passage thou hast translated many times always with the same faults. What! What! cried Fulbert, deceived. Always the same faults, said Abélard, and to continue in our faults deserves punishment; whereupon he struck Héloïse twice across her hands. But it were better to strike thee than that Fulbert should suspect us, and the greater hurt, he said, was in my heart, and the heart suffers more than the hands. He kissed her hands and her eyes, and hearing the front door close he took her in his arms. So, Abélard, no woman has pleased thee till I did? and he answered her that till he met her, music and philosophy had claimed him so fully that he had had no thought for life till now. From that day their passion for each other took new forms and refinements; to none did he find her loath. Yet there was a shadow on her happiness, for their desire of one another became so importunate that Abélard could not leave her to go to his school, and she watched the shadow darkening in his face and heard him say that the thought of his school was distasteful, and that he could not overcome his dislike of these lessons.

But thy lessons are thyself, Abélard, she answered, and thou wilt return to me with pleasure, excited by the separation. Have I not earned a holiday? he replied; and art not thou my holiday, Héloïse? But if thou wish it,

I will leave thee; and to soothe the pain his words caused, he said: Thou art right, I must go, and thine absence will increase my pleasure in seeing thee again. And when he returned and she said: Didst speak with inspiration? he answered: No. I unrolled the scroll of memory and repeated the old lessons. But on my way hither, verses came into my head without being asked: love songs that are thou, songs that are I. Then sing to me, she said, plucking the lute from the wall. She was the first to hear songs that would capture town after town, delighting all by the charm of the verses and the tunes that accompanied them—all except the disciples, who said in the school: Music and poetry have captured our master; he is no longer a philosopher, but a trouvère. And Abélard, noticing his own estrangement from his scholars and disciples and from books themselves, began to think of his own honour and asked himself with what words he would answer Fulbert if the Canon were to surprise them one day in each other's arms, or if the Canon were to give ear to the gossips who were already busy with their names. It is true, he said, that a man is blind to the evil within his doors and goes his way unaware of the vices of his children and his wife, the laughing-stock of the crowd. But what is known to all sooner or later cannot be hidden from the victim whom it most concerns, and one day Fulbert opened the door with a suddenness, almost a violence, that was unusual, and the lovers were afraid, for it seemed certain that the news of their love had reached his ears. Neither doubted that it was so when he said: Héloïse, I would speak with Abélard alone. I have some orders to give to Madelon, she answered, and left the room, assuming an air of indifference that was not lost upon Abélard.

Abélard, said Fulbert, the common talk about the

Cathedral and in the town has been for some time that
my niece is your mistress, but these lies have only just
come to my ears, and I told him who brought them to me
that he had been listening to liars. I am not mistaken in
you? No, sir; you're not mistaken, Abélard answered.
Your niece is no more to me than a favourite pupil, which
is as it should be, for I have never met such intelligence
before as hers, and——— Nothing of what is said is true,
Abélard? Fulbert interjected. Nothing, sir. At his
words the gloom lifted from the Canon's face, and his
voice became lighter. It was my duty to tell what is
in every mouth, and it is my duty to tell her, too, though
it would have been better that such stories did not reach
her ears yet. They reach the ears of all sooner or later.
But say once more, Abélard, it is not true. I put my
faith in you. Our relations have always been what they
should be, sir: those of an affectionate pupil to a devoted
master. Give me your hand, Abélard. And holding the
door, he called to Héloïse: Héloïse, come to me. Abélard's heart seemed to stop beating and he felt the colour
die out of his face, for if Héloïse were to admit the truth
—his thoughts did not carry him further than a vague
sense of horror and shame—yes, uncle, I am coming. He
heard her feet on the stairs, and a moment later she was
in the room. My dear child, I have come to tell you of
the wickedness that is being spoken in Paris to-day, about
the Cathedral, and in the street corners and in the tav-
erns; it is said everywhere that you are Abélard's mistress. How did you answer the scandal-mongers? Héloïse
asked, with an unchanging countenance. I answered
them that they were liars, the Canon replied. He had
intended to lay a trap for Héloïse so that he might get
the truth, but the words revealed to Héloïse the knowledge
that Abélard had denied the truth, and she answered:

Uncle, you did well to tell them they were liars. I am sorry there are people who would speak ill of a girl who has done them no harm. She has saved me, Abélard said to himself, and the Canon took his niece into his arms and kissed her. My heart told me it was not so. I did not suspect thee, dear, but hearing that such talk was about I had to come to you both; but you have lifted a great weight from me, and he turned aside to disguise his emotion. And when he thought he could speak without faltering, he said: It will be well, despite your innocence, that Abélard leave my house. Oh, uncle, Héloïse cried, must I lose my friend, my first friend, my only friend, because people speak evil? It is hard, Héloïse, but I do not see how Abélard can remain here. What do you say, Abélard? And Abélard answered: It will be better for me to withdraw. I shall lose a dear pupil, but, Héloïse, your uncle is right, I must leave, and now.

Héloïse turned to the window and picked up a book: Never shall we read Virgil together again, and the Canon answered: Now I will leave you; Abélard will tell thee that it is as I say, and he will be able to make plain better than I that his absence is necessary if an end is to be put to this evil talk.

They waited for the door to close, but when it closed Abélard did not take Héloïse in his arms for shame of the breaking of the trust that had been imposed upon him. But Héloïse, knowing only love, was thinking wildly of how the days would pass apart from Abélard. It is hard that we should be divided just as we have become used to each other's thoughts and ways, and each needful to the other, she said; when thou art with me life is full, and when thou art away, empty as a desert. It cannot be, Abélard, that we shall not sit in that window-seat again arranging plans, plans in which I had a share; didst thou

not say that I could help thee, and will it be that somebody else takes my place? Abélard did not answer, and
they stood each a melancholy gazing-stock for the other.
We must wait until the scandal dies, he said at last; now
I must go. But why shouldst thou be the first to say:
I must go? she cried. Do not make the parting worse
than it is, Héloïse, he answered. Wouldst thou then have
us part, she replied, as if the parting were but a welcome
diversion in our life? Héloïse, the strain is too great, I
cannot bear it; my tears will flow if I strive to endure it
longer. Only this I have strength to say, that this parting
cannot be for long; for those who love as we do cannot
be parted. We shall always be united in thought, and
thought is a great magnet, Héloïse. I have often spoken
to thee of reason, now I speak to thee of faith; good-bye.

CHAP. XIV.

IT might have been better had we confessed the truth,
he said, as he sat alone in his old lodging, dreaming of
Héloïse, unable to sleep, his mind torn by thoughts of
his love and his duty towards Fulbert. Everything seemed
crooked, and life was a greater load than he could bear,
but he would have to bear it. The night went by and
the dawn came, and he said: I shall have to prepare
a lesson to-day and another lesson to-morrow whilst
Héloïse is——- His thoughts died, and soon after, or
long after, he awoke, asking himself of what he had been
thinking—his long absence—and then he fell to thinking
of the last lesson he had given in the cloister, for it
would not do to repeat what he had said a few days
before: he must repeat something he had not said for
many months. But he could think only of Héloïse, and
suddenly the thought came upon him of the words she

had used and all that had followed. Her words were:
I will have no partial love from thee, the risk is mine;
and he fell to thinking how the Canon had burst in upon
them, the questions he had put to them, and their denials.
And while recalling those last moments in the rue des
Chantres, he remembered that he had had no thought in
the few minutes left them to take leave of each other
to ask her to send him a message saying: The danger is
past. Now if it should befall him to have gotten Héloïse
with child, how would he help her, what would be the
next step? A fortnight went by in fitful anxiety, and as
the next week brought no news of her he welcomed the
letter that Madelon brought to him, certain that it contained the good news. While reading it he became aware
suddenly that Madelon's eyes were upon him. She may
be reading my face, he said to himself, and it might be
well to cast the letter aside carelessly and so deceive her.
He was about to do this when he read a few lines lower
down: Madelon knows all and can be trusted. So the con-
tents of this letter are not unknown to thee? he said,
raising his eyes and looking her straight in the face.
Héloïse tells me that we can trust thee. I hope indeed
that I can be trusted to do all that I can to help her in
her woman's trouble. Poor damosel, whom I knew in
her cradle and who has been ever since in my care, more
or less. All the years she was at school at Argenteuil,
I never let one pass without going to see her and bringing
her cakes and fruit, and that is ever since her father was
killed in Jerusalem after finding the spear that pierced
good Jesus's side. It is said that the spear is coming
back—— But, my good Madelon, we have to think how
we have to save our damosel. Yes, indeed we have,
interrupted Madelon. For when the news reaches the
Canon's ears he will be beside himself, tearing at his hair

and talking all kinds of wicked things of how he must be
revenged upon you, good sir, and going out of his mind
perhaps and drowning himself in the river, for the store
that he puts on that child is more than anyone can tell.
And what wilt thou be saying—what, Madelon? Of
course I shall be saying whatever comes into my head—
that none need know about the baby, and that everybody
has babies, and it is the fault of nobody, for it is in the
nature of things for the little lambs to skip. Should I
be far amiss in saying these things, sir? Thou hast thine
own words and ways of saying things, Madelon. But
our damosel asks me what she is to do, and I would know
what thou hast said, and what advice given? I have told
her, Madelon replied, that there is nothing for it but for
us three to take the road to Brittany, for are we not all
Bretons together, and coming from within a few miles
of the same part? We three should take the road together, for the ride through the Orléans forest is a long
one and full of danger in winter, the wolves being hun-
grier in the snow than in the sunshine. So if she is not
to be frightened out of her wits with fear that the Canon
will suspect something, as well he might, for there are
women that show the child in four months just as there
are women who don't show it until the eighth—I was like
that myself, standing behind the tables so that the Canon
shouldn't see my belly, and should be loath that our little
damosel should be put to the same strain as I was. The
ride is a long one, and she is better able to bear it now
than she will be in six months' time. The floods in the
Loire sweep the country in winter, picking up trees and
steads as easily as wolves do lambs, even whole towns.
Do I not know the Loire, having lived by it all my life
till—but we won't speak of that again. If we don't start
out on our journey now we shall have to ride the most of

it, and the leagues are long between Tours and Nantes.
It is true that your folk are nearer this way, but it is
only a few miles between Nantes and Le Pallet; about ten
or a dozen I am reckoning it. No more is it than that.
So we may count it from Paris to Nantes a matter of
three or four hundred miles or thereabouts. Three weeks'
jogging on a packhorse is good for neither a woman in
the family way nor the baby. So methinks Héloïse cannot
do better than to start at once, she and I together, for she
will never find her way alone. Nor wouldst thou find it,
though I put much faith in thee, Madelon, Abélard said,
faith in thy leal, courage and truthfulness and common-
sense to help you both out of the difficulties ye would
meet on the way. But I must go with you, and we must
start at once. Not at once, said Madelon, but in a week
from now. Why is that? asked Abélard. The Canon is
going away to Soissons for a few days, Madelon replied,
and won't he be in a tantrum when he finds his niece gone,
and with her his old servant, who has looked after him
all her life. But we will leave a letter for him telling
the truth, for we might as well all three murder him as
not to do this, for it would be the same thing. We will
leave a letter, Abélard replied. And when does the Canon
leave for Soissons? The first day of next week, on the
Monday. On Tuesday morning I shall be waiting for
you by the Little Bridge with the hackneys at daybreak,
for none must know of our departure. I will come in a
friar's garb, and between this and then thou canst fit, cut
and sew a nun's habit for Héloïse; and thou must wear
a habit as well. Two nuns and a friar we shall be riding
towards Orléans on Tuesday morning. So be it, sir, and
though I am leaving the Canon, who will be breaking his
heart for me and his meals, it will be pleasant to be in
charge of our damosel, going with her to our own country,

for are we not, as I said before, sir, Bretons together?
We are three Bretons, Abélard interjected, and on Tuesday morning we shall be riding towards our country.
Thou hast much talk, Madelon, and whilst listening to
thee I am thinking as well as listening, and it has come
upon me that our ride to Orléans will be a slow one, for
although thou hast ridden many a pony over the hills of
Brittany, our damosel, as thou callest her, has never been
astride, nor yet sat on a pillion. It will be slow indeed,
sir, but our damosel being no more than seventeen will
learn riding easily, for at that age the limbs are supple
and soon fall to any labour that may be laid upon them,
whether jogging on a pillion or gripping a pony's side
with the knees. She will soon fall into it, but let the
pony be a quiet one, a slow pony, one loath to move out
of his walk. Even a walking pony can do ten miles a day,
and the Canon will hear nothing of this for about three
or four days, so we shall be in Orléans before he returns
to his empty house. I am sorry for the good man, for he
has been a good master to me and I am leaving him in a
great trouble, and I had always looked to myself to be
by his side to console him—— With such words, Abélard
interrupted, as God's little lambs will skip. Now thou
art laughing at an old woman and her talk. But isn't
it true, sir, and it may well be that if you skipped with
her it is because you did but a little skipping in your early
days? Sooner or later we all skip, and myself is a token.
One foggy night it was, and—— A story that will beguile
our ride, Madelon. But now I would have thee return
to Héloïse with the good news that if we do three leagues
a day, we shall be in Orléans in five days from Tuesday.
She will be a bit stiff after the first day but I will give
her a hot bath and, as you say it, sir, we may reckon on
being in Orléans the next week, not that I am much good

at counting, but as an old woman makes it up on her
fingers it will be about that.   And twenty leagues takes
a lot of catching up, and the Canon will not know which
road we have taken, nor guess perchance our journey's end.

CHAP. XV.

ON the day appointed Abélard was at the Little Bridge
an hour before dawn, watching the stars, wondering how
long it would be before they began to pale, rise higher
and vanish out of sight.   The watchman's voice crying
the third hour told him that his hopes would not be fulfilled for yet half-an-hour.   He must have dozed in the
saddle, for he remembered nothing after the watchman's
cry till, rousing his drooping head, he saw the towers of
Notre-Dame showing above the murk in which the city lay
buried, and was inspired to think of the coming day as
rising out of the night like a phantom, grey and empty,
unreal, almost vindictive; soundless, too, he added; for
the owls are back in their tower, the fox has gone to
ground; not a chitter in the jasmine; and we shall be far
away in the country before the daws come out of the
hollow boles.

   But why am I astride of the mare, wearying her with
my weight? he asked, and dismounting, he stood in admiration of the strength of his young chestnut mare:
Well worth the money I paid for her, he said, five or six
years old, of great girth and up to almost any weight.
Then his eyes falling on the tufty fetlocks, he remarked:
How short she is from the fetlock to the knee, with chest
and shoulders like a bull; a pretty head, a winning countenance starred white.   He liked to hear her whinny when
he approached with the nosebag, and to see her fling it
from side to side in her greediness when it was strapped

behind her ears. A good feeder, he said; a little long in
the body, but finer quarters and hocks would be sought
for in vain. His eyes turned to the two grey hackneys,
and he saw in them good roadsters, sound in wind and
limb, who will, he said, take us to Orléans without a
breakdown. We needn't press them, for Héloïse will not
be able to ride more than four leagues a day; Madelon,
perhaps, for she was used to riding in her childhood.
Four leagues the first day, three the second; on the third
we shall have to rest longer. After that, riding will come
easier to Héloïse.

The horses continued to feed, and when the watchman
cried the fourth hour Abélard looked across the bridge
into the dusk, and seeing two figures in black hurrying
towards him he began to unbuckle the nose-straps. Are
we late? said Madelon. I was here before daybreak,
Abélard replied, and that was about three-quarters of an
hour ago, maybe an hour, but the horses are now baited
and ready for the long march that lies before us. As he
spoke these words, he overlooked his travelling companions, admiring their garb, the long Benedictine habits
that would allow them to pass for nuns; himself in the
surcoat and hat he wore would be taken for a friar—a
friar conducting two nuns from convent to convent we
shall be to all eyes. I will pull up the girths a hole
tighter, he said, turning to Héloïse, for I do not want thee
to find thyself under the horse's belly. Find myself under
the horse's belly! Héloïse cried. Master Abélard, such
talk is likely to frighten one who has never been on a
horse, as you should well know, and Abélard answered
Madelon that he had spoken thoughtlessly (indulging himself in a joke), for there was no danger of such a thing
coming to pass. For, you see, he said, turning to Héloïse,
the pillion is attached by a strap going under the horse's

tail and by another strap around his neck. And the talk
turning on the greater fatigue it was to a horse to carry
a woman sitting sideways than to carry one astride, it
behoved Madelon to speak of her habit to ride astride.
But thou art a nun for the time being, Madelon, and the
religious should never be seen astride; it is not befitting
for them, who are taught to keep their legs always in one
stocking. Come, let me lift thee on to the pillion and
strap thee into it, Héloïse. Hoist Madelon first, she said.
Madelon caught at the bridle like one who knew how to
use it, and Abélard turned to Héloïse, who quivered with
the wind or with alarm, she knew not which, asking why
the horse whinnied, and why he laid back his ears. Now
if he should run away, what am I to do? He told her that
that was not possible. For thou'lt ride between us, and
there will be two leading reins on thy bridle; one will be
in my hand, the other in Madelon's, and little by little
thou'lt learn how to turn the horse to the left or to the
right, to rein him in and to urge him forward. But I am
foretelling the fortunes that await thee a week hence. Be
not afraid, and of all believe that I did not bring thee out
of Paris to lose a life that I hold more precious than
mine own. His words heartened her; and she felt that
she could confide herself in all such things to Abélard,
but even so, it was hard to be calm, for if the horse did
not put back his ears he whinnied; a rabbit darting suddenly across the path awoke him from his dream, and
uttering what seemed to Héloïse like a frightful snort, he
jostled to the right, once almost overthrowing the horse
that Madelon rode. He chooses to bump Madelon's horse,
Héloïse said, because he is smaller and thinks he can overthrow him; he never bumps to the left, for thy horse is
too big to be upset, and he looks upon every heap of stones
as an enemy. Abélard answered that it might be well for

her to change horses with Madelon, for a stumbling horse
is tiresome to ride. But he wished to get away from Paris
quickly, so nothing more was said about changing horses;
and the little cavalcade rode on in silence, the world unfolding field after field unperceived, Abélard's eyes being
always on Héloïse's horse, watchful lest the awkward
animal should trip and unseat her, and it was not till the
first timid ray struck across the roadway, revealing in its
passage some budding larches at the corner of the brown
wood, that his eyes were diverted from his charge to their
spires, whose traceries, he said, show delicate as the
groined roofs of the new cathedrals—his meaning not
being plain to Héloïse till an hour after, when an old
Romanesque church, lying low, almost squat, served him
for an illustration, and he made it plain to her that the
round arch was superseded by the pointed; for it allowed
the builders to build higher, to raise their roofs to over
a hundred feet, thereby inspiring the worshippers to lift
their thoughts as well as their hearts Godward. The
Romanesque church represents faith, he said, and the new
church faith enforced with reason, a little exordium that
filled Héloïse's eyes with wonder and her heart with reverence, though she would have wished to hear of faith and
reason at some more suitable time, for at that moment the
green streak of morning was passing away and rose-
coloured clouds were beginning in the sky. A lovely day
is preparing, she said, and the trouvère getting the better
of the philosopher he forgot faith and reason, and said:
The beauty of the larches is enough. But his apology
was not to her taste, for she felt that any concession
from him was out of keeping, and answered that it was
reason, not faith, that helped men to an appreciation of
the spring for itself. She put it to him, asking if it were
not true that if we fail to turn to reason each spring-tide

must seem like a separate act of God. Her words were pleasing to him. I will not deny that the words Faith and Reason exalt me, he answered, for they represent a battle that is in progress between the Church and human nature, but I am often afraid that when I meet people they will say: ah, he will talk to us now about faith and reason, and instead of speaking about what is nearest my heart, I speak of other things, for though no one would believe it, I am at heart a shy man.

As in a bird, the spring awakens the singer in thee, Héloïse said; and I have thee always in mind going forth with the great Comte de Rodebœuf on horses, attended by gleemen. A pleasant picture that spring morning makes, Rodebœuf and thyself riding from castle to castle, watching the trees coming into flower and leaf; first it was the larch, he's always one of the earliest; see, the hedges are blossoming on this side of the path, but on the other side they are not so far advanced. The trouvères, he said, love the spring, and the flowers and the birds owe much to us, for we know all their calls and feathers, petals and leaves; we have them all by rote, birds and flowers; our hearts are uplifted when we see the white glint of the chaffinch's wings and we stop to admire the handsome little bird when he comes down to the runnel to drink; and our eyes are ever on the watch for the flowers as they arise in the hedge bottom, after the long, dark winter. Our thoughts arise, too, like the flowers; like them we come out of a dark winter and we think of it when we catch sight of the purple of the ragged-robin in the wood. Flowers and birds owe much to us, for without us they would be nameless, except to peasants; everybody knows the violets, oxslips and primroses, but only the trouvères have eyes for the stitchwort, jack-in-the-green, country wench and ladies' smocks. He did not

know the names of the flowers in Latin, and the French
names gained Madelon's attention. How is it, she asked,
that with all the learning that ye have in abundance, ye
were short of the Latin and had to speak French when
talking of the country-side? Because French is the language of our roadsides, I'll warrant neither one nor the
other can put the Latin name on chaffinch, and maybe the
name of the wren is not known to you, and if it be known
it's only because it chimes with other words that it is
your craft to put into your songs. Put a name, philosopher, on the tree we see at the corner of yon wood coming
into yellow. Madelon, Madelon, thou must not speak
to Pierre Abélard as the philosopher, though he be a
philosopher, Héloïse cried. But why should I not take a
lesson from her in the things she knows better than I?
Abélard interposed. Thou askest what is the yellow
tree at the corner of yon wood; a fair question, and to
my shame, Madelon, I cannot put a name on it in French,
nor yet in Latin. It may be that at closer view, she
said—— But no, Madelon, neither at closer nor at distant view, Abélard answered, can I tell it. A sycamore
it is, said Madelon, and a yellower tree there is not in
all the springtime, which the trouvères call the green
springtime. But the spring is not green, but yellow. Tell
me if yon birch be green or yellow; near by is an aspen
deeper in colour than the birch; both are yellow. Let
your eyes run along the roadside and tell me if the crown
of the King of France is brighter yellow than the gorse.
Those who sing about the springtime have no eyes for its
birds or flowers or trees, except as matter for rhymes.
I'd have it from you, which is the poet, he that loves the
woodland for itself, or he that makes rhymes out of it?
The rhymester gets the credit, though there isn't one
among you all who knows that every tree has flowers,

except, perhaps, the fig. Does the oak bear flowers? Héloïse asked, and Madelon answered that if she were to look into all the greenish chains she would find flowers; and at the word greenish, Abélard said: I think we heard the word greenish, Madelon. Whereupon Madelon replied tartly that she had not denied that there was green in the springtime. Green there is but not much. The corn is green in the spring; the buttercups hide the grass, and the meadow over yonder, she said, is almost as golden as the gorse; and I would have you tell me why all poets speak of the springtime as green. She waited for Abélard and for Héloïse to answer her, but got no answer from them.

Though misfortunes may betide us, Héloïse, said Abélard, at the end of a long silence, we shall not forget this happy morning. We shall not forget it, Abélard, Héloïse answered, and storing it among their memories, they rode through a pleasant undulating country, now all white with bloom from pear and cherry trees, breaking the silence rarely, very often riding a quarter of a league, perhaps even more, without speaking, Abélard pondering what his life would be when he returned to Paris, Héloïse, whose eyes were rarely off him, wondering what his thoughts might be, so absorbed was he in his thoughts, as well he might be, for he had begun to ask himself if Fulbert, after the rape of his niece, would tolerate his (Abélard's) authority in the schools and if he would not seek means to bring about his overthrow. While thinking these things his eyes often went to Madelon, who rode without noticing the country they were riding through, sitting on her pillion, he said to himself, forgetful of the fields that are green and the fields that are yellow, thinking only that Fulbert had always been a good master to her and that she liked to do her duty towards him. But she had betrayed him. She is thinking, he added, of Fulbert returning to his house, wandering from empty room to empty room, his eyes at last catching sight of the letter they left for him. Madelon's thoughtfulness at last claimed Héloïse's attention, and she, too, fell to thinking of her uncle, her picture of him bringing into her face a pensiveness that forced Abélard into further talk about birds and flowers. Listen, he said, to those three birds in a cherry-tree, all singing together. But I would know the names of the birds, she replied; canst thou tell them to me? The bird with a flash of wine in his wings is a chaffinch, Abélard answered, but I don't like his song; he has wearied us with it, for he and his fellows have never ceased to utter it since we left the Little Bridge, trolling it out in every fir, a wearisome run of notes ending on a defiant little flourish; over and over again he repeats it. I have forgotten the Latin name of the bluish bird, a stocky little fellow with a harsh cry, but lean thy head to me and I will whisper it in French. She bent her head over, and in a kiss Abélard whispered: titmouse. And the bird whose note is single? she asked. He whispered: greenfinch.

Sometimes a hundred or two hundred feet passed under the horses' hooves without a word being exchanged, and these silences were not less sweet than speech, for each enshrined the other in thought and worshipped before the image. At the end of such a silence the horses were entering a rooky wood, tall boles rising fifty or sixty feet from the roadway, the nests in the high branches, and a great clamour about them. The wayfarers stopped to admire the parent rook crawling gingerly into the nest with some snail or grub for the speakers within it. There is even a young rook or two on the edge of the nests; a precocious season truly, he continued, pointing to a fledgeling that had ventured far out along a branch. And what are the rooks saying to him, since thou knowest them so well, Abélard? They are telling him that he must return to the nest till his wings are stronger if he would not fall to the ground and become a prey to prowling cats and foxes. At that moment the droppings of the rooks becoming more numerous, Madelon cried: I will not wait here to be covered with filth, and she struck her horse with her heels, bringing the other horses after her. The next thing they saw were some lambs skipping up the banks and butting each other, as glad to be alive, Héloïse said, as the lambs were when thou and Rodeboeuf set forth on an April morning many years ago. I remember those lambs of old time, Abélard replied, and the clamorous rookery in the trees over the castle gates. On that day even the sheep joined the lambs at play, but now they are feeding more industriously, for the grass is not as forward as it should be, despite the warm rains we have had. The lambs can afford to play, for they feed from the udders; and at that moment a lamb's belly gave him warning that hunger was nigh upon him, and leaving his mates he galloped to his dam, thrusting his nozzle against the full udder as if he would drink it dry in a draught. How patient the yoe is with him, for he is her own; but were another lamb to come she would drive him away. It is all very wonderful, Héloïse said, and putting aside thoughts of germination, she said: a wonderful day that was when you two went forth and gave a display of singing in the castle of—I cannot remember the name—and before Abélard could tell her the name, her thoughts had gone back to Virgil. But all we see to-day Virgil saw more than a thousand years ago; and the *Georgics* rising up in their minds, each tried to outdo the other in quotations, saying: match that if thou

canst, till at last Abélard said: if the *Georgics* were lost
we could recover them all from our memories, for where
mine failed thou wouldst come to my aid, and together
we could give back to the world the book it had lost.

Madelon, how is it, he said, that thou findest no joy in
the springtime? The birds do not seem to delight thine
ears, nor the skipping lambs thine eyes, and the yellow
meadows pass by without stirring thee into speech, except
to say that the trouvères speak of the green meadows
whereas they would speak of the yellow if they had eyes
about them. Having no language but French, said Madelon, and being no rhymester in it, I have no thought for
the buttercups in which the cattle are standing knee-
deep, except that the fences seem weak and hardly able
to keep the sheep on the bare fields. And why wouldst
thou keep them on bare fields? Héloïse asked. For the
sake of their own precious lives, for were they to get
in among the meadows full of vetches they would swell
with wind and die if none were ready with lancets to
relieve them. And is it not as well to think of such things
as to stand under a rookery listening to all the squeakings
and squawkings up in the branches, and getting your eyes
filled with filth for your pains? You think that I have not
been watching you and guessing a great part of your talk,
though it was in a foreign language; making a genius of
the little chaffinch, who rattles through a dozen little chit-
terings ending up with a kweek-kweek. Neither chaffinch
nor rook is worth a fine spring lettuce made tasty with oil
and vinegar and hard-boiled eggs and beetroot; nor is the
song of any blackbird or thrush equal to spring spinach
or asparagus; nor would either of you be listening to a
lark if a dish of asparagus were waiting. No more than
Madelon would herself. But do not think that I am without thoughts for the early cauliflowers. I love the spring

as well as any gleeman or gleemaiden living, but I love
the spring in a more natural way, for they love it only
for their rhymes, whereas, being a cook, I love it for
my belly and for other bellies. Now is there anything
more natural than the belly? For all that crawls and
swims and flies and walks on two feet or on four has a
belly; we are bred in the belly and we live by our bellies;
no sooner is the lamb out of the yoe's belly than he's up
against the udder, which is part of her belly; and we are
as dependent upon the lamb as the lamb is upon the yoe,
for we, too, have bellies to fill and the lamb fills them
excellently well, and never better than in the month of
April, above all other months the month for lambs. For
though I would not disdain a lamb in the month of March,
an April lamb is sweeter, but leave the lamb till June
and July and you'll be eating what is neither lamb nor
sheep; even May is a bit late for the lamb, and while you
have been praising green leaves that serve no purpose
whatever, especially those of the beech and the oak, for
even the goat, that is a hardy feeder, likes them not, I
have been thinking that the lambs we saw a while ago
should be on the spit before another month, else the flavour
of the meat will be lost. I know well enough that all I
am saying seems hard to the poet, who goes about with
his nose in the air, sniffing the hawthorn breeze and putting rhymes to it, and I will tell our philosopher poet who
is taking us back to his country, which is our country
(for if not altogether a Breton, thou'rt half a one,
Héloïse), that the finest eating I have ever known, and
I have known some good eating in my time, was a lamb
that had lost his yoe. She was taken by a wolf, and
he'd have died, too, before the next wolf would have taken
him, for he was near gone before I brought him into the
house and put him in a basket and fed him; he used to

put his nozzle into my hand and follow me about every-where, but Lord! if we were to give away to those feel-ings, we would be worse than the village idiot, for the lamb the yoe nourishes was given to us to eat. Did not the Lord himself say to Peter: Kill, and eat? and Abé-lard, who knows the Bible better than any man alive, maybe as well as the Pope of Rome himself, will tell us what part of the Bible the three words come from. The words thou hast in mind come from the Acts of the Apos-tles, Madelon, and I will go with thee thus far, though I could not cut the throat of a lamb that I had brought up in a basket by the fireside and that thrust his nozzle into my hand and followed me about. But if you'd nobody to cut it for you, you'd cut it fast enough yourself, Master Abélard, for you wouldn't eat him alive, would you? Madelon asked; and if we didn't eat him, and left him to multiply his kind there would be no lambs, for we would have so many lambs that there would be nothing left for us to eat, and we'd be calling the wolves to rid us of the pests. Now, am I not right? said Madelon; come now, you two who are disposed to laugh at poor Madelon who knows no Latin, deny it if you can that she speaks the truth on this morning better than you do yourselves.

But, Madelon, said Abélard, though we should grant that the lamb is no service to man if he be not eaten, thou'lt not have it for thy whole creed that we have not ears and eyes and nostrils wherewith to take out our pleasure. The song of the thrush on the branch, and the song of the lark as he flies heavenward, the fluting of the blackbird in the orchard, and the robin's dainty ditty from the topmost spray of the coral hedge are voices that we would be loath to be without. But these voices are not the only voices the spring brings us, Made-

lon interrupted; in the spring the peacock squalls till
you'd think he'd bring down the vault of heaven.   It's
true that the spring gives back to the seas the sea-birds,
that scream all the winter up and down the Seine.   And
what is all this squeaking and screaming about? Nothing
whatever, for the birds don't understand each other.
How canst thou say that the birds don't understand each
other? Abélard asked.   The crow talks, and the parrot
too.   I've heard of talking birds, she answered, and know
not if they can say all the words that are reported of
them, but am full sure that the words they learn from us
are roted in them without meaning, just like their own
cries.   The rook whose caw pleased you a while ago is
hardly a better bird under the pasty than the crow that
nobody eats.   The pigeon is better if he be laid out
between slices of good beef, for the neighbourhood of
the beef favours him, and the slices of fat bacon with
which whoever knows the pigeon overlays him help him
a lot, and the hard-boiled egg helps him, too, and we've
begun to forgive him his monotonous coo, coo, coo,
when—— But Jesus, Mary and Joseph! listen for the
life of you, for the bird that has just flown from the rail
yonder, flapping like a rook across the fields, is the noisiest
bird that spring brings us; from overseas he comes.   Hark.
And reining in their horses, they heard, cuc-koo, cuc-koo,
cuc-koo, repeated from every hillside.   No need to wait
much longer; we shall have heard enough of those two
notes before we get to Brittany, Madelon said, her heels
striking her horse into a trot.

    Before the travellers had ridden another league the cry
began to strike tediously on the ear, and to forget it
Abélard and Héloïse were glad to listen to Madelon, who,
nothing loath, continued her patter, asking them, or asking herself, it was not clear which, how it could be that

a Christian man should bear with that tiresome bird, his
ears cocked at the beginning of the noisy month for his
cry, and making it his brag that whereas the neighbour
heard cuc-koo on the fifteenth, it was his luck to hear it
on the twelfth. Now, she said, the Latin poet of whom
you're always talking, Virgil, did he ever speak of the
cuckoo? As neither Héloïse nor Abélard was able to
say that he did, Madelon took advantage of their lack of
knowledge to declare her belief that the bird had come
into favour with the trouvères, for like them he is a
wanderer without a home of his own or wit to build
one, or too lazy to try, we know not which; the hen just
laying an egg on the ground and carrying it about in her
bill till a sparrow's nest is spied in the hedge, or a lark's
nest or a wagtail's. One is as good as another, for the
cuckoo leaves her egg and her offspring. A knowing
bird, I will say that for the cuckoo, for she lays but one
egg, whereas if she were to lay two, neither the hedge-
sparrow nor the wagtail nor the lark would be able to
feed the young ones; a voracious bird is the young cuckoo,
that turns the natural chicks out of the nest so as he may
get all the food that the parents can collect; and Lord!
They say that the two sparrows, the cock and the hen,
work so hard to feed the ungainly fowl they have hatched
that they never get through the winter but drop off at
the first touch of frost, having no strength left in them
to fight against hard times. Nor is it strange that I
should have no liking for those birds, for it was one of
those birds that dropped his egg in me and left me
to feed the chick all the days of my life, poor little
hedge-sparrow that I am. The story that was on thy lips
to relate when thou camest to my lodging to tell of
Héloïse's trouble is again almost on thy lips, said Abélard,
and he waited for Madelon to begin; but she kept a

stubborn silence, as if she were sorry for having said so much. Héloïse knows the story well enough, she remarked suddenly, and to encourage her to tell it, Abélard asked her how long it was since she had seen her boy's father.

A week come Tuesday, she answered. So he is still in Paris? Abélard replied. Yes. And the boy? Abélard asked. The boy is in Brittany, he is indeed, and in troth my heart is the lighter for the hope of seeing his bonny face again. Madelon doesn't make the fuss that you do about green fields and the songs of birds. Her spring-tide is in the west yonder, she said. But does the father do nothing for his son? Abélard asked. His son! Madelon answered; he has never owned the boy, though I had him brought to Paris to show him to his father when he was ten; and anybody could see that he was his son, the very spit of him, but he would have none of it. An evil soul must be in him, Abélard said, to deny his son. I could always see that he didn't believe me. But he must know whether he lay with thee or didn't, Abélard interjected. Ah, that's just what he doesn't know. Doesn't know whether he lay with thee? It has often seemed strange, Madelon answered, that he should have doubts about such a thing, and the only way I can make it plain to you—— Is by telling us how a woman may lie with a man unbeknown to him. Well, there isn't much of a story, but just this, she said. We'd been keeping company for a couple of years, or more maybe, when one evening returning home along the river we walked into a fog and lost our way, and he said: Madelon, we may be going towards Nantes or we may be going away from it and it would be better for us to sit down and wait till the fog lifts a bit. We hadn't been sitting there very long before we saw somebody coming through the fog and we called to him; and when he came to us

he looked us in the face and said: Aren't you the twain
that asked me in the morning the way to an inn? And
I said: Yes, we did ask the way to an inn in the morning,
and had our dinner in it, and ever since have been
walking about talking over the years to come, for we
are going to be married. Going to be married? he said.
In about six months, said I, when Jean comes into the
farm that his parents have been promising him this many
a day, for they are too old to work it. So the man before
us said: You will never be working the farm if you sit
on in this fog till it lifts, for there will be no lifting
of it till the wind changes, and that will not be till
daybreak, if then; the fogs lie heavy and long by the
river. Well then, what shall we do? we said, and he
answered: A wedded couple like you, for you are as
good as wedded, shall never sit out in a fog whilst I
have a roof over my head. So we went into the man's
house, and not to make a fool of myself before them
all, I said: As we'll be wedded in six months we may as
well be bedded this night. And the man of the house
said: Well, you can do that, and if I had a sword I
would give it to you so that you might lie on either side
of it, which is the token that the twain kept their virtue
in the old stories; but I have nothing better than a
broomstick, but if that will serve, you can have it. We
just laughed at him, for he was a comical fellow. And
it was some two months after that night that I went to
Jean and said: I am quick. And he said: By whom?
So I said: By whom could it be but by thyself? And
he said: but I never touched thee the night we lay with
a broomstick between us. And I answered him: I know
naught of a broomstick. He said: Broomstick or none, I
never crossed over thee that night, nor any other night,
and of all nights that was the one that I couldn't, for I

had drunk too much and fell asleep the moment my head was on the pillow, as I remember well. A fine story, a true cuckoo story, said Abélard; and I am minded to hear what answer you made to it. I said: I don't know what you did, but I know what I did, and that more than once. But you talk, Madelon, as if you believed him. Believed him! I know what happened between us, sure enough, but for all that he thinks that he didn't beget his son, for by his manner of talking I can see that he is speaking honest, however strange it may seem to me who knows the truth. And that was the only night that thou hadst knowledge of a man? Troth and faith, the only night; and a great hardship it has been to me, but the boy was worth it, and I don't begrudge any year of labour he has cost me. My heart is light now as the hearts of the birds and the beasts, as your own hearts are light, for I am going to Nantes to see my Jean, who'll be glad to kiss his old mother again. But let's push on, or we shall be old people before we get there, and let there be no more talking.

But they hadn't ridden many minutes before Madelon reined in her horse, and the other horses stopped too, there being leading reins on either side. Now hark to those birds; a dozen if there be one. Tell me if your ears be not wearied of their calling, and wearier would be your bellies if you were to eat him; as well eat a hawk; no good for the spit or the pot or the pie, a polluter of other birds' nests, a pander, a bawd, and a—— Madelon looked to see if she had listeners.

Do not answer her, Héloïse whispered to Abélard; else her tongue will never cease. It has become as burdensome to me as the bird itself. Talk to me in Latin and I'll answer thee in Latin. I read distress upon thy face, Héloïse, Abélard answered, and guess thy thoughts

to be back in the rue des Chantres at the moment when
thy uncle returns to the empty house, and, finding no
one, runs to my lodging. It is even so as thou sayest,
Abélard, Héloïse replied sadly. While Madelon prattled
of the springtime my uncle was plain before me; and I
can see him now wandering about the town like one
bereft of all reason, talking of indifferent things, only
to break off suddenly, remembering that his niece and
his servant were taken from him. And that I was the
robber, Abélard answered.

CHAP. XVI.

IT was at the end of the third league that Héloïse asked
how far they were from the village at which it was
arranged they were to rest and bait. Abélard answered
her: when the shoulder of yonder hill is passed, thou'lt
see it. Her eyes sought the plain vainly for a village.
Thine eyes do not see all that's in the plain, for it rises
and dips, he said. Thy village is a phantom, an idea of
thy brain, she returned, laughing, to keep me on my
pillion, which I have kept till now, wishing to please
thee. But the lurching stride of my hackney breaks
down my will, and as we shall reach Mortemer on foot
as easily as on horseback, I pray thee to let me walk.
So the last half of the journey was accomplished by
Héloïse on foot, holding on to her stirrup, Abélard walking beside her, Madelon leading the way by a few feet.
Now is not my promise fulfilled? he said, pointing to a
white gable showing through the morning mist. That is
Mortemer, not a thousand feet from here, so get thee
into thy pillion, for we shall strike a better appearance
if we arrive on horseback.

On arriving at the inn she could but fall from her

horse into the arms of the innkeeper, so weary was she, and in the inn parlour plead that she was stiff and sore. A tub of hot water will take the stiffness out of thee, said Abélard. And while the water is boiling let us walk about the village, for a change of movement to-day will benefit thee almost as much as the bath, and remember that if the Canon should return suddenly from Soissons he will start in pursuit of us. We shall not be safe till we are sailing down the Loire, she said; and obedient to his every wish, followed him down the village street, too tired to eat, and too tired to sleep until the afternoon of the next day. The next village, Coudray, was but two leagues from Mortemer. We must be in Orléans before Fulbert returns to Paris, was the burden of Abélard's thought as they rode away from Mortemer. At Coudray they passed the night, and to remove all stiffness from Héloïse's limbs she seated herself in another tub of hot water to which Abélard added a bottle of vinegar; a sovereign remedy, he said. Even so it proved, and Héloïse, now completely refreshed, mounted her pillion in the belief that she was a perfect horsewoman. May we not trot a little? she asked. Abélard answered: Trotting on a pillion is barely possible; a slight amble is the only change of movement that can be attempted, for to trot one has to rise in one's stirrups. If we do not get a boat to take us to Tours we shall throw aside our disguises and ride astride to Blois. And with this promise for encouragement Héloïse sat her hackney, watching the country change from an undulating, pleasant, orchard, garden country into a long, somewhat dismal plain. This plain was once forest, and it would not take many years for it to return to forest, Abélard said. Trees are springing up everywhere; groups of trees and woods, but kept within bounds by man's labour. The words carried their thoughts back to primal Gaul, through which the Druids and their congregations wandered in search of the sacred mistletoe, seeking it where now were large fields of corn many inches high. Pillaged by the ring-doves, Madelon interjected, voracious birds, that the boys armed with rattles can hardly drive back into the forest. But I'll say no more to you bird-lovers, who take pleasure in every kind and sort of bird cry, even that of the worthless cuckoo, a bird that cannot build herself a nest or hatch an egg, but destroys other birds, their eggs at least, and is not herself fit for roasting or boiling, baking or stewing. But I'll say no more, for I can see that neither likes Madelon's talk, but would rather listen to the bagpiping of the larks as they go up and come down. Singing a feverish song, Héloïse said: let us hope that we feel our love deeper than the lark feels his. Abélard asked her if she were tired, if she ached in her joints, and would like to spend more than a night at Étampes. She answered him that it might be better to press on to Orléans, for is it not most true that we shall not be safe till on board a barge sailing down the Loire? But how wonderful it will be to sail down a great river, seeing the towns and villages go by. Thou art tired, Héloïse, almost too tired for speech, but rest awaits thee, for we are close to Étampes. A pleasant town, he continued, telling the town before it came into view; one great street with by-streets straggling in and out of the forest, and the principal street not packed like a Paris street, but each house standing in its own garden.

As they rode into Étampes he asked Héloïse to watch the storeyed houses and high-peaked gables filled with picturesque lights and shadows, for they will help thee to forget thine aches, he said. I did not know that a village could be so beautiful Héloïse answered, as she rode. And riding down the rutted street, and thinking that Étampes wore an air of exaltation and welcome on this fine May afternoon, she snuffed the faint fragrance of the chestnut-trees, now all in flower. Lilac was in bloom in every corner, and laburnum hung golden tassels over every gate. But the best scent of all was the haw-thorn, and looking round, they caught sight of the tree hanging over the roadway. A little farther on, hard by the inn whither they were going, a more powerful scent stopped them. Why, sillies, it's nothing but a flowering currant, the strongest of all scents, said Madelon, and her words set them laughing. Madelon, said Abélard, if the country were less known to thee, perhaps thou wouldst appreciate its beauty more. But here is our inn, and a handsome inn it is, with pink roofs overhung with green branches—Madelon will not deny them some green. Give your horses to the ostlers who come from the archway, and I will help you from your pillions. It would be in keeping with our religious garb to seek a secluded room, but to-morrow we shall be on our way, finding it as best we can through the intricate roads and paths of the forest, so we may indulge ourselves this evening on this terrace overlooking the road. We need a bottle of wine after our long ride, Abélard called back to the innkeeper, and the hour before supper was dreamed under the boughs in Étampes, a forest town, or almost one, not more than ten leagues from Paris. In it Fulbert was forgotten by the lovers, by Madelon, mayhap, for when the sun sank, leaving a quieter sky behind, life seemed a perfect gift, and their joy increased at every moment till they thought their hearts would break.

We shall always remember Étampes, Abélard said, lay-ing his hand on Héloïse. Hark! some gleemen are singing in the street, and he asked Héloïse if she remembered the gleemen in the rue des Chantres. Do I remember! she answered. And they descended the long stairs to listen to the love song the gleemen were singing to a lute accompaniment; but on perceiving the religious they stopped singing the song, thinking it unseemly for a friar or nun to hear it in public, and began an Ave Maria:

Qui de s'ame
Veut oster le fiel amer,
 Nostre Dame
Jor et nuit doit reclamer.
Fole amor pour lui amer
 Jetons fuer:
Qui ne l'aime de douz cuer
Bien se puet chetif clamer.

Porte du ciel,
De Paradis planche et ponz,
 Sorse de miel,
De douceur pecine et fonz
D'enfer qui tant est parfonz
 Nous deffent.
Qui non crient peu a de sens
 Car n'i a rive ne fonz.

Douce dame,
Par mult vraie entencion
 Cors et ame
Met en ta protection.
Prie sanz dilation
 Ton fil douz,
Qu'il nous face vivre touz
 In terra viventium.

The words are better than the tune, gleemen, Abélard said.
I will write you another to-night which perchance will
be worthier of the words than the one you sing to it;
and hoping that he would be inspired, the gleemen thanked
him, but he noticed that they did not begin to sing at
once.   They are waiting, Madelon said, till the friar and
the nuns are out of hearing before they commence a song
more welcome to their customers.   It may be so, Abélard
answered indifferently, for his thoughts were on some
quiet spot in the forest where he might be alone with
Héloïse.   But the forest seemed full of voices, voices came
from every side, and, seeking to escape from the towns-
people out for an evening stroll, the lovers struggled
from one sandy hollow into another, through tall pines
rising out of the sand.   Lovers would be here keeping
trysts, said Abélard, if the town were not amusing itself
awaking forest echoes.   You'll not miss my company,
said Madelon; my tongue has clattered in your ears since
early morning, so I will leave you to your own thinkings.
Do not go too far, Abélard replied, for we cannot return
to the inn alone without raising suspicion against ourselves.   I shall sit in the vale beyond and tell my beads,
as is my wont before going to bed.   But sleep not, said
Abélard, for the darkness is so deep that we might not
be able to find thee.   I shall not sleep, she answered, and
Héloïse drew closer to Abélard.   All this afternoon I
have been thinking of thee, she said.   Abélard answered:
Is it strange that thou shouldst think of me?   We think
of each other always, she replied, but there are moments
when each longs for the other more intensely than at
other moments.   If desire were without ebb and flow,
we should not be able to bear the strain, Abélard answered.   Abélard, I would speak plainly with thee.   It
was not for kisses then that we came here? he asked,

and she answered: Thy kisses and thine embraces I
would not be without, nor could be without. Abélard, do
not kiss me, for I would speak to thee of thyself and I
would speak of myself. If we were caught and taken
back to Paris! Think not of Fulbert, think only of me,
Abélard answered. Madelon watches for us, but she
prays for herself, telling her beads, and will fall asleep
over them.

Héloïse forgot to answer her lover, and in the silence
of the pines they lay in each other's arms, happy in each
other's atmosphere, afraid to speak, for a word would
break the spell of their delight. It was for moments
like these that we met, Héloïse said at last; it is for our
love that we live, but it's only now that I begin to know
love, for in the beginning, Abélard, I was not true to thee
nor to myself. It was not thy manhood that I loved,
but thy genius. Thy genius exalted me, compelled me to
throw myself at thy feet, but that was not love but vanity.
Abélard, I would tell thee all things. I would have thee
know me as God knows me; but words are vain, and
oneself is a burden to oneself. I would have thee, Abélard,
love me as I love thee: I would have thee love the
woman that I am. Ah, I know it is the woman in me that
thou lovest, but in the beginning it was the learned girl
of whom Paris was talking that drew thee to me, and I
was proud of my learning and grateful to it for having
gained thee to me. But now I would cast the learned
girl out of myself and I would cast the philosopher out
of thee, leaving naught but the woman and the man for
each to love the other through eternity. We meet in
this vale at night for love, but methinks that we must
have met long, long ago in the ages back, perhaps before
the beginning of time. This moment is but a moment
in a love story without beginning and without end. It

may seem to thee that I am talking only as the mad
talk. But I am not talking, Abélard, I am thinking;
I am not thinking, Abélard, I am dreaming; I am not
dreaming, Abélard, I am feeling; and in this moment
I am consonant with the tree above me and the stars
above the tree; I am amid the roots of the hills. It
may be, Abélard, that I am a little mad at this moment,
but we are all too sane, and whosoever has not passed
from sanity to insanity has perhaps never tasted the
final essence, the residuum of things. I would, too, that
thou wert a little mad here in this vale, the dark trees
above us, the stars shining through the tree-tops. And
Madelon, Abélard answered, saying her beads in the vale.
Thou wouldst strike a jarring note, for alas, we are
divided, Héloïse answered sadly, and I am sorry that
thou canst not love as I do. So already, Héloïse, even
in this moment thou hast a fault to find. No, I find no
fault, but I would have thee tell me why I was sent to
thee, for hast thou not often traced the hand of God
in our meeting? There is a reason for all things, though
we cannot trace it, Abélard replied, and I might ask thee:
Why was I saved from love of woman till I met thee
in the cathedral? Words fail us, Abélard, and truth
eludes us. Am I the true lover, or is it thou? Canst
thou answer, or is it that time alone holds the answer?
We are divided again, we who have been united. We are
not divided, Héloïse; we shall never be divided. We have
existed always, united in the end as we were in the
beginning, and it cannot be said that we shall be parted
come what may.

It is even so as thou speakest it that I feel my love,
she said, as a thing that always was and ever shall be.
That our love, he answered, was before the beginning of
time is my belief, and I believe, too, that it shall not end

with time. Then I have heard what I wished to hear,
Abélard, for it has always seemed to me that our love
came to us from the stars, and since our love awakened
almost the same thought in thee thou wilt be spared, as
I shall be, the shame of regret. Regret nothing, Abélard,
for I swear thy love of me shall not steal a single jewel
from thy crown of glory. How came I into this knowledge? It was revealed to me as my love was revealed
to me, as thy love was revealed to thee, as all things are
revealed. And now I have told thee all. Our love shall
not cost thee a single jewel, not one, she repeated, rising
to her feet, and they stood, looking at each other, Abélard
marvelling at the beauty of her eyes; and remembering
that he had seen them wistful and far away, he wondered
at seeing them open and confident. My love is dearer——
Our love, Héloïse interrupted, is part of thy renown; it
is our business to protect it, for without it we perish,
that is what was upon my mind to tell; now we must go
in search of Madelon. And they went from vale to vale
calling; at last a sudden ray of moonlight discovered her
asleep. Madelon, hast thou no ears for the nightingales?
A thousand are singing about thee. She roused a little,
and, moaning for her bed, followed them to the inn.
Begin telling thy beads, Héloïse, for it will make a good
appearance. Begin telling thy beads, Madelon, and myself will make show with my breviary.

And in their different beds all three slept till the
prime of the morning was over, and the hope of reaching
a certain village by evening was almost gone. But morning and evening the forest is safe for the religious, so
said the innkeeper. The robbers that infested it would
not dare to attack them, he averred, and he knew the
ways of the forest robbers, having himself on more times
than one had to pay blackmail to save his house from

plunder and his guests from being carried off and held for ransom. But the religious have no cause to fear, so severely were the robbers punished on different occasions for robbing them, so cruel were the punishments inflicted upon them when caught, and so rigorous was the search made for them after every robbery or murder committed. A friar like yourself, reverend sir, was murdered and robbed on a lonely bit of the road between here and Saint-Jean-de-Braie, a large village or town within the skirts of the forest, two leagues, two and a half, maybe, from Orléans. The robber fled, but the religious have power with the King, so a price was put on his head, and money, as you will know, reverend sir, produces every virtue as well as every vice. The robber was betrayed at last, and as he had been a terror in the district for some time, a curious death was devised for him, one that would bring the people far and wide to see; and they came in thick crowds, for the robber was to be laid at length on the floor of the scaffold to have his belly eaten out by a dog trained for the job. The condemned was told what his punishment was to be, and he must have suffered in thought as much as he did upon the scaffold. The agony his eyes bespoke when he saw the dog straining at the chain will never be forgotten by those who saw it. He was shriven by a friar of the Order of the man he had killed, and allowed to kiss the Cross before the dog was let loose upon him, an animal well trained, who in less than ten minutes was pulling out the entrails, casting them to and fro while the man was yet alive. A cruel punishment, full of sickening forebodings before the moment came, but not worse, I ween, than the punishment inflicted upon him who stole the sacred vessels from the cathedral in Orléans, for I was there at the time and can tell that the flaying was skilfully performed, the

skin of the robber's leg being withdrawn from the flesh
even as a stocking might be. He screamed terribly and
begged to be killed outright, but this could not be, for his
punishment included the lifting of the skin from his
belly, and my word! it was thrown over his face like an
apron. The water test is maybe as fierce a suffering as
any, so the executioner himself told me, for pouring pints
and quarts and gallons into a man until his guts are dis-
tended like bladders tends to suffocation, and the drying
of him in a warm room is not less an infliction than the
pouring. It is in the warmest room, it appears, that
his will yields, and the heresy that he cherishes is fore-
gone and denied. So it was upon a heretic that the water
test was practised—and Abélard asked what his terrible
heresy might have been. One of the Pastorals, for certain,
but his name has gone from my mind, answered the innkeeper; a rebel against his Lord and Master, one that
believed the reign of the Father and the Son was over
and that of the Ghost had begun. A terrible belief
to hold indeed, Abélard replied, and did he die in this
belief? Troth and faith he did, reverend sir, though it
was held as truth at the time that if he had taken a little
less water, or if the drying had been less quickly done,
he would have repented and died shriven and received
into the Church again. But if there are no robbers to
fear, Abélard asked, in the forests, thanks to the condign
measures thou hast described so well, innkeeper, there
are wolves? The wolves, reverend sir, feed so well at
this season of the year upon young deer and fawns, picking up the young of the wild swine occasionally, that
the traveller goes his way unafraid. Of what are you
talking, brother Pierre? Héloïse asked. Of wolves, Abélard answered, whereupon she related the story of the
wolf which she had not succoured in the great wolf-hunt

though he howled plaintively at her door for it to be opened. Yet we are venturing into a forest filled with wolves, she said. Abélard whispered in her ear: The two-legged wolves are more fearsome than the four; let us away. Whereupon he helped his nuns into their pillions and they started forth on the next stage of their journey, hoping to reach before sundown the village of Chécy.

But to reach Chécy before nightfall they would have to hasten, and the innkeeper told them that the road through the forest looped so that the village of Lorris might be taken into the circuit; but there was no need for him to follow this winding, he would find a by-path across certain low hills which he could not miss. Abélard did not feel sure that the by-path might not be missed, but to hear the road explained out again would be merely a waste of time, and so they hastened towards the forest in a sort of half-knowledge of the way, allowing the horses to trot a little, thinking that they might draw rein when they passed through the fringe of birch-trees that encircled with their pallor the great district of pines that showed in black masses over against Étampes. Now we are well within the forest, Abélard said, as much in the forest as if we were in the middle of it; and he asked Héloïse to peep over the undergrowth that lined the rutted path down which they were riding, so that she might see the pines rising up naked and bare some fifty or sixty feet, some straight, some leaning, in endless aisles. Like the spears, Héloïse said, of Crusaders going into battle; and how penetrating is the smell of the resin. But the pines were in patches only, and the forest passed quickly into rocky hillsides overgrown with oak and beech; and so faint was the path they followed that Abélard often asked Héloïse and Madelon to draw rein while he went forward in search of the path. For if we

all went forward together, he said, we should not be
able to go back to where the path ends: a tree is no sure
landmark; one forgets which tree, and wanders in a circle.
I've got it, he cried to them, and they came forward,
the forest getting lonelier as they proceeded into it.

All bird cries have ceased, and we hear only the sighing of the boughs, Héloïse said, and the smell of the
forest is different from all other smells; a more mysterious
smell is about, a smell of earth and moss. There is also a
warm smell, said Madelon, that reminds me of our Brittany forests, the great forest about Clisson, where we
shall be—Héloïse, myself and my boy—before the
month's end, should we catch a fast-sailing barge from
Orléans. Did he not say that a little over three leagues
from Étampes we should find the by-path that would save
us several leagues' journey? Abélard asked, and some
hundreds of feet after he told them to rein in while he
went on ahead in search of the path. Here it is, he cried,
from a clearing; we have but to follow the path that
leads through the hollows yonder up to the rising ground
that the innkeeper spoke of. He spoke to me of oak-
trees, and here they are. And they rode beneath the
boughs not yet in full leaf, following the path as it
wound through hollows, losing it and finding it amid
rocks, pushing their way through thickets that seemed
impenetrable at a distance but did not prove so hard to
force through as they had appeared. There is a rutted
way under the brambles, Abélard said; cattle and horses
have been through here; and stooping low in their saddles,
they broke through somehow, losing bits of clothing in the
passage. Soon after the path led them up hills, through
thorn and hazel mingled with interspaces, till it brought
them to a heath, and Abélard said: those pines standing
so solitary at the end of the lake embedded in rocks are

the trees the innkeeper told me I was to look out for. We have not missed the way, he continued; look back and see the forest that we have come through. And he pointed to a dark ragged line of pines flowing down the northern sky. But is our way to the right or to the left? Madelon asked. To the left, he answered; we have to ride southward, keeping the setting sun on our right.

Once more they plunged into the forest, and this time it was all birch, and while wandering they learnt some facts regarding this tree from Madelon, who told them that in Brittany, in the wilder parts, birch bark was used by the peasants to thatch their cottages. But this was not all. The birch possessed many qualities which Madelon was willing to tell, but her loquacity was interrupted by the spectacle of many uprooted trees. The great storm of some three years ago, she said, has laid them low, turning their roots up into the air, leaving great holes behind. A sad sight it was truly, all these dead trees, dead or dying, for some, though their roots were broken, were coming into leaf; The last leaves they will bear, Abélard said; next spring they will be lying leafless. The travellers were sorry for the poor trees, and wondered how it was that a clump remained here and there unharmed; sometimes it was a single tree that had managed to keep its roots unbroken. The wind seems to have whirled about the forest at random, Abélard said; leaving some spots untouched, tearing the slender rooted birches as if they were reeds, unearthing the great elms and sparing only the oaks. The oak, said Madelon, is rarely uprooted, for its roots go deeper than any other tree; some say its roots go as deep as its branches go high. Fine trees, she said, are those about us, almost as great as the oaks of Clisson, over against the castle of Clisson. You know it well, master philosopher; I needn't tell you how far it is between Clisson and Le Pallet; you know it better than I do. And you know, too, that in our country it is said (and who should know the value of the oak better than the Breton?) that no tree is as useful to man and to beast as the oak. Many a good meal myself, my father and kindred have made out of the oak mast. The oxen rejoice and eat the oak mast greedily and fatten on it, and the pigs rejoice in it even more than the oxen. In the forest of Clisson, as master Abélard knows well, Héloïse, every farmer garners as much as two hundred and forty bushels of acorns for the oxen, mingling them with a like quantity of beans and lupins and drenching them well. For the building of ships and the making of houses there is no timber like the oak. A man with an oak rafter over his head is always sure of his roof. The oak is a good tree from end to end; there's nothing about the oak that man can't put to his use and benefit. The leaves of the oak make the best litter for cattle, and at the Canon's I heard a Crusader, who had been as far as Hungary and come back, tell a tale of a certain water that turns the leaves of this tree into brass, iron and copper; and in Brittany the leaves steeped in wine make an excellent gargle for a sore throat. Even the shade of the oak is good to man. If he has walked a long distance and is hot, no doubt he rests well, Abélard said. There's more in the shade of the oak than that, replied Madelon; many a paralytic has sat down in the shade of an oak with his crutches laid against the tree, and if he sleeps long enough in the shade, he will rise up and walk, leaving his crutches behind for sign of his cure, and that others may do as he did.

The oak is not like any other tree; it is magic, a spell, for him who would turn a black horse into a dapple grey; he has but to give the animal oak buttons mixed with his oats and he will alter his colour in a few days. Thou'rt forgetting, Madelon, the power of the oak over the mind, said Abélard; the oak grove was the cathedral of our ancestors. Not a whit does that surprise me, said Madelon, for who can walk in these shades without awe? Awesome indeed they are, Héloïse whispered, in Latin, and they continued to talk together in that language, for of Madelon's tongue already they had had enough. A thought of Valeda, the prophetess maiden, came into their minds, of her strange story, and of Cæsar, Cato and Virgil, for all these great folk were associated with the oak-tree. They remembered too that every tree has a spirit that lives and dies with it, its titular deity, and their eyes roved over the aged oaks under which they were riding, in expectation that at some moment or other a gracious apparition would step forth to meet them. But as none came forth, Héloïse asked if the hamadryad was found in oaks or in beeches, for a great beech had just come into view, and it seeming a likely habitation for one, they drew rein and began to recite verses, to Madelon's great discontent. For the beech, said she, is not as serviceable a tree as the oak, but the pigs fatten finely upon the beech mast, almost as well as upon acorns. What else besides its mast is the beech good for? Abélard asked. Why, you, a philosopher, surely should know that buckets and shovels (and the best) are made out of beech wood. We should have been glad of a little beech wood last winter in the rue des Chantres, for not once did we go to our beds without feeling like ice to the knees, as Héloïse can tell you, master Abélard. A beech log is the best of all for burning, better than oak or elm. And is that all the beech can give? Isn't that enough? she answered, but there is more; the finest charcoal is gotten from the beech. And a charcoal burner is hereabouts, lopping the trees for his kiln, pollarding, as some call it, Madelon continued; we may come upon his hut at any moment, and I'll warrant it to be the same as his father and forefathers built before him, beech poles bent together, tied at the top, and thatched with birch bark, a clerical hat it is, for all the world. Without a hole to let the smoke out, said Abélard. Of what use, she answered sharply, would a hole be in the roof to a man who never lights a fire within, always without? But his dinner? interposed Héloïse. His dinner is cooked in front of his hut, where there's plenty of fuel. A happy man is the charcoal burner, or should be, for he is the one amongst us who can be sure of never going to bed with cold shins. More than that, he is the one amongst us who can get out of this world easiest. Of all deaths charcoal fumes are—— Hast forgotten that hell awaits him who seeks death? Abélard interrupted. I haven't forgotten that God is good, she answered; and his goodness is always in my mind when I'm saying my beads. But let us not be talking of the man's soul before we look inside his house and find him lying stark, mayhap. How she enjoys hearing her tongue clatter, Abélard whispered to Héloïse, and Madelon continued to talk all the way across the clearing till they drew rein before the hut. As their shouts brought nobody's head out of it, Abélard dismounted and looked inside. The nest is empty, the bird has flown, he said, and returned inside to look round for traces of the charcoal burner, finding only some potsherds, the residue of a broken pipkin or crock. These are what remain of him who is gone, he said. But whither, we shall ask in vain. For where are last year's birds, and where is the man, the wife and the little ones? Let us away, said Madelon, for the wolves may have eaten them, and the ghosts that those lolloppers leave behind are the wickedest of all.

But we have lost our path, Abélard answered, and reck,
oned on the charcoal burner to put us into it; we must
encamp here. Not here, cried Madelon, the charcoal
burner and his family will be about; not for all the
money you will ever earn will I spend the night here.
We shall have to water our horses, Abélard said, and I
see no well. Wherever man is, water cannot be far away,
Madelon said. Dost not hear a sound of rippling water,
Abélard? Héloïse asked, and riding down the shelving
ground through the beech wood they came upon a shallow green river rippling pleasantly over pebbles, the low
grassy banks putting the thought into their minds that
they would not find a better ground for encampment.
Nor a better place for a camp fire than the flat stones
lying about this high rock, Abélard remarked. A fine
shelter it would be for man and beast if a storm were
to arise. Let us build these flat stones into a hearth, and
when that is done we shall go into the beech grove and
return with armfuls of sticks and dried leaves and pile
a fire that will keep away the wolves and bears. But
we shall have to seek better grass for our horses; here it
is sedgy and tough, and our horses will not crop it willingly. I like not to separate ourselves from them, but
they are quiet animals and will not break their tethers.
He returned soon after burdened with the three saddles,
and Héloïse and Madelon having built a hearth, he set
himself to the task of lighting the fire with beech branches
and dried leaves that had already been gathered for him.
Not an easy task, he said, as he flicked steel and flint together, my tinder being none of the best. Héloïse watched
the lighting of the fire. Now it catches, she said, it
begins; we can blow it into a blaze, and she went down
on her knees to blow, amused at the lighting of the fire as
a child would be. Abélard chatting gaily of the Israelites

coming out of Egypt and finding their way through
deserts, just as we are finding ours, casual Israelites of a
day and a night, antitypes in a small way of those in the
Bible, he said, helping the time away with such light
discourse till the evening meal was eaten and Madelon
brought out her beads.

The moment had come therefore for them to seek their
souls in the twilight, and leaving Madelon, already nearly
asleep, before she had only half her rosary accomplished,
they walked, hearkening to the forest sighing for weariness of the prattling river. As they passed out of the
dark beech wood into the grey moonlight they were caught
by a sudden awe that brought them back through the
birch-trees, whither they had gone thinking to hear the
nightingales; but not one was singing, and the stillness
set their hearts almost fluttering and sealed the words
upon their lips. I am afraid of the forest, Héloïse said,
and Abélard sought to calm her fears, saying: The forest
is wonderful. Listen to the silence, for silence in the
forest is different from any other. But the forest is
never silent, Héloïse interposed. It is always mumbling
to itself. I am afraid. Shall we go back to Madelon, he
asked, or sit here among the ferns? And in answer to
her question if he were afraid, he answered that he was
not, which was barely the truth, for with the decline of
the light the forest seemed to him to have put off its
casual associations with man and to have returned to itself,
a strange, remote self, nearer to beasts than to man. We
are all aliens to the forest, he said, all save charcoal
burners and wolf-hunters. Héloïse, who would put the
forest and its mysterious mutterings out of her mind,
begged him to tell her of the first stirrings of his genius,
for there must have been a moment, she said, when it was
whispered to thee that thou wast not as other men. I

think I always knew that, Abélard answered, but if thou
wouldst hear a truthful account of the self that inspired
thee in the cloister, I must tell that it first appeared one
day at dinner some thirty odd years ago. My mother was
filling a large bowl with lettuce, cucumber, beetroot and
onion (she made excellent salads) but my father looked
upon salads as waste, saying that he did not believe that
anybody cared to eat raw vegetables, and being always
hard to curb, and restless beyond most boys, I began to
argue with him, and he said: Pierre, keep a quiet tongue
in thy head. He passed on the salad bowl, and seeing
that I helped myself largely, a smile began to trickle
into his eyes: Pierre, I checked thee a while ago, but now
I give thee leave to plead the cause of raw vegetables.
Whereupon I talked for ten minutes, my father not answering, and, hurt by his silence, I fell to thinking that I
had failed in argument. It was my mother who, reading
dejection in my face and taking pity on me, told me in
secret that my father had said to her, when they were
alone: I can't answer for the red-haired ones (my brothers
have red hair) but Pierre is wonderful. For these words
I have never ceased to think of my father with affection.
I am sure no boy ever talked like thee, Héloïse said.
But afterwards? It seems to me that afterwards I talked
to everybody who would listen to me, Abélard answered;
taking pleasure in the argument for the sake of it, caring
very little which side I took, my pleasure being to quicken
dead minds, to awaken thought; for the world, it seems
to me, is sloughing its skin of centuries very slowly,
almost unwillingly, too lazy to use its wits, liking nothing
so well as to lie like a pig in a sty; lacking reason, the
world is no better. It seems to me, he continued, his
interest in his portrait of himself waxing as he talked,
that I began to look upon myself as a swineherd who,

irate at the sloth of the swine, was moved to prick them
up with a goad. Thy simile is a false one, Héloïse replied, for the swineherd would like the porkers to lie and
fatten. All similes are defective if pressed too far, Abélard answered, but I cannot find a better image of myself
and the world than a swineherd poking a pig out its
unclean straw. I'm sure I'm telling truth of myself if I
say that I came very soon to see the world as a sty full of
pigs that it was my business to compel to rise up and go so
that the sty might be cleansed. I like to goad the porkers.
But is it cruel to desire a clean world? I begin to
understand, Héloïse interrupted, why the Church did
not attract thee; in the Church thou wouldst not be thyself. I was always more interested in my own thoughts,
he answered, than in the thoughts of any body of men,
but this is not egoism, for only our personal thoughts
are human; the thoughts that we collect are unclean as
straw that has been lain in too often, and the fine
phrases that Champeaux and Anselm wrap their thoughts
in fail to conceal their evil smell. I have often wondered
if these men lack the courage to express their own
thoughts. It may be that they are without individual
thoughts and find their pleasure in trying to cleanse the
ideas prevalent in the streets, treating them like dirty
brats, whose faces are washed with spits, and whose
noses are held between forefinger and thumb. But thou,
Abélard, wouldst cut the brats' throats and throw the
corpses into the river, Héloïse remarked; and Abélard
thought he detected a tone of regret in her voice. I would
like to humble the swine in their own sight, till to escape
from my sarcasms they would throw themselves over
precipices into the sea. But if they did, their heads
would bear them up, for their heads are but bladders. I
think thou art sorry, Héloïse, that I am so immodest a

man. And if that thought has come into thy mind I cannot blame thee for it, for it's often come into mine. Time and again I have tried to check myself, to conform, but no man checks himself or even conforms, if he be a man. And because thou couldst not conform thou art not a priest, Héloïse said, half to Abélard, half to herself. As a priest I should not be myself, he answered. But once a priest, she said, thou wouldst speedily be made a bishop, and from bishop to archbishop thou wouldst rise quickly; a cardinal's hat would soon be thine, for the Church cannot pass over men of genius; they are too rare to be passed over, and once a cardinal the papacy would fall into thy hand like a ripe plum. In St. Peter's chair I should be less than I am now, Abélard answered; there have been hundreds of popes but only one Abélard. It was on Héloïse's tongue to say: A man cannot spend his life wandering in thickets by himself, springing on the unwary from time to time, and as if he discerned her unspoken thought, Abélard said, speaking to himself as much as to her: It may be that I have been myself and nothing but myself for too many years, and there is a time for everything, for personal and collective endeavour. It may be, too, that the time has come for me to make my peace with the world, for one of our oldest proverbs is, that an old monkey pleases nobody. But can we change ourselves?

We are always changing, it seems to me, Héloïse answered. We are always changing, but we do not know in what direction we are changing. If we did . . . I am fain to believe that thou lovest me, Abélard, she said at last, but thy mind is the dearest thing in the world to thee, dearer than life; dearer than I can ever be. Abélard was moved to dispute this saying that he taught philosophy for money and nothing else. We all speak

many vain words, she answered, and a man may be better
judged by his acts. If thou wert moved to philosophy
only by the money's worth, how was it that thou didst
part with thy lands, throwing them to thy brothers like
an old coat? Thy lands were given away so that thy
mind might be saved, a mind that would have dwarfed
in Brittany. And it was to save thy mind that thou didst
turn from the priesthood. It matters naught to thee
that there is no advancement outside the Church. And
it was for thy mind's sake that a deaf ear was turned to
the women who came before me. It was not lest a wife
might rob me of some of my mind, he answered, that I
am unwed, and since, O subtle Héloïse, thou wouldst see
thy Abélard from end to end like a valley seen from a
hill-top, I will tell thee that the young seek new lips
always, never caring to kiss the same more than three or
four times, and you women are as easily wearied as men,
and seek change as often, for it is our mortal fate to seek
till we find. At last thy love came, and I believe it to be
the sum of all my early desires and aspirations, a love
that will abide in me always, for it is a truth that whosoever has loved in his youth does not return to love. We
can drink of the love draught but once; whether we
drink it in youth or in middle age matters little. In
middle age the wine is headier; and he who drinks at
forty never escapes from the swoon and intoxication.
How wonderfully thou speakest, Abélard; how wise, oh,
how wise, she said, laying her hands on her lover's
shoulders. But thou must not turn from philosophy, for
I love my philosopher, who is greater than Plato or
Aristotle. But what is that sound going by? she asked.
A nightjar, Abélard answered, seeking its food; it will
be gone presently. But any sound is better than this
stillness, Héloïse replied, and as if in answer to her a

long wail as of a soul in agony came out of the heart
of the forest. It is but a brown owl, Abélard said, but
its cry is the most melancholy in nature. And since thou
art afraid of the forest and its cries, let us return to
Madelon. Hush, Abélard, speak no word, but look;
and raising himself on his elbow, it seemed to him that
he caught sight of a grey form slinking across the moonlit glade. A wolf, maybe, Abélard whispered, and thinking of what other animal it might be, they returned to
Madelon, whom they found dozing by some embers; on
these some dry wood was thrown quickly, a great fire
was built up, and Héloïse was assured, in Latin, that they
need fear no attack from the wolf. Wolves attack men
only when they are in numbers, and driven to it by hunger,
Abélard said. We have a long day's travel before us
and would do well to sleep as far into the dawn as we can.

Whereupon the three rolled themselves into their cloaks
and slept till the grey silent dusk of day awoke them
one by one, Abélard being the first to awake; and he lay
thinking between waking and sleeping for a long time,
wondering when the birds would begin to sing. All were
asleep in the branches, and the animals that he had heard
moving in the darkness overnight were fast in their bur-
rows and lairs. At last he heard Héloïse's voice. Art
awake, Abélard? she asked. Yes, he answered, and
Héloïse whispered: Madelon is still asleep, let us not
awake her. But hearing them telling their dreams, Madelon awoke. I too dreamed of horses whinnying, she said,
and instinctively all three sprang to their feet and hastened down the river bank, afraid to speak their thoughts.
Our horses are safe, God be merciful, Abélard cried; for
being in advance of the women he caught sight of them
first, grazing peacefully about a dead wolf and her cub.
If the horses could speak, they could tell a tale, said

Madelon; and they continued talking through a cloudy morning of May, puzzled to discover in their imagination how the wolf and her cub had come by their deaths, all wearing thoughtful countenances till midday, when a likely explanation of the mystery came into Abélard's mind. He was about to tell it to Héloïse, but a cry from Madelon checked the story on his lips. We are well at the world's end, she said, and looking round they saw a blasted oak and a few pines at the end of a desolate track filled with great rocks. Truly a desolate place, Abélard said, visited only by the winds. And the witches, said Madelon, who come hither by night on their broomsticks to assemble under that tree. After a little while it fell that two ravens should come out of the forest and alight upon the white branches. I will not ride past them, Madelon cried. Abélard too was afraid, but conquering his emotion, he seized her bridle. Tell thy beads with bowed, devotional head, he muttered, and the power of the ravens will be taken from them. We owe Madelon a good deal, Abélard said in Latin, and we are paying with our patience all that we owe her. A troublesome old thing, he grunted, and began to tell Héloïse that the dead wolf might have had a den by the river, but scenting rain—— The sky was clear at midnight, said Héloïse. Animals have a foreseeing that we have not, he answered. To-day is all cloud, it will rain before night, and if not to-night, to-morrow. But go on with thy story, Pierre. Afraid that her den would be flooded by the rising of the river, the wolf remembered the hollow beech up the hillside. She seemed to be carrying something, a cub more likely than anything else, for she returned the way she came for another (as many as three and four go to a litter) and while carrying the last cub, or the last but one, my thought is that to avoid some scent that the wind carried down to her, that of a bear maybe, she came through our horses and was kicked and trampled to death, for horses like not the smell of a wolf. Thy sleep was disturbed, Héloïse said, by horses neighing. Yes, but they seemed to me to be screaming rather than neighing; it was the screams of the horses that put it into my head that the wolf and the cub met their deaths under their hooves. It may have fallen out differently, he continued; nature is rich in imaginations. However the wolf and the cub met their deaths, Héloïse answered, certain it is that a cub, or maybe two, are starving in a hollow beech-tree, and one or more may be starving by the river. Those by the river will drown when the river rises, Abélard said. We are fairly lost in this forest, Madelon cried, drawing rein, and the twain forgot the wolf cubs in the dread that a long roaming might be their fate, trying to keep in a straight line by the trees but turning in a circle always. It was yesterday we lost the track, Abélard said; let us keep our eyes on the ground, for tracks there are always in the forest. Any track is better than no track, be it the hooves of deer or of cattle, or of the wild ponies that abound in the forest. At most we may rouse a wild boar from his lair, Madelon muttered.

And they rode on and on through endless aisles, losing heart, for it seemed to them that they were under a spell. At last Madelon cried: Somebody is living yonder, for I see a drying shirt, and Abélard answered: A drying shirt is a good token of a man. And they rode towards the shirt, but on their way thither a great dog bounded forward, causing Madelon's pony to shy violently, bringing down the drying shirt. Whereupon a savage fellow came out of a hole or cavern in the hillside flourishing a great club, whereat Madelon's pony began to rear. Abélard cried to him to withhold, but he did not seem

to understand and continued to flourish the club. At
last the strap that held Madelon to the pillion broke,
and at the same moment a woman came from the dwelling-
hole towards them, her face aflame, but seeing that her
mate was not in danger and that a woman had tumbled
heavily, she called the dog off and returned to the cavern
for water. The water or the sound of her own language,
or both, brought Madelon back to herself, and she murmured thanks in Breton, their common language bringing
them into a reconciliation, which was quickly passed on
to Héloïse and Abélard. Tell them, said Abélard, that
we are on our way to Saint-Jean-de-Braie and lost our
way yesterday in the forest. Tell him that he will be
rewarded if he will lead us to the village we are seeking.
The man appeared not to understand Abélard's French,
but as soon as the French was translated into Breton a
brighter light broke upon his face, and he seized the
bridle of Madelon's horse, and called upon the others to
follow him. His house, said Abélard, seems to have been
begun by the dislodging of a rock from the hillside, but
it must be a poor sort of place to live in; and what his
purpose is in living in this wild forest is not clear, for
he is not a charcoal burner, and what other trade may
be practised here it is not easy to guess. The woman,
said Héloïse, is his wife, but how did he persuade her to
follow him? Wherever a man goes he will find a woman
to follow him, Madelon answered; and she began to put
questions to their guide, and on their way to Saint-Jean-
de-Braie they learnt that the man was a wolf-hunter, and
on hearing that such was his trade they told Madelon to
tell him that they had seen a she-wolf bring her young
from the river and lodge them in the bole of a great beech-
tree, not far from the sheeling of a whilom charcoal
burner. Tell him, said Héloïse, that it will be a kindness

to kill those cubs and save them from a lingering death. But when this message was transmitted to the wolf-hunter a bleakness came into his face, and it was some while before it became clear to them that he was unwilling to kill the cubs.   Madelon was bidden to inquire out the reason, and she reported that he was minded not to kill the cubs but to feed them, a gentleness of heart that they did not think to find in the hunter.   At which Madelon was charged to return to the Breton language and to keep to it throughout, it being the only language in which he could make plain his reasons for preferring to feed the cubs rather than to kill them, and the story he had to tell, translated from Breton into French by Madelon, was that he owed his appointment to his skill in imitating the cry of the wolf; his business was to counterfeit the wolf from the top of a fir.   The cry begins, he said, low down in the throat and rises into the howl that you know of.   For a long time I get no answer to my cry; I repeat it now and again from the fir-tree, and sooner or later the wolf prowling in search of lambs or fawns to feed his mate begins to think that she is calling to him for help; and leaving his quest he comes, and the hunters who are stationed at various corners of the wood have fair shots at him as he passes.

Men do strange things for a livelihood, Abélard answered, after having had the story transmitted to him; and in all my travels I have never heard of a stranger way of getting a livelihood.   But why will he feed the cubs?   Ask him that, Madelon.   The wolf-hunter's answer was that wolves were scarcer now than they were formerly, and that if they continued to lessen in numbers he might lose his job.

CHAP. XVII.

ONCE more saying that they were weary of their pillions Héloïse and Madelon dismounted, and giving their horses in charge of the guide they walked through the darkening forest, hoping to be safely in the inn at Saint-Jean-de-Braie before the rain fell. The guide seemed doubtful, saying that they might be caught in the first shower of rain, but he hoped, however, to arrive in the village before the storm broke. But thou'lt get the full force of the storm on thy way back, said Abélard, at which the guide smiled vaguely, his shoulders, face and gesture seeming to say that rain could not hurt a serf. A deeper twilight gathered and a faint pattering was heard on the leaves overhead, and the forest, hitherto so morose, seemed to become friendly, even sociable, the pattering seeming to Héloïse like the feet of the fairies. Or the very voices of the fairies themselves, Abélard answered. The forest welcomes the rain, he continued; it was parched, and all the young leaves are opening to receive the warm shower; the rain will freshen the waters of the streams and ponds.

A green snake hissed through the grass, showing a beautiful mottled belly as it went by, and a little bird sang despite the rain. A robin, Madelon said, and she began to tell stories; but in answer to the guide, who seemed puzzled at the travellers' sudden delay, she called upon Héloïse and Abélard to mount their horses. We must hasten, she said, or we shall be caught in all the storm. But the rain is so pleasant to listen to, Abélard answered. The guide warned them that it would be well to get out of the forest before the wind arose, but they took no heed of his warnings till the wind sent down all the rain that had collected in the leaves above them, drenching

them to the skin. How far are we now, Abélard asked,
from Saint-Jean-de-Braie? The guide answered: Less
than a third of a league. Anything to be away from
those drenching trees, Abélard answered, and the women
drew the hoods of their cloaks low down over their faces.
But the rain penetrated everywhere, and very soon they
began to talk of rain behind their ears, of rain on their
necks, of rain flowing down their backs. They seemed to
be sitting in water, so they said, and their shoes were filled
with rain. My ankles and legs are soaked, there's no part
of me that isn't wet, Héloïse cried. It matters little how
much more falls, for we are as wet as we can be, said
Abélard. But ten minutes later Héloïse answered: I am
much wetter than I was ten minutes ago, and seem to be
getting wetter every moment. I am wetter than I was,
he answered, but we are out of the drip of the forest at
last and within sight of Saint-Jean-de-Braie. Ask the
guide if the inn is a good one; and while Madelon was
translating French into Breton and Breton into French
again, the trees were again shaken, this time so roughly
that it was as if a cistern had been emptied over them.
Never were human beings as wet as we, Abélard said;
and when they reached the skirts of the forest the rain
fell so fiercely that it was hard to force the horses through
the downpour.

So a welcome moment it was when the innkeeper came
forward to meet them and took charge of the horses, and
Abélard, after rewarding the guide with money, and
thanking him, followed Héloïse and Madelon into the inn
kitchen, where there was a fire burning on a great hearth
built into the middle of the floor, the smoke curling and
escaping as best it could through a hole in the roof
sheltered from the wind by a louvre, a sort of tin screen
shapen like a conical hat. And the fire being a big

one, they were already enveloped in a cloud of steam,
whereupon Abélard warned them of their wanton disre-
gard of their health. God will look after his own, Madelon murmured humbly, and the innkeeper's wife said:
But this kitchen is used by carriers, pedlars and gleemen;
and it is in truth no place for such as you, turning to
Madelon and Héloïse; nor is it a place for you, reverend
sir. Alas there are no guest-chambers, so I will bring
the sisters to my room, and you, reverend sir, will dry
your garments as best you may before this fire, and make
yourself easy on one of the couches. My husband will
see you get a good rug and a pillow. And then, turning
to Héloïse and Madelon, she said: You will eat something
before you lie down to sleep? A little milk is all that
I could swallow to-night, said Héloïse; we have come a
long way from our convent at Saint-Denis and are too
tired to eat, but hope to reach, with God's good will, a
convent of our Order near Nantes. As soon as you see
one of my omelets, appetite will come to you, the innkeeper's wife answered. To-morrow I will eat an omelet,
but to-night I am too tired to eat, Héloïse replied. We
have ridden twenty miles through the forest; we were
lost in it till we came upon the sheeling of a wolf-hunter,
and it was he who led us out of the wilderness. It seemed
to her that this was a sufficient account of their journey,
but Madelon could not withhold her tongue and began a
long narrative, to Héloïse's great weariness, who was
thinking only of when she could rid herself of her clothes
and lie down. You too, reverend sir, will sleep better
if you have something in your stomach. Abélard promised that he would allow her to cook him an omelet, and
she led Héloïse and Madelon to a spiral staircase at the
end of the kitchen. In about half-an-hour I shall be
with you again, reverend sir, and in this half-hour Abélard

stripped himself of all his clothes and laid them out to dry, and was within the sheets of a couch in an alcove before he caught sight of the long, lean shanks of the innkeeper's wife descending the spiral staircase. You have promised to eat an omelet if I make one, and should it be to your liking, you will remember me, good father, in your prayers. Like the good sister who has left us, I am too weary to show a good appetite even for your omelet, said Abélard; but I will remember you in my prayers. And he set up a mumble that would pass for a prayer while the innkeeper's wife prepared the omelet. Your omelet, my good woman, is the tastiest that I have ever eaten, he said. My omelets are liked by all who come hither, she interjected; and he handed her back the empty plate, saying: My prayers to-night will be that God will send you much custom every night of the year, but to-night I would that you lacked some, for your custom is no doubt gleemen, pardoners and carriers, wandering folk that make much noise before getting into their beds. Have no fear lest you should be roused from the sleep you need, she replied; should any vagrant come to our door after dark, he will enter my house under promise that he does not raise his voice above a whisper and draws off his boots noiselessly. Nor delays long between the right and the left boot, said Abélard. We must make the good father easy, she said to her husband, who had just come in from the stables, for he is going to pray that God may have mercy upon my soul, and send us good custom. My soul is as important as thine, the innkeeper grumbled, a small, red-headed man, with weak eyes like a ferret. I have relics that I would show him if he be not too weary, he said. Abélard's eyes were closing and he was asleep before the innkeeper returned, and the wife began a grumble that the promised prayers were forgotten. But that is no reason why he should not have a pillow and a rug, the innkeeper answered, and Abélard slept till the voices of some gleemen who came in overnight awoke him with talk of distances and loads. The newcomers could not be else than gleemen, for their talk rolled on the money that they might gather from the pilgrims they hoped to meet, but whom they might miss, the forest being well-nigh impassable. The words: Heavy muddy roads, reached his ears, and later a river was spoken of which he could not but think was the one by whose banks himself, Héloïse and Madelon had slept. A green, shallow stream, a gleeman said, in dry weather, but rising after rain into a swift race of water. We shall not cross it to-day, nor to-morrow; we should lose our bear and our dogs in the current, and ourselves, mayhap, and the gleemen began to mutter against their evil luck till Héloïse and Madelon stepped down the staircase in garments borrowed from the innkeeper's wife.

The sight of women restored confidence to the gleemen, and they called to the innkeeper for his permission to train their animals in the kitchen during the afternoon, saying that if the pleasant company assembled cared to reward the animals with a small coin or two, the animals and their owners would be grateful. The innkeeper laughed and shrugged his shoulders for answer, saying from the foot of the stairs that they might train their animals, but his guests must not be pestered nor asked to move out of their places, and of all, he would have no hat going round his inn kitchen. We are not bullies or cut-purses, the gleemen answered, whereupon the false friar and his nuns retired into a distant corner to read their breviaries and watch the performance furtively till the company in the kitchen became oppressive, which it did during the course of the afternoon. The rain has stopped, or nearly stopped, Héloïse said; let us get a mouthful of fresh air or I choke. And rising to their feet they went towards the door, Abélard rewarding the vagrants with some money, hoping thus to gain their good will and courtesy. As they passed out the innkeeper and his wife warned the friar and his nuns that the rain had not stopped and would begin before long to fall heavily as before, but Abélard answered: we must get a breath of fresh air, and will go no further than the stables. The talk of the ostlers will be a change from the talk we have been hearing all the morning, he whispered to Héloïse, who was asking for bread for their horses, and when the bread was eaten, naught remained but to return to the kitchen or follow the single street which seemed to be the entire village. The dropping chestnut-trees with all their standing bloom seem to lament the bad weather, Héloïse said; how sad they are under the low sky—— Like the lid of a pan, Madelon interjected, with the pan simmering underneath it. For the life of you look at the rain jumping out of the puddles. We shall be wet to our skins. But neither Héloïse nor Abélard could return to the kitchen. We must go to the end of the street, said Abélard, and at the end of the avenue they found other streets striking right and left; and it was while standing in the middle of these, asking each other how it would be to hire a house and live all their lives in Saint-Jean-de-Braie, that the rain began to fall, very dree, straight through the still air without mercy for man or beast. From the eaves, from the gutters between the low gables it flowed, making the street look like a brook, said Abélard. It will be no use taking shelter in a doorway, sooner or later we shall have to run to our inn. Summer rain hurts nobody, cried Madelon. Abélard

answered that the innkeeper's wife would not be able to
provide them with a second change. But if we hasten we
shall escape a soaking, Héloïse replied, as she ran down
the street past the patient cattle come under the chestnut-
trees for shelter.

Everybody was running for shelter, any porch, any
door; and on returning to the inn they perceived some
newcomers, wet and miserable as themselves, crowding
round the hearth drying their clothes. One of these
arrived at the same moment as themselves, and after
shaking himself like a dog who has been into a river, he
began to unstrap his pack, his goods, which were many,
making a fine show upon the floor. Now I would that
all here should cast an eye over the good things that I
bring you, he said; for all that you see is of the best
quality, and all were made in the fair land of France,
which is good warranty for everything that you may be
minded to buy. You all lack something, and here you will
find everything you lack. All of the best quality, I say
again, for everything you see was made in the fair land
of France, and all things made in France are the best in
the world. Let not the evil luck I met with in the forest
follow me into this fine kitchen, where I am glad to be,
though it would have been better for me if the sun were
shining, for the sun brings us all out of our houses, and
the women of this village, were they to see it, would not
leave any of this fine thread for the next village, nor any
of these needles, the finest I have ever known, and I have
been on the road these thirty years.

A thick-set man he was, whose bulk and build may
have inspired the belief in him that he had been cast
for a pedlar's life, and Abélard began to look upon his
cozening talk and self-depreciation as a concomitant of
his trade. The lads of this village will find knives, he

continued, of all kinds and sorts in my pack; all blades and handles; little knives handy to cut a goose quill into a pen, long-bladed knives to slice up a loaf or a cheese with, sheath knives to wear in your girdles to put a robber to flight with, knives that a girl can defend herself with when her lover begins to handle her knees; knives, knives, knives, and girdles too. Girdles and gloves for wenches and wives, all things that you need you will find in my pack; tell me what you lack, girls and boys, tell me what you lack. Now, gentle sir, what will you give to your lady? A comb for her hair, a purse for her girdle, a ring for her finger, a brooch for her bosom? And if none of these suit you, I will return to-morrow with a little dog, who will love her as dearly as you do, sir, for dogs love their mistresses, and your lady would like a small, gentle dog to keep her company when a bad cold is upon her, for I can see the lady there is sniffing; three times has she sneezed, and a finer necker-chief than this she will not find to wear, and as long as she wears it no cold will dare to attack her, for it has been blessed by many a holy man, and the blessing and the quality of the silk will keep her from colds for evermore. The ladies to whom thou speakest, pedlar, Abélard answered, are nuns dressed in the casual raiment of the innkeeper's wife; we all came last night soused to the skin after a long journey through the forest. Take no offence, good sir, said the pedlar, for I only know a nun by her habit; and if the nuns that wear the clothes that have been lent to them would like a scapular or a rosary, I can let them have either at a fair price. My goods are cheaper than those sold by any other pedlar on the road. But nuns, reverend father, have nieces, and I would offer the nuns silk coifs for their nieces. You too, reverend sir, have nieces, and here is a fine comb of tortoise-shell.

I will have thy tortoise-shell comb, pedlar, Abélard replied, for my niece whom I shall meet at Tours; meanwhile, I will give it in charge to the good sister whom I
am conducting thither. No fault have I to find; but
thanks, thanks, thanks, the customer is never wrong, never,
he cried, as he dropped the comb into a linen purse which
Abélard handed to Héloïse. The man speaks well, he
said in Latin, and a moment after, in French: there is a
hoarseness in your throat, sister; get you to your bed,
for should a sudden illness fall upon you we are undone.
I had counted to reach Orléans to-morrow. You speak
wise words, reverend sir, Madelon answered. I will see
that our sister keeps to her bed and has plenty of warm
drinks. With the help of these and God's help she will
be able to travel to-morrow. Whereupon the women
withdrew to the staircase, and were about to mount it
when another arrival stayed them, one who looked as if
he had come a long way, some five and twenty miles;
more than that, maybe, so wearily did he let down his
pack. But he had not laboured in vain, for he had come
upon generous pilgrims who had money and had purchased
something, if no more than a little dust from the bones of
the saints, some teeth that they had shed, some parings
of their nails, some hair from their heads and beards.

A pardoner, Abélard said to himself, whose business
lies with troubled consciences, with men and women who
dread the punishments in the next world for their sins in
this; and looking once more into the long, brown face, he
said: Of the next world of which he prates so gaily he will
soon have practical experience. An opinion this was that
Abélard soon found himself obliged to abate, for no
sooner was the pardoner's tongue loosened than his looks
began to belie him. Or is it that his greed overcomes his
weariness and his wetting? Abélard asked himself, and

he listened, with a half-amused, half-contemptuous smile on his lips, to the patter of the relic-seller.

Wet as I am, tired as I am, I have still a tongue in my head to tell a good story, and I will tell one to you, unless I am interrupting somebody in his story? No one has told a story this day, so if thou'rt minded, tell thine, Abélard said, and the pardoner answered quickly: Since the good father bids me tell my story, I will. It is of a woman who coveted her sister's husband, and coveted him with success, for she enjoyed him in her sister's bed, a drug having made sure of her own cuckold. But such love as hers the devil puts into our minds, and very soon he withdraws the love that has tempted us into sin and we suffer much torment in our consciences. Such is the way of men and women, and the woman about whom I would tell you began very soon to hate the man from whom she had not been able a little while before to withhold herself. His face and name reminded her that the temptation she had yielded to had lost her long happiness in heaven and plunged her into endless misery in the gulf of hell, maybe. But what had been done could not be undone except by the aid of a priest, who would shrive her. But the penance he imposed upon her could not be fulfilled, and it is in this penance that the point of my story lies. The woman confessed that she had lain with her brother-in-law, and many other sins of such tremendous nature that the priest was taken aback. I know not how to deal with you, daughter; you have earned hell ten thousand times over, for of theft and lies, adultery, fornication and incest, you seem to be guilty. I can think of no sin you haven't been guilty of except murder. The woman bowed her head and began a new story, for even of murder she was not wholly innocent, and the priest, more affrighted than ever, sat trying to think of a penance that would keep the woman quiet for the rest of her life. But her whole nature seemed to him so bent upon the pleasure of sin that he could think of none that would make her soul's salvation certain. Yet he couldn't reconcile himself to telling her that he was unable to help her, and forgetful of her body, he sat thinking of her soul, leaving her on her knees all the afternoon while he meditated, she asking him from time to time to pronounce the penance that would insure her soul against burning. The priest sat thinking how this might be done, and the best penance he could devise was to send her all over the country from shrine to shrine, muttering Paternosters and Ave Marias at each one. Only by bodily exercise can her soul be saved, he said to himself, and again fell to thinking, till the woman, unable to keep on her knees any longer, rolled over, crying to him to speak any penance, for whatever it was she would accomplish it.

It was not till many weeks afterwards, when far away on her pilgrimage, that the truth broke upon her that the penance the priest had imposed, and that she had accepted so joyfully, could not be performed, life not being long enough. Whereupon she cried out in her misery that her soul was lost. Now it was the devil tempting her, for her next thought was: Since my soul is lost for ever, let me return to my sinning, for even God cannot punish me more for the sins that I have committed than He will for those that I am ready to commit. The woman's steps turned from the holy shrine whither they were going to a tavern, and at the first step she took thither a great rejoicing began in hell, all the devils crying as they danced circlewise: We shall get her, we shall get her. But there is a proverb that runs in hell as well as upon earth. that it is not well to think how we shall jug our

hare before we have caught our hare.   The woman's
soul was not yet lost, but it would have been lost if she
had not met me, who was able to tell her that the priest
that imposed the penance spoke thoughtlessly, for a
penance that cannot be performed is not a valid penance,
and can be revoked.   I might indeed go further and say
that a penance that cannot be performed has never been
pronounced.   The Church is always practical; her teaching has ever been that the sinner must not despair.   So
did I speak, the woman was soothed, and the good father
present will not gainsay me: despair is the only capital
sin.   We must never despair; our feet must ever strive
upwards, however thorny that way may be, and a relic
is a great help.   We hold it in our hands, we press it
to our bosoms, and forthright strength is given to us.   I
come to you from the Holy Father, who charged me to
ease all troubled consciences.   In my wallet I have the
Holy Father's testimony on parchment for all of you to
read.   He conferred upon me the right to give sacraments,
to sell relics.   I have it all under his own hand; the brief
he gave me is in that wallet, and if you cannot read for
yourselves the friar yonder will read for you.   The
pardoner produced from his wallet a large brief with
many seals, which he said came from famous Rome, the
city of God on earth, founded by Saint Peter, and it being
no part of Abélard's business to challenge the authority
of the relic-seller, he gazed into the parchment and
handed it back, his face wearing an expression of aston-
ishment rather than approval, and forthwith the pardoner
began another vouching of his wares.

Here is a piece of the sail of Saint Peter's boat that
carried Our Saviour Jesus Christ on the day the storm
arose on the Sea of Galilee, the day he walked upon the
water as if upon dry land.   And here is another piece of

the same sail. Three small pieces are all I have left, but I sell none for less than five shillings, which is a small price to pay for a great benefit. As none of the gleemen had five shillings to spend upon a relic, they sighed, afraid that their souls might be lost; but as soon as the pardoner produced the candle-end that the angel lighted in the tomb over against Golgotha, they forgot their souls, and their minds were gathered in admiration when the pardoner exhibited a feather from the tail of the cock that crowed the morning that Peter denied Christ three times. He exhibited these relics without putting a price upon them, for the price of the candle-end and the cock's feather, and of all, the ointment that Mary Magdalen spread over the feet of Christ, were far beyond any money in the inn that day. And what is this? cried one of the gleemen: a tress of the Magdalen's hair? No, not the Magdalen's, said the pardoner, but a curious tale hangs by this tress of hair, and I will tell it to you. This tress of hair belonged to a woman who prized her hair more than all other things. She spent all day combing and brushing it, rendering it sleek with ointment, till God in His great goodness was sorry for the woman who wasted her soul in vain attendance on her hair; so what do you think He did? He took the woman's sight away from her, and from that day she was unable to see her beautiful hair or to attend to it. It became matted and unkempt, whereupon the woman, whose whole life was now given up to God, was much grieved and affected by the thought that at the special judgment which awaits everybody on the day of their death she would appear untidy before God. So God, taking pity upon this poor woman, gave her back her sight; but no sooner was it given back to her than she returned to the tendance of her hair, forgetful of all things but the men who admired her for it. But God, knowing in His infinite wisdom that there was a core of good in this weak woman, and determined to have in heaven the soul which she was going to lose, took her hair from her. But what matter the loss of my hair if it be restored to me when my body is raised from the dead? she said. Henceforth all her life was spent praying that her hair might be restored for God to see it on judgment day. She became one of the greatest saints ever known; and now that you have heard her story, look into this tress, every single hair of which is worth a penny, and a penny is not too much; everyone here has a penny, or should have one, to spend on the hair of a great saint, who lived in a cave for five and twenty years and is now standing near to the throne of God. What is this? cried one of the wayfarers; a piece of stone? Yes, a piece of stone, answered the pardoner, of the carven statue of the Holy Virgin that stands in a niche in the chapel of Rocamadour. A pious workman was mending her crown one day, but the ladder he was standing on was unsafe and gave way beneath him, and he would have been dashed to the ground if the Virgin had not taken him in her arms and saved his life. So great a miracle as that could not fall to any man's lot without it becoming a great power over his life. He left his bag of tools at the foot of the ladder, and wandered away like one bereft of his senses. One of the Church's greatest saints he became, and this statue is one of the most famous in France, worthy of a great pilgrimage. It would seem, pardoner, that all thy relics are worthy of ten times the price thou askest for them, Abélard said, and having so many holy relics thou wilt be glad to hear that the greatest relic perhaps of all has been discovered by the Crusaders in Nazareth, a phial containing a pint of the Virgin's milk.

At that moment the words: Sancte Thoma adiuva me,
came from a far-off corner of the kitchen, and on looking
thither every face changed colour, for nobody was to be
seen.   Be not afraid, said the pardoner, and he went
whither the voice had spoken and uncovering a cage
revealed to the company a grey bird with a red tail. This
bird, said the pardoner, prays continuously, and his
favourite prayers are Paternoster and Ave Maria, the
two prayers most closely associated with our holy religion.
The bird is among my merchandise, and if I do not put
him up for sale in this kitchen it is because of the price
that I am obliged to ask for him, having paid a very
high price to possess him and spent many years rearing
him in piety, if not in faith, though there is some reason
to believe that he has faith in God.   Let none think that
a terrible heresy is involved in this belief.   The Church
will take into account that his utterances are often so
fitted to the occasion that it is hard to doubt that he
attaches some meaning to his words.   A good, pious bird
he is, without doubt, one that has never been known to
indulge in evil speech, a habit that birds of his kind often
indulge in, not perhaps of their own fault but because of
the society into which they have drifted.   My bird's
vocabulary I will guarantee to be altogether ecclesiastical,
and his repertory includes not only the prayers I have
mentioned but some Latin hymns.   I will guarantee him
to repeat the Veni Sancte Spiritus without a fault; also
the Regina Coeli, and—— Forgive me, good pardoner,
but myself, and I think all here, would be glad to learn
from thee why thou wert at pains to teach the bird prayers; for his own benefit, or for ours, which?   After
having said our prayers we are allowed by the Church to
think of other things, the pardoner answered; we cannot
think always of heaven and hell, and I am truly grateful

for the question that has been put to me by the good
father; a more intelligent question I have rarely heard,
for the value of that bird is in the fact that he prays all
day. At the present moment, it is true, he is silent, but
there can be little doubt that he is learning prayers,
conning them over in his silence, for he's always learning
new prayers and brings out a new prayer when one least
expects it. He is never satisfied, as we are, with sufficient
piety; the word sufficient is unknown to him. I will
avouch it, for by long living with my speaking bird I have
been led to believe that he dreams prayers; our dreams
are but echoes of thoughts that we have forgotten, that
or something quite different; our dreams may be therefore
memories of evil desires and acts, but my bird has no
knowledge of evil. His dreams are pure dreams, his
sleeping hours are prayerful, and the natural affection of
the bird leads him to offer up his prayers for his master,
for, poor bird, he knows well that himself cannot go into
heaven, being but a bird. If my bird be not as I tell
you, how else may we explain his love of his prayers,
unless indeed we suppose him to be an angel incarnate.
But that savours of heresy, and I would not advise anybody among us to harbour such a thought. My bird is but
a bird, I don't offer him as anything else, but he is a
unique bird, one that prays without ceasing, and his prayers will save his master's soul from the many thousand
years of purgatory which his master's soul may be earning
in this life. If that be so, these years melt away before
the bird's prayers as wax melts before a fire. But a
bird's prayers are not answered, Abélard interrupted.
Good father, your question is an excellent one, and for it
I thank you, for I have proof that a bird's prayers are
granted. The one misdeed chargeable to this bird is that
finding the door of his cage open one morning he flew

across the fields, but he had hardly crossed the first before he was pursued by a goshawk, and seeing that he could not escape by swiftness of wings he screamed aloud: Sancte Thoma, adiuva, and no sooner had these words passed his beak than the goshawk fell dead. Good father, the story I tell is the truth. Mine own eyes saw the bird pursued and saw him return repentant at having attempted an escape which nearly ended in his own death. That day he recited a chaplet of Paternosters and Ave Marias. How then—— Ah, scepticism always appears, I regret to say, in the religious; I read it in the good friar's eyes. Good friar no doubt he is, but his eyes are sceptical eyes. I, who have travelled far and seen all kinds and sorts of people, can read the thoughts that lie behind the eyes. Our friar is sceptical, as all friars are, of my miracle, a fault of all the religious, who believe only in their own miracles. I will say, therefore, no more about my bird.

The pardoner's voice was mournful, and excited pity, and won most of the company from Abélard to himself, and they begged of him to tell them more about his speaking bird, which has, said Abélard, uttered no more than four words up to the present. The two men stood looking at each other, Abélard seeing a man of middle height, broad-shouldered, deep-chested, with a great mane of black hair in which there was here and there a streak of grey, and in his forked beard, too, which was thick and black as his hair, there were a few grey hairs. He saw too a long, sun-tanned face with grey, piercing eyes watching him under bushy eyebrows. The pardoner's forehead was broad, the cheek-bones were high, and in his nose, of comely curve, were nostrils long and open. Abélard judged him to be a man between forty and fifty years, but still in the prime of life, able for a day's work with anyone, whether it was a day's mowing or a day's travelling in a forest, a pack on his back. The only sign of age was in his neck, which was full of veins and sinews. A good traveller he must be, for his trade demands it, but his legs are slender for long marching; and his feet? Abélard asked himself, and his eyes went down to the pardoner's feet, and he considered them well. Good travelling feet, he thought, but his ankles are slender like a woman's. A high instep, he added, and continued: A man who spoke the truth when he said that he had travelled far, and can read men's thoughts from their faces. One who can tell the morrow from the aspect of the stars and sky, one like the pedlar who came upon his trade by instinct, one unlike the pedlar in this much, that the day will come when he will hold his merchandise in less esteem than heretofore. A saint, maybe, in the making.

CHAP. XVIII.

THE women, who were still standing in their wet clothes, got a scolding for their imprudence. We shall not start to-morrow, he cried after them, and his fears were realised, for the news next morning was that Héloïse's cold was passing from her head to her chest. I knew that we should not be able to start to-day, Madelon. I cannot think how thou couldst be so stupid as to let her stand in her wet clothes. Go to her, attend upon her, let her have warm drinks, get her well; thou knowest that every day here is a danger. Madelon bowed her head, and Abélard turned to the gleemen with whom he sang and with whom he watched the weather, always in great anxiety lest the Canon might be following them with hirelings. Ah, if he were to overtake them in this inn!

His courage and his pride in himself were great; he stood so high in public esteem and his pupils and disciples were so numerous that he did not believe that anybody could prevail against him. But Fulbert was a canon of Notre-Dame and had many adherents. They would not be safe till they reached Orléans, and in obedience to the impulse of the moment he called up the staircase for news, and the answer he got from Madelon was that Héloïse was in her bed and would not be able to travel for the next few days. On the third, on the fourth, and on the fifth days the answer was the same, and when they rode from the inn on the sixth Madelon was still in doubt whether their departure was altogether a wise one. Women like Madelon only think of one thing at a time, Abélard muttered; and she has forgotten the Canon, who may be at this moment inquiring us out at Étampes. But we are on horseback at last, and not more than an hour's ride from Orléans, he added, judging this to be so from the appearance of the forest, which had begun to dribble into fringes and scattered clumps of trees, as a city does into villages. All the country that lies before us, he said, was once forest, the residue of the great wilderness of Sologne, the desert lying along the left bank of the Loire whither the King and his nobles go for hunting. The clearances we are riding through were forest once, but corn is now all about us, a green country to-day, a yellow country in two months' time. But he spoke into deaf ears, for Héloïse's thoughts were not on the plain before them but on the kindly forest that had sheltered them, and her eyes falling at that moment on an oak, she said: Is there anything in the world more beautiful than an oak showing against a blue sky? A moment after she added, speaking almost to herself: A young man before age has warped him. A masculine tree the oak certainly

is, Abélard replied, and forgetful of her remark, began
to speak his own thoughts, saying that the green country
about them stretched without further interruption from
the forest they had left behind to the very banks of the
Loire, which they would come into sight of at the end of
an hour's ride. Almost the first rise in the ground will
show the river to us, and Héloïse answered: And I shall
be glad to see the river, for one wearies of plains and low
horizons. I like wide expanses, with hills in the back-
ground.

And they continued to talk in this manner while their
horses plodded up a gentle acclivity with bent heads, as
if they were asked to perform some heavy task, Héloïse
waiting for the Loire, which did not come into view for
another hour; and when it did flash into sight it was not
the course of the river that captured her eyes, but a
great barge sailing fast on a wind blowing from the
east. She will reach Tours in three days, Abélard said;
maybe less. And shall we sail in a barge, and will the
sails be yellow or white? Héloïse asked, but seeing that
he was deep in himself and averse from any interruption
of his mood, she gave herself wholly over to an unaided
admiration of the smooth, finely bending lines of a bluish
river sweeping through a grey-green country, the right
bank tame and cultivated, with some of the original forest
here and there, and an almost immeasurable forest along
the left bank, with scrub and marsh where the ground
was low, great trees where it was high, her romantic
imagination summoning to her mind the sound of the
hunting horns echoing round the lakes and ponds as the
hounds and the huntsmen pursued now fleeing deer, now
wolves and bears. She knew from Abélard that there
were no lions nor tigers in France, and she would have
liked to ask him about the King's hunting in Sologne, but

his humour did not seem to invite questions; so she persisted in her admiration of the river, seeing that it bent
a little as it came round the town of Orléans, straighten-
ing out soon after into its seaward course, certain that
the distance that her eyes embraced represented many
leagues; many leagues lay between her and that blue-
tinted line of forest, and nearly as many now lay between
her and Paris.   Towards that blue-tinted distance we
shall be sailing to-morrow or the next day, she said to
herself, and as they had by this time come into full view
of the river, she began to hope that the ship to take
them would be one of the great two-masted ships with
which the river was speckled, and that it would be borne
along beautifully by pointed sails like wings.   The ships
go towards Nantes, towards the seas, sailing with sails
crossed over, she said, and they come up from Nantes
to Orléans with their long peaked sails in a line, making
first for one shore and then for the other, gaining a little
on each tack.   She had seen boats perform the same
feats on the Seine at Argenteuil, and knew that the task
of working a boat against the wind was a slow one.

The city lay on the left under the low shore, the twin
towers of the cathedral striking firmly against long droves
of dove-coloured clouds through which the sun was breaking, illuminating the landscape, showing the line of the
fields, spreading wonder and delight, bringing the sails
of all the ships into relief, filling the river with reflections,
and doing many other wonderful things that Héloïse hoped
to remember; but so extraordinary and so various was the
play of light that she was sure she would have forgotten
a great deal of what she was now seeing before Abélard
thought fit to rouse out of his taciturnity.   Of what can
he be thinking? she asked herself, but refrained from
asking him, and forgot him in a sudden wonder at a long,

low island filled with fair trees, walks, and some houses,
and a long bridge of many narrow arches, whose gently
curving line was broken by roofs of shrines and dwellings,
rising from high piers like the prows of ships, and defended by pointed turrets.   Hast thou no eyes, Abélard,
for the river and its city? she asked.   And he answered
her that he would have had eyes for both had he been able
to rid his mind of Fulbert.   But Fulbert would not follow
us to Orléans? Héloïse asked quickly.   For who would
there be in Paris to tell him?   And he answered her that
although he had regretted at first the illness that had
kept them for so many days at Saint-Jean-de-Braie, he
was now disposed to look upon the delay as advantageous,
for if Fulbert went to Orléans inspired by the thought
that we should sail from thence, and got no news of us
in any of the inns he would return to Paris forthright.
And to her question whether he thought that Fulbert had
come to Orléans, Abélard answered that had Fulbert
come to Orléans he would not have waited; getting no
news of us here, he repeated, he would return to Paris
at once.   But if his thought should be: They are still on
their way hither? she said.   Then it will be bad for us,
he answered, for we cannot resist, he being surrounded
by hirelings.

It was then that Héloïse began to apprehend her lover's
danger, and she rode by his side silent, seeing the city
very distinctly but unable to appreciate the beauty of the
trees, the acacias and the limes and the chestnuts that
filled the Mail with perfume.   There are no trees in
Paris like these, she was about to say, but the words
died on her lips, for Fulbert might dash out of a side
street at any moment.   If we get no tidings of him at
The Red Dragon he has not followed us to Orléans,
Abélard whipered to her as he helped her from her horse,

and it seemed to her that her heart ceased to beat while
he put inquiries to the innkeeper, but as these elicited
no tidings regarding the Canon of Notre-Dame, she drew
an easier breath, and began to think that luck was on their
side after all. In answer to his inquiry if he could get
a ship to take them to Nantes the next day or the day
after, the innkeeper told him that he could get one that
very night, whereat the three were elated. Each ship
takes six passengers and it looses as soon as the six have
paid their fares, said the innkeeper. But the passengers,
reverend sir, are often noisy and unruly, and you and
the good sisters that are with you will suffer much in
such company; and the price not being a large one you
would do well to hire a ship for your use, for you will
then be free to stop at different towns. There is much
to see in Meung and Beaugency. At Meung there is a
great abbey, and they are building a new church there
designed by a young man of great promise. And our
beautiful river has much to show for pleasure and instruction. But your horses, good sir, you will leave with me.
I will care for them well. And should your stay at
Blois, at Tours or at Nantes be a long one, I am ready
to bid a good price for your horses. Whereupon Abélard
said he would want his horses when he returned, which
would be in a month. In a month a horse has time to
eat up a great deal of his value, averred the innkeeper,
and in a month's time horses will be more plentiful in
Orléans than they are to-day, and Abélard allowed himself to be swayed by the innkeeper's arguments.

The sun is no longer at height, the afternoon has
begun to steal upon us; remark, reverend sir, how the
shadows are lengthening. It may be that you would like
to rest yourselves at my inn, to eat and drink, and make
a start to-morrow or the next day? If so, I shall not

charge for the keep of your horses. You have not seen
all our city, you have had but a mere glimpse of it. My
rooms might tempt you to spend a few days in Orléans
if you will deign to see them. Abélard thanked him, but
feeling that Fulbert might be still on their traces, he
decided to leave Orléans within the next hour if he could
hire a ship to take them to Nantes. You will find plenty,
reverend sir, lying by the wharf; but do not accept the
first offer, for the avarice of these sailors is notorious;
they will come down to half of the first price if you
show firmness. Or if you would like it better, reverend
sir, I will take the matter into my hands, and your ship
shall be ready to-morrow morning. Abélard thanked the
innkeeper again and said that he would walk to the end
of the wharf and look over the ships that might be lying
by. Come, Sister Héloïse and Sister Madelon, I would
have your advice about the ship that we shall travel
in. And having taken the way to the wharf from the
innkeeper, the three walked thither, finding themselves
suddenly confronted by a dark-skinned man, portly and
about medium height, from whom all three felt a sudden
aversion, owing perhaps to their fears of Fulbert. For
the moment every corner was a hiding-place for a hireling. Moreover, the man's very courtesy roused their
suspicions. Reverend sir, he began, may I say without
intruding myself unduly upon your attention and on that
of the good sisters who are with you, may I say that if
your search is for a fast sailing ship that will take you
to Blois in a day, to Tours in three, to Nantes in four,
mine is the ship you are in search of. May I—— Wilt
show me the ship that thou ownest? Abélard inquired
abruptly. Most certainly, reverend sir, I will show you
my ship; she lies alongside; and if you will do me the
honour to step on board and overlook her, I shall be

most happy; and if everything is not to your satisfaction
it shall be made so as far as it is in my power, for I am
but a poor skipper owning only a single ship, but the
best, I can say truthfully, that lies at this end of the
river, and it would not be too much of a brag were I to
say that it is as good a ship as you will find in Nantes,
where assemble all the good ships of the world. The best
ships in the world are built at Nantes, and if thy ship
is all thou sayest I ask nothing better than to hire her,
thyself and thy crew; and the cost will be——? Reverend
sir, my ship is at your service; any recompense that you
make will be enough for me. Vain words are these, Abélard answered; one cannot be buyer and seller at the
same time; the seller names his price, and the buyer
accepts or declines. Whereupon the skipper, after eyeing
Abélard sharply and turning over in his mind that he had
come from Nantes and knew the prices, named a sum of
money that seemed to Abélard a fair one considering the
length of the journey. If thy ship has two sails, my good
man, the bargain is clinched. Two sails! replied the
skipper, could I get you to Nantes without two? I was
thinking, said the false friar, of the sisters, for this one
looked to seeing the sails cross before the wind. And
the skipper, taken aback, thinking that he had to do with
fools, male and female, regretted that he had not asked
much more, and invited them into a long, narrow ship
that Abélard said would make fine way before the wind.
But it is hard, he continued, to sink them enough into
the water to save them from slipping backwards when
sailing near to the wind. See this deep plank, sisters;
when the ship's head is put up to the wind this plank is let
down into the water, for without it we should not be able
to tack. And these remarks restored the skipper's confidence in Abélard as one who might have been able to

make a keen guess at the sum of money that it was right
for him to pay for the voyage from Orléans to Nantes.
It is pleasant to sail with one who can put his hand to a
rudder, keeping the ship's head straight, he said, and all
that you can do, sir.   And now I will call my boy, who
will divide the cabin, leaving half for the sisters and half
for yourself.   But to my thinking not much of your time
will be spent in the cabin; in preference you will sleep
on deck under the full moon to-night; but that is how
it may please you.   Have we loosed yet from the quay?
Abélard asked, and the skipper answered: see, they are
loosing already.   A moment after the great rope came on
board, and the long, narrow ship floated into the middle
of the stream.

And all danger of meeting Fulbert being now past, the
lovers fell to talking, Héloïse saying that she liked watching the boats go past at Argenteuil, their sails filling,
bending the boats over.   A lovely sight it is to see the
boats bending over, but the boats at Argenteuil have not
long, pointed sails like these.   Hear how the water ripples
past.   She would have said a great deal more, but the
skipper was by again, asking Abélard to take note of the
pace the boat was making over and above the current,
running, Abélard said, at the rate of a league an hour;
we shall be at Meung, which is two leagues from Orléans,
in not much over the hour.   We shall be at Meung under
the hour, the skipper answered, and may I not land you,
for if you have not seen the Abbey, one of the largest
and finest in this part of the country, you should see it;
and there is the new church that is being built alongside
of the old one.   We shall reach Beaugency before seven,
so if you would like to spend an hour at Meung you have
but to say the word.   Abélard answered that he had matters to settle with the sisters and would tell him later.

Madelon was certain that the Canon had not followed them; he is angry, and he can be very angry, she said, but he can be very lazy, too. But what if he be waiting at Meung? Héloïse asked. You did not know yourselves that you would stop there. Forget the Canon and live your lives according to your liking, was her advice to them. So when the square tower of Port d'Amont rose up against the western sky, Abélard sought the skipper and said: There are not much more than four leagues between Meung and Beaugency, and with this wind we cannot fail to reach Beaugency before nine. We cannot, the skipper answered, and leaving Madelon on board, who was always happy with her rosary (her piety will relieve the skipper of any thoughts he may have formed about us, Abélard said), they walked for an hour or more in Meung, admiring its green gardens and the brook that flowed through the town turning many mills. Wherever they went they seemed to be always meeting mill wheels. A good little worker is this brook; it wearies never, turning the last mill as quickly as the first, Abélard said. And he called Héloïse's eyes to the church that the builders were just finishing, showing her the pointed arch that had come into fashion and praising the skill with which the architect harmonised the new with the old, for in his scheme the old round Romanesque tower did not seem out of keeping with the slim, mullioned windows. Reason coming to the aid of faith, Héloïse said. And after admiring the gravity of the round eleventh-century church and the gaiety of the new Gothic, they forgot all about faith and reason and wandered side by side along the river's bank under the shade of pleasant trees, forgetful of all else but themselves, till they were awakened from their dream by the skipper, who said:

Maybe it would be better that we get up the sails, for the wind may change a little towards evening.

How like our sails are to swallows' wings, Héloïse said, and, Madelon, if thou wilt lay aside thy rosary—— I am always willing to lay it aside when the talk is in French, but when it is in Latin I might as well be saying my prayers. You would have me answer if our sails are like swallows' wings: the sails are peaked and so are the birds' wings, but the sails are yellow and the wings are black, and the wings move up and down and the sails are still. It would seem to me that there be more differences than likenesses, but that is the way always. And no answer coming to Héloïse to make, her eyes followed the countless swallows flying up and down the river, through the arches of the bridge and back again, skimming the surface of the water. A certain sign of rain, Madelon said; but there were hundreds, maybe thousands, of swallows in the sky, high up aloft, collecting, retiring, dividing, collecting again, some passing down to the river, others rising high out of sight. It seems, Héloïse said, that birds never tire of flying. It is by flying they get their living, said Madelon; nobody ever tires of that. All day long they have been flying, Héloïse continued, and before retiring to their roosts they are flying more madly than ever, as if to lose a minute were a loss indeed. The swift, sudden, incomprehensible gyrations of the birds above contrasted with the steady flight of the swallows that flew back and forwards, their wings dipping the surface of the river as they passed through the arches and back again. Never was there such an evening of swallows, Abélard said, more because he wished to be at one with Héloïse's thoughts than because the birds interested him. An evening of swallows, he said, but those birds going up and down the river are not the true swallows; he was not certain that they were not bats, for the dusk was deepening, and it took him a long time to decide that the stronger-winged birds were aloft, the weaklings keeping to the surface of the river. The first brood cannot yet be flying, he mused, and fell to thinking of the many species of swallows, and to which might belong the birds that flew up and down the arches mechanically as soldiers at drill.

Look, Héloïse said, how the sunset is coming up, and raising their eyes from the river they saw a great herd or flock of rose-coloured clouds coming up from the west, reminding them of rose-coloured sheep returning to the fold driven by the shepherd. Madelon prattled, and the lovers thought of each other, of their love, of the destinies that had guided them, till remembering suddenly the rose-coloured sheep on high, they raised their eyes. But none was to be seen, all had vanished or had passed into the dun-coloured clouds in the east, out of which the moon rose. Are we in night or in day? Héloïse asked, and Abélard answered that these summer nights were short, the twilight lasting till dawn. Only two hours of transparent darkness, and then the dawn. Sing to me, she said; the dawn song with the burden: Ah God, ah God, the dawn! it comes so soon. But I have no lute, he answered. The sailors will lend thee a rote or gittern—— If I sing the skipper will know that we are fugitives. From an angry uncle, Héloïse said, and she sang the tune under her breath.

CHAP. XIX.

WHEN Abélard opened his eyes the summer dawn was breaking, soft as the bloom upon a peach, and on raising himself upon his elbow he overlooked the ship from bow

to stern. Héloïse and Madelon lay side by side, wrapped
in their cloaks, deep in slumber, and the slumber that
had overtaken the crew in the bow seemed hardly less
deep. A long day is before us, and only five or six leagues
between Beaugency and Blois: even if the wind should
fail us, those stout fellows now sleeping will be working
at the oars, bringing us easily to the wharf at Blois during
the course of the afternoon; that is why they are with us,
in case the wind should drop. His head fell back upon
his pillow, and when he awoke again the sun was bright
upon the river, all dancing silver, and the boatmen were
eating their breakfast before making ready for sails for
departure.

You would do well, said the skipper, good sir, to seek
your breakfast in the town. The inns are open, and
there is no need to hurry back to us after breakfast, for
these summer days are long. You will dine at the inn at
Blois and sleep in a bed, if you wish it, but it seems that
none of you have slept too badly upon the deck. And
when all the skipper had said was related, the cunning of
the peasant awoke in Madelon, who said that she would
feign sickness, and keep watch; for should the sailor,
who has received his money, weigh anchor and return to
Orléans, our plight would indeed be a pitiful one. I will
keep watch, and you will bring some food back with you
when yourselves have eaten and visited the town. And
her words seeming wise to Abélard he made them known
to the skipper, who shrugged his shoulders and said:
It is just as you wish it, sir, and continued his own breakfast, leaving Héloïse and Abélard in doubt as to their
conduct, which they soon forgot, so excellent was their
appetite when the king of fishes, the shad, was laid before
them: Of more delicate flavour than the bass, better than
the turbot, a fish that makes the sole seem common, said

Abélard. The shad comes, he continued, to us in his prime
in May; the glory of the Loire is the shad. Some mutton
cutlets brown from the grill, smelling sweet of roasted
fat and gravy, revived their appetites; in the sauce there
was a flavour of onion, and they forgot the shad for a
moment, and he did not return to their thoughts till a
dish of asparagus was eaten and they sat together finishing their bottle of the white wine for which Beaugency
has always been famous since vines first came to France.
And after this good breakfast they went out into the town,
gaping and gazing at the storeyed houses, very like those
they had left behind in the rue des Chantres. It seemed
to them that they could find happiness and contentment
in any of the beautiful houses that they came across, one
of those they had caught sight of coming up from the
wharf, houses overlooking the river, from whose windows,
Héloïse said, we could catch sight of our ship, for we
would not be without one; and when weary of the hearth
and the home we would loose and sail past all the towns
that we shall see on our way to Nantes, past Nantes and
down to the sea. And then? Abélard said. And then,
she replied, we would dash over the sea waves as Jason
did. Like Orpheus thou wouldst sing at the prow. New
horizons would open up and I should have seen the sea,
a thing I have seen only through Madelon's eyes. She
has spoken to me of the sea, telling me of the great rocks
it roars about and the caverns it has worn among the
rocks, but—— Here we are at the fortress that the skipper
told us to go in search of, Abélard interrupted, the Tour
de César, and having walked round it they made their
way back through the narrow intricate streets to the
river, pausing under the trees of the Mail to indulge their
eyes with all the bend of the river and the bridge, as
beautiful as the bridge at Orléans. The river is more

beautiful here than it is at Orléans, Héloïse said; it wears
a welcoming look, seeming almost to take an interest in
its travellers and its towns. At that moment the bells of
Saint-Cléry began singing, and the sound was borne by
the breeze over the great wide smiling river. It would
be beautiful to live here, Héloïse said again. But we
must not forget Madelon's breakfast, Abélard remarked,
thereby breaking the spell of the moment. We must
go back and fetch her some breakfast from the inn at
once; which they did, and found her hungry and glad to
receive what they had brought her. The skipper, too,
was glad to get away, and when they had passed under
the bridge he bade them notice how deep the water was,
how it whirled, creating dark whorls here and there, like
those one sees in glass, great knots such as one meets in
trees. Whirlpools, he said, these are, that have sucked
down many a swimmer. As he talked the wind caught
the sails, and they were carried past long, narrow islands
and yellow sandbanks lined with tall reeds. It is among
the reeds yonder that the shad loves to lie and bask, a fish
worth catching, the skipper said. Well worth catching,
Abélard answered, as we know well, for we ate of one
to-day for breakfast.

And the men talked of the eating of shad and the drinking of Beaugency wine, Abélard admiring, while he talked,
the sun driving shafts of light through the dove-grey
clouds that enhanced the extraordinary silky blueness in
the sky that day. The river, he thought, is in harmony
with its sky and with its grey-green landscape. There is
nothing a man would change, for God was in a good
humour when he made France. A puffing little wind
brought them into view of some shallows, and the skipper
said that the Loire often shifted its sands and made steering difficult, and Héloïse cried: Look at the herons wading

in the silt. And look, Abélard answered, at the gentle folk coming towards us on horseback with hawks on their wrists. But they are not going to hunt the herons? she asked; rooks or crows or choughs or jackdaws or magpies, but not herons? The beater will send up the herons, Abélard answered, as soon as the hawks are at pitch, and almost as he spoke the herons were driven from their fishing, and ascending high into the air the beautiful grey birds tried hard to keep above the hawks, knowing that their safety depended upon their doing so. But the swifter wings of the hawks carried them higher, and the ladies and gentlemen watched from their palfreys the stooping hawks, always forced to glide aside, for the spear-like heads of the herons were deftly raised to meet them. At last, with closed wings a hawk fell swifter than any arrow upon a wearied heron, bringing him to earth. The other heron, seemingly swifter of wing than the hawk, promised more exciting sport, and part of the company went away in pursuit, part remaining to capture the successful hawk. The falconer will find him tearing the heron open, Abélard explained, looking round from time to time, fearing an intruder, but recognising his keeper, who will approach very quietly, lest he should frighten the hawk. The hawk will allow himself to be taken by the jesses. And what will become of the heron? Héloïse asked. His brain will be awarded to the hawk as recompense for his flight, and some serf will boil or roast the heron for his supper. A wonderful match it was, Héloïse said, and I would like to see another flight, though the beautiful grey bird with long neck and head like a spear is dear to me. And then they talked of the other birds that the hawk might be flown against, Abélard saying that the best sport of all was afforded by the magpie, a cunning bird that flew from hedgerow to hedgerow

with much wiliness before he was driven into crossing
an open space where the hawk might strike. And there
was talk, too, about the ducks and snipe that the hawk
could catch if he were at pitch; and what is meant by
being at pitch, Abélard said, is when the hawk is high
in the air, which might well be called at pounce, for the
falcon does not fly after his birds, overtaking them like
the goshawk; he waits on high for the birds to be put
up for him, a good hawk understanding the game as well
as the falconer. As their ship drew away on a fair wind
they talked on about the keeping and breeding of hawks
till the subject became wearisome, and their eyes roved
over the grey-green valley, seeing long herds of red cattle
with many bulls among them, for, said Madelon, there's
nothing that the wolf fears so much as the bull; he may
bite the bull's legs, but that matters little to the bull,
for he very soon treads the life out of the wolf; and if a
number of wolves come out of the forest to attack the
herd, the heifers put the calves inside the ring, and then
the bulls chase the wolves hither and thither, helped
sometimes by the heifers, for a heifer will put up a good
fight to save her calf. But the sheep? said Abélard.
Well, the sheep know their danger and come into the
circle if they get the chance, so while protecting their
own heifers and calves the bulls save the sheep from
the wolves, who never get more than a yoe that has wandered too far in search of a straying lamb. But do not
the bulls fight each other for the possession of some beautiful heifer? They do indeed, and whiles they kill each
other, which is a great loss, for no herd or flock would
be safe but for the bulls. There's more forest in Brittany
than here, and there's a good deal here as you can see
for yourselves; it sprouts up, for, however much you
may strive to clear away the forest, wherever forest has

once been it is likely to come up again. One year's
seed makes seven years' weed, as the saying is, and it
will take many centuries, perhaps thousands of years, to
free France from forest and wolves. An acre of forest
gone means a wolf gone with it.

We shall be alongside of the wharf at Blois in another
half-hour if this wind holds up, a vexing, puffing wind
it is, that carries us a little way and then leaves us, said
the skipper; but it comes again; look, and their eyes
following his hand they saw a great hill rising steeply
above the river, and began to think of their dinner in one
of the inns at Blois. Wilt thou come with us? Abélard
whispered to Madelon. No, she said, but thank you
kindly, master and mistress; I will remain where I am,
having no dependence upon our skipper, who would play
us a trick if he could. Go to your dinner, but do not
forget to bring back some for Madelon. Is it, Héloïse
asked, because she knows that we would like to be alone
that she refuses to come with us, or does she suspect the
skipper? That we shall never know, Abélard answered,
for Madelon herself may not know the reason of her
obstinacy. But we must get the name of an inn from
the skipper.

From the terrace of the inn he recommended to them,
and on which they dined later, they could see a great
prospect, the forest of Blois and the marshes and scrub
of the Sologne. It put thoughts into Héloïse's mind of
the herons they had seen chased by the hawks that morning. One of the mated birds will never fish again in those
marshes, more beautiful to a heron than a vineyard or a
rose garden, she said. Both may have been killed, he
answered, but let us not forget Madelon's dinner in our
sorrow for a heron's death. Whereupon a basket was
purchased, and with it on her arm Héloïse wandered with

Abélard about the steep streets of Blois, up and down the
many staircases that led from terrace to terrace, filling
the basket with dainties, for Madelon remained at her
post in spite of the skipper's efforts to persuade her to go
ashore to listen to some gleemen who were seeking to
attract a crowd at the bridge-head.

Wilt sing a song, Abélard, and shame these gleemen as
thou didst shame those who came to sing in the rue des
Chantres? said Héloïse, and Abélard, though afraid that
if he were to play the lute he would betray himself to the
gleemen as being no friar but one of themselves, could not
keep himself from talking to his whilom companions of
the road, thereby awakening suspicions of him and
prompting them to offer him a lute on which he accompanied himself so well that one of the gleemen said:
No friar art thou, but a brother, whereat Abélard laughed
and answered them: Before I was a friar I was a gleeman
like yourselves, but the grace of God was vouchsafed to
me and I laid down the lute; and the songs that I wrote
in my unregenerate days haunt my mind and give me
pain. That is why I am now a wandering friar, for were
I to become a priest my fate might be to end in a bishopric, and what then would be my sorrow were I to hear
my own songs of old days sung before me? A joke thou
art putting upon us truly, for no bishop or gleeman art
thou, cried a player on the gittern, for if thou wert a gleeman thou couldst play the gittern and the sackbut. I can
play both, Abélard answered, rejoicing inwardly in the
imbroglio he was weaving; on all the instruments you can
bring to me: the lute, the vielle, the gittern, the sackbut,
or the virginals, bring them all. Give him thy gittern,
Jacques, cried another gleeman, and we will see what he
will do with it. And Abélard striking a chord upon it,
they cried: that is a fair one. And Abélard striking

another one: that is a fairer one still, they said, and now
we believe that some part of thy story be true. A
lutanist thou art for certain, but of thy friarhood we
will say nothing. So said the vagrants, mingling with
their talk so much laughter and rough jests that a hermit
on his way from the river to his cell stopped to listen
to them. Many lutanists pass this way, he said, but
seldom a better one than this friar. Whereupon Abélard
and the gleemen laid their minds to the preparation of
a concert, but just as they finished playing some opening
chords and were about to sing, a sound of voices was heard
in the distance and afterwards the thumping of staves
in the roadway, a sound well known to the gleemen, who
said: Pilgrims are coming, and they will give us a fine
audience. Nor did the gleemen speak more than the
truth, for tired of their own singing the pilgrims were
glad to stop to hear music less mournful than their own;
and they enjoyed the minstrelsy, forgetful of death and
burial, till the sound of a bell coming towards them reminded them of the approach of a disease easily con-
tracted.

A leper is on his way hither, let us begone, they cried,
but Abélard said: A leper is in need of music as well as
you. And when the sick, sad man came into sight, Abélard hailed him cheerfully: Wouldst hear music, good
friend? he asked. And the leper replied: I would indeed,
for I was a gleeman before I was a leper; but my fingers
have gone from me and now I can do no more than to
rattle a bell to warn people of my approach. There were
gleemen here just now, but they fled from me like all
mankind; I heard lutes. But they have gone. If I had
a lute I would sing to thee, good friend, Abélard said,
I had hoped to hear a little music, for while listening I
would forget my misfortune. The leper began to weep.

I would sing to thee, Abélard said again, if I had a lute, and my singing and playing is as good and better than that of those who have run away; but I have no lute. But if you were a gleeman you have exchanged the motley for a friar's hood. I have done that, Abélard answered, for life is brief and eternity is long. Give me bread, said the leper. We have none, Abélard replied, but will leave some money on this stone. None will accept money from me, the leper replied. Then since I have no bread and money is of no use to thee, I'll sing thee a song. A true gleeman you are, though you wear a friar's hood, and I thank you for your music and will sing it on my sorrowful way. Since thou thinkest well of my music, good friend, do thou do the musician a service. What service can I do you, sir? the leper answered. Thou who wanderest all over the country must know the inns, Abélard said; tell me the best inn between this and Tours, which marks our journey's end. You will find, sir, no good inns between this and Tours, but a good monastery, with kindly monks, who will let you and your sisters in Jesus Christ sleep in the guest-chamber. There is too little straw in the leper chamber, but why do I complain, for I have to face evil and eviller days till God takes me. The bell tinkled out of hearing, and Abélard, like one in a dream, returned to the ship. The breeze, said the skipper, that has just sprung up will take us to Tours before evening, if it lasts.

Very soon they began to pass by yellow sandbanks and green islands, with osier beds; deserted islands they seemed all to be, save for one cow, which came down to the water's edge and gazed at the passing boat with moist eyes. Does she wish, Abélard asked the skipper, to come on board? No, the skipper answered, but they have forgotten to milk her. We might perform that kind office for her; and one of his sailors landing with a pail, the animal was relieved of her pain. But of a theft they are certainly guilty, Héloïse said. Children may lack milk to-night, Madelon added. We shall lack a breeze to take us into Tours, the skipper muttered, and he began to wonder if the dropping of the wind was sent by God for their punishment. The wind freshened a little but dropped again, and with the sunset it died languid on the river opposite a great monastery that tempted Abélard and Héloïse on shore, this time with Madelon, for, he said, we are within a few miles of Tours, and it would not be worth the skipper's while to cheat us; moreover, he would have to get out his oars to do so, for there will be no wind to-night to take him up the river. And no doubt yonder is the hospitable monastery the leper spoke to us of, Abélard said to Héloïse, as they made their way up the stately park. But neither their knocking nor their words, spoken through the grating, persuaded the porter to open for them. The monastery is closed for the night, he said; and they protested in vain. The monastery is closed for the night, the porter answered again and again, and slammed back the slide, leaving the friar and his nuns to find their way past the great firs, whose shelving branches seemed to be the roosts of innumerable peacocks, ghostly birds in the mild moonlight, whose long white tails set Madelon crying: Ghosts or angels! let us away; and her cries, awakening the peacocks, set them all screaming, till Abélard began to think that the angels beyond the stars could not fail to hear.

CHAP. XX.

HÉLOÏSE had wooed sleep continuously and from side to side, but the hot, breathless night kept her awake, and

at last, too weary to try to sleep again, she rose from the
deck and, leaning over the taffrail, looked down the river,
now wide as a great lake. A scent of peppermint and
sedges came across the water, and from time to time
another scent roused her, and she turned to ask Abélard
whence it came. But Abélard slept, and it was Madelon
who told her that the pungent odour was of the sea, blown
up from the great estuary by the fitful breeze. For on
these wide waters the breeze never wholly dies. She
could hear it stirring in the reeds that filled the bays and
inlets of the green islands, keeping the sleepy ducks
awake; and her thoughts being set any whither and no
whither, she remembered that she had seen wild ducks
at sundown swimming in and out of the reeds followed
by downy broods. A heron too had come down the sky
and settled himself in a quiet corner to take his rest on
one leg (his spear-like head hidden under his wing), for
it is thus that birds rest themselves. From birds and
their habits her thoughts moved on to flowers, for they
were nearing the month when the river wears yellow and
white lilies in all its quiet backwaters, and the dikes out
on the marsh are lined with long-bladed leaves, whose
austerity is atoned for by a furled blue flower of delicate
hue. How beautiful the earth is in May, she said, sur-
passing by far the heavens; and her eyes sought the twin
towers of the cathedral in the grey moonlight, for on the
morrow they would go straight to the Cathedral to ask
for tidings of Denise, Abélard's sister, and Alan, his
brother-in-law. Or maybe they would have to call at
all the inns, for they knew no more than that Denise and
Alan would be in Tours at the end of May. For it was
she who wrote to Abélard saying that as they had not
seen each other for some years, it would be well that
they should contrive to meet at Tours. a sort of half-way

house. All families, she said in her letter, should fore-
gather from time to time. And Abélard was overjoyed
writing: We will meet in Tours, thereby setting Héloïse
wondering why he liked to meet his family in Tours rather
than in Nantes. She had noticed that he talked of his
relations with feeling and interest in Paris and that it
was not till the time approached for him to meet them
that he sat apart brooding (if he were not asleep), his
gloom increasing and his customary gaiety failing him
altogether on the way from Blois to Tours. He likes
to talk of his country, she said to herself, and he takes
pleasure in remembrances of Brittany and its people,
but any thought of finding himself standing in its fields
distresses him. How is this, why is this, and will he
ever tell me? Does he know himself?

From time to time the lapping of the water against
the ship's side reached her ears, and she had forgotten
everything but running tide and evanescent distances,
when Madelon's jarring voice begged her to lie down
beside her and try to get to sleep. To-morrow will be
a big day for both of us, she said, lifting her head out of
her rug; Abélard will be by to see us through it, but
he'll be anxious to get back to his lecture hall in Paris,
and—— Sleep seemed to have fallen on both of them
suddenly, for when their eyes opened the river was laughing silver under the sunny sky. We must be at Tours,
cried Madelon, and the women began to talk of the search
they would be engaged in for the greater part of the day
perhaps. We shall have to ask, Madelon said, at the
Cathedral first of all, and then at all the inns. There'll
be weariness enough in our legs, I'll warrant, before we
find them. And it was just as she said, walking till midday from inn to inn, from church to church, meeting
blank faces and vague answers, the upshot being that

the innkeepers and clerics had not heard of any travellers from Nantes answering to Abélard's description of his sister and brother-in-law.

It was on one of these journeys up and down and round about the city of Tours that Héloïse and Madelon heard Abélard calling them back, and turning they saw that he had stopped to speak to a small woman and a tall man. Who may these be? said Madelon, and a moment after Abélard began to tell how he had only just escaped passing his sister in the street without seeing her. If it hadn't been for Alan, he said, who is as tall as a steeple, we might have walked once more all the way round Tours missing them. Alan and Denise waited for Abélard to tell them who Héloïse and Madelon were, but he could not tell Héloïse's story in her hearing, and being embarrassed as to how he should begin it, he spoke some vain words, breaking off suddenly, saying to Héloïse: Alan will walk in front with thee and Madelon; I have important matter to talk with Denise. The words: with Denise, drew Héloïse's eyes to Abélard's sister, in whom she discovered very little real likeness to Abélard. The very last person I should have thought to be Abélard's sister. And as she walked on in front with Alan and Madelon, the words: Abélard's brow shorn of its significance, came into her mind; Abélard over again with all that is noble and inspiring left out. While speaking on matters of no interest to her, she remembered that her lover's eyes were penetrating and far-reaching, and she contrasted them with Denise's eyes, which she was constrained to admit were not unlike his, but shallow, almost foolish eyes. Good and kind she doubtless is, and there's no reason why we should not like each other. Her voice, too, she said to herself, is the same temper as Pierre's, and she being of cheerful mind we shall live together pleasantly. But it is strange that two human beings should be so alike yet so unlike. Now they are talking about me, and I must talk to Alan.

Denise, said Abélard, I have a story to tell, so let us walk slowly, for I would have thee hear it all before we reach the inn whither, I suppose, we are going for dinner. Denise answered him that the inn they were staying at was at the other end of Tours, built, she said, where the bank is higher, and overlooks the river. But a eulogy of the Loire seeming to Abélard to be out of place at the moment he was about to confide important matters, he said, with a change of voice that caused Denise to quake: I have a story to tell; thereby getting her attention at last, he related how Héloïse had thrown herself at his feet at the end of a lecture. Denise forgot the view of the Loire from the windows of the inn, and he remembered that he had always liked his sister, despite their differences of temperament, Denise being interested in practical things, his thoughts being engaged exclusively by ideas. All the same, it was to Denise he wrote whenever he sent a letter to Brittany, and it was Abélard she singled out whenever she spoke of her brothers. Héloïse is very striking, Denise interposed, and it doesn't surprise me that she should have won thy love, though I never thought that any woman would be so fortunate. Abélard thanked his sister with a faint pressure of his hand for her words. She is now about two months gone, he said, and Denise repeated: only two months; and she began to ask for details till once more she saw she was annoying her brother, and hoping to mend matters she said: Thou'lt marry her in Nantes? Nothing is settled, Abélard replied sharply, again frightening his sister, who quaked like a sheep in front of a storm. For what reason, he asked, should I marry? But if you love each other——

Let us not waste time talking, Denise, of what cannot be.
I shall be ordained, I hope, within the next year or two.
But does she know, that thou art going to abandon her?
Abandon her, Denise? There is neither question of aban-
donment nor marriage. And in the hope of enlightening
her he related his own place in the world at present and
his ambitions, saying that these could not be gratified
outside of the Church. I am, it is true, thought by many
to be the greatest philosopher that has ever lived. And
so thou art, cried Denise; thy fame has reached Brittany,
and we often talk of thee as having surpassed all that
have gone before. When people speak of me as the
greatest philosopher in the world, he answered, it may be
that they are right, indeed I think they are, but my
admirers are not satisfied with that share of praise; they
would have it that I am the greatest philosopher that
ever lived, afflicting me—— And how dost thou answer
the praise that afflicts thee? Denise asked. I ask them
if they have read about the Greek philosophers, and
when the answer returned to me is: No, I tell them that
if they were to read the works of Plato and Aristotle they
would be able to appreciate how insignificant the present
is compared with the past. Humility is thy fault, Pierre,
the admiring sister answered. Every man is aware of
his worth, Abélard replied; the difference between me
and other men is that I have been at pains to understand
Plato and myself. But let us not waste time discussing
Plato and Aristotle. Héloïse knows then that thou'rt
about to enter the Church? Denise asked, and Abélard
would just as lief that this question had not been put to
him, but he answered it fairly, and Denise replied: I
never heard before of a girl who was willing to sacrifice
herself to her lover's ambition. Thou'rt wiser to-day then
than thou wert yesterday, Denise, and as I am going to

ask thee to take charge of Héloïse for the next year, it is important that thou shouldst know all. Héloïse wants me to enter the Church, but speak no word of this to her, for to do so could not fail to awake dissensions that I may have to come from Paris to Brittany to settle. But a marriage will reconcile thee to Fulbert, Denise interposed, and immediately afterwards she added: Canons of Notre-Dame are rich, whereas—— We are wasting time, Denise, as thou couldst not fail to understand if it were possible for me to tell the whole story. But I know the story, she said; thou hast told it to me. One may tell the truth as far as it can be told in a few minutes, Denise, Abélard answered, and it was with difficulty that he restrained his temper; but knowing himself to be dependent on his sister he kept it at bay, saying: I shall be ordained in a year, or maybe two years; some delay there may be, but—— Why should there be delay? Denise interrupted. To make that plain to thee, Denise, I should have to tell thee that there are two philosophies at present in Paris, Nominalism and Realism, and that Nominalism in its extreme form has been declared to be heretical. Even the mitigated Nominalism that I teach is suspected. I hope, Pierre, that thou wilt never teach anything contrary to the doctrines of our holy Church, for the Church is all-powerful. Whosoever comes to the grapple with Saint Peter gets a fall for his pains. Thou'lt remember that thou hast a sister living in Brittany, a country devoted to the Church, and if it became known that her brother was guilty of heresy—— Denise, Denise, thou'rt putting me past my patience; matters so subtly implicated as these cannot be explained in the short journey from one inn to another. I beseech thee to acquaint thyself with the facts; thou hast an excellent understanding, and all the rest will come to thee in time.

But the two philosophies on which the world depends cannot be discussed quite thoroughly, as I have said, by passengers on their way from one inn to another. I shall come to Brittany to see Héloïse and to see my child at the end of the year, when Héloïse has come into her figure. I don't think that a husband considers his wife's figure; he is too overjoyed that she has borne him a child. My dear Denise, perhaps I was wrong to use the words: as soon as Héloïse has come into her figure, but the words are not mine, they are Héloïse's own. She has forbidden me to come to Brittany till—— But there is no reason why I should repeat words that offend thee, my object being not to offend but to ask a favour. A very strange phrase for a young woman to speak, and of all, in her condition, Denise answered, her alarm having worn off. But, Pierre, thou wast always strange among us, different from thy brothers from the very beginning, giving up all thy lands to us so that thou mightst wander the world over and teach; so it is not strange that thou shouldst have met one like thyself, and in meeting Héloïse thou hast met thine own image and likeness, so it would seem to me.

Now I am beginning to hear again the Denise whom I left behind in Brittany years ago. Thou'lt do all that I ask thee? Thou'lt rely upon me and believe in me, sister? Abélard said, drawing Denise closer to him. And lifting fond eyes to his she answered: Pierre, I believe in thee; and give no heed to the poverty of my words, for they are not myself; but thy words are thyself. And surprised at this sudden comprehension, which endeared him to his sister even to asking her for some account of her life in Brittany since he had been away, Abélard said: All I have heard of thee, Denise, is the occasional birth of children. Yes, she answered; I have had too many. Thou hast written books, and I've had children. And that is the way of life in some form or another. Abélard was about to speak of abstinence and of those days in the month when the womb is not fruitful, but some random thought led him to speak of the tall, silent, lean man, whose mind was always upon his farm, upon its crops and beasts. But it would have been strange if his sister had thought of another man, she being what she was, and he fell to thinking that they were beyond each other's ken, or only faintly visible to each other. Had she not said: Thou wert always strange, giving up thy lands so that thou mightst be freer to wander the world over, teaching, and she had added that she hoped he would teach nothing that the Church did not approve, not understanding that the instinct of teaching is but the fruition of a man's belief in the truth of his ideas. Such was the origin of his teaching, but he had learnt long ago that he was an exception, and that the interest of many teachers is not in their own ideas, for they have none, but in gabbing to one school what they had heard in the last. All the same, it was strange that his sister should have allowed her husband to use her so wantonly, and on his speaking to her of the folly of many children, she related her misadventures—— So-and-so was not wanted and his sister was not sought for, Abélard listening with a superciliousness on his lips that she recognised and that caused her to break off suddenly, saying: But thou'rt at fault even as we; and Abélard answered: It was not my will but her will. Thou tellest me strange stories, Pierre, but thy life has always been different from other men's, and what befalls thee is exceptional always. And that is why I believe thee.

A moment later they overtook Héloïse and Madelon. Yes, my husband speaks Breton, Denise said to Héloïse,

but he speaks French too. Speak to Héloïse in French,
Alan. And the long, lean man replied with a few mono-
syllables. Abélard, cried Héloïse, Alan has twelve oxen
in his byre for the farm work, and the garden is full of
hives and I shall live the life of the country, watching it
from season to season like Virgil. All I know of the
country, Alan, she said, detaining him, is from books, and
the few sights of it that show in the window of the company-room in the rue des Chantres. The labourers on
the farm sleep on couches all around a kitchen, Abélard,
just like the kitchen we saw at Saint-Jean-de-Braie; and
there is a spiral staircase leading to Denise's rooms. The
dais on which the table is set—— But, Héloïse, I know
my own country, Abélard said; Le Pallet and its farm-
houses are commonplace to me. A cloud of disappointment rose up in Héloïse's face, but it quickly disappeared
and she continued to ply Alan with questions.

It was at the inn, in answer to a remark dropped by
Denise, that Abélard asked his sister for news of their
father and mother, who had by mutual consent broken
the marriage bond and retired into the religious life, one
to a monastery and the other to a nunnery within hail
almost of each other; and in reply to Héloïse as to why
Bérenger and Lucie had taken this step, Denise told her
that Bérenger, their father, had been a soldier in the
service of Huet IV., but feeling that his life with the
world was closed, and his wife feeling the same, both
had judged it wise to devote their old age to making their
souls ready for God's acceptance in the life to come. But
did Pierre never tell thee, Héloïse, that his father and
mother had entered the religious life? Denise asked. No;
this is the first time I have heard it, Héloïse answered,
and Denise raised her eyes and looked at her brother,
who replied somewhat sharply: Denise, thy face is doubt-

ful, as if I were guilty of withholding something from Héloïse. Of what matter can it be to her that our father and mother retired to monastery and convent? None, so long as thou dost not leave me for a monastery, Héloïse answered gaily. Whereupon Denise asked her brother when he would be ready to start for Brittany. To-morrow or the next day, which? Since I had the good fortune to meet thee in Tours it seems to me needless that I should follow you back to Brittany, Abélard replied, knowing as I do that Héloïse will be well cared for. But can it be that thou art not coming to Brittany with us and that we are about to part now, to-day or to-morrow? Héloïse cried. Was it this parting thou wert brooding in the ship coming from Blois? So this is thy secret. Héloïse, I will talk privately with thee, and if it seems wise to thee that I should not leave thee here but follow on to Brittany, so it shall be. Then do thy best, Denise said, to persuade him, for his father and mother will be grieved to hear that he came more than half-way, only to turn back. We will leave you to persuade him; we have business in the city, and in thy place, Pierre, I would take Héloïse into the fields, where she can snuff the meadowsweet and become winsome again. Talk is easier indoors than in the fields, Abélard answered her, and feeling that her words had not met with his approval, she said many others to gain it, till at last his impatience frightened her out of the room with her husband and Madelon.

When the door closed behind them, Abélard and Héloïse were standing by the window overlooking the Loire without words to praise or even eyes to see the great sunlit river and the low-lying undulating country in which herds of cattle grazed between belts and patches of forest. Nor had they a single thought for the low horizon melting into violet, nor for the sails of shipping going back and forth; all their minds were intent on themselves, on each other, on the future, on the past. Art thou going to leave me at Tours? Héloïse asked, and Abélard answered her stupidly, great man though he was, for the emotion of the moment exceeded his intelligence. Denise talks always, he said, without thought, and is therefore often tiresome to hear. It annoyed me to hear her speak of my father and mother who, having entered the religious life, would not understand that in opposing certain bishops I seek to raise man's soul from the common sensuality of prayer, as we saw at Saint-Jean-de-Braie. My father and mother would not understand me, and to meet them would be painful to me and it would be painful to them. We had better remain apart from those who cannot share our thoughts. But hast no thought for the country in which thou wast born? Héloïse asked, for the town on the steep hillside above the river, shaded at the bend with poplar-trees? Alan has been telling thee of Le Pallet, he answered, and before long he had dropped in spite of himself into a second discourse, asking Héloïse if he could love a people who were prone to hate everything that he loved and to love what he hated, and when she answered him: but the country, the forest, the river, the sails, and the skies? I could not see the whole of Brittany, every field and every laneway, every garden, every tree, every orchard, were I to give my whole life to the quest, he said, and waited for Héloïse to answer him; but although she heard him, her mind was not engaged with what he said, for she was thinking of her loss, and she did not awake from her reverie till he told her that if he were to follow her to Brittany he would be detained there for many days, perhaps many weeks, and during that long while his pupils and disciples would be looking round like hounds for the huntsman to lead them unto the scent they had lost. Even now his presence was required in Paris to put a stop to the stories that were no doubt being told about them: if thy presence be needed in Paris, she said, go thither at once, delay not a day nor an hour; go, for though thou art dear to me there is one thing dearer than thyself—thy glory.

END OF VOL. I.

HÉLOÏSE AND ABÉLARD

VOLUME TWO

HELOISE AND ABELARD

VOLUME TWO

HÉLOÏSE AND ABÉLARD

CHAP. XXI.

THE ship that brought the twain from Orléans to Tours was still lying alongside the wharf, and it was Denise's project that they should hire it to take herself and Alan back to Nantes, for Abélard had seen a horse in the inn stables that pleased him, and was saying that horses might be dearer at Orléans than at Tours, and that it was not likely that he would see one that pleased him more than a certain bay stallion. A moment after the ostler led the horse into the yard, and Alan whispered that he was a bargain. Abélard sprang into the saddle and rode around the yard, the bay stallion bucking a little, Abélard balancing his long body, his short legs tight about the horse like a girth——a broad, lean man, who sat the bay stallion well, his shoulders square, his hands low down on the horse's withers. The horse bounded across the yard, bucked and bounded again, till, feeling the task to unseat his rider to be hopeless, he suddenly stopped, and stood champing the bit, in a rage. Alan had his hand on one rein and the owner of the horse had his on the other. He bucks in no evil intent, said the horsedealer; it's only his play. He will not kick again, for he has learnt his master, Alan said, returning to Denise, who was anxious that Abélard should not buy so headstrong a brute. Dissuade Abélard! cried Alan; look at him and tell me if his body and mind are not as like as twins, as stubborn one as the other. Alan is quite right, Héloïse an-

7

swered quickly; were the world searched, nothing more
like his mind would be found than his body. But like
Denise, she was averse from savage animals, and Abélard,
to cut a story that was beginning to be a long one, short,
rode away waving his hand, saying to himself: Everything
is settled; protracted farewells may be borne only by
those whose hearts are cold. And knowing himself to be
already sick with grief at parting from his dear Héloïse,
and that his pain would grow worse day by day, he began
to think of the book that she wished him to write (the
title they had discovered together: *Sic et non*), and rode
in meditation of it for her sake, till he caught sight of a
tall man walking very quickly in front of him. To pass
him by he would have to push his horse into a trot, and
he did not do this, for he could not put it out of his mind
that he had known somebody who walked with that very
gait, somebody whom he had known long ago and intimately. But though he rummaged his memory he failed
always at the last moment to recall his former friend,
and in his perplexity, as he was about to pass the way-
farer by he drew rein, saying to himself: It cannot be, and
yet—— He trotted his horse on again and looked back.
It is the Comte de Rodebœuf, he said to himself, tramping
the road in tatters like any common gleeman, a lute upon
his back. The Comte de Rodebœuf himself, or the devil,
he said aloud. The Comte de Rodebœuf I am, and maybe
on my way to the devil, but whose are the eyes that can
see the Comte de Rodebœuf through these sorry rags?
The Comte de Rodebœuf's eyes are blinder than mine,
Abélard answered, for seemingly he does not know his
gleeman of old time, Lucien de Marolle. Lucien de Marolle, Rodebœuf repeated, but I remember him well; my
horse found him asleep under a tree, and afterwards we
sang and composed together for many months, eighteen

months or two years, maybe, I have forgotten which. Abé-lard replied: My name is now Pierre Abélard. Now a trouvère, the Comte interjected, ascended from gleeman to trouvère, while I descended from trouvère to gleeman. Sir—— began Abélard, but the Comte, stopping him, said: we are equals, and had distinctions to be indulged in it would be for me to honour thee with plurality; but I have not forgotten Lucien altogether, so we'll thou and thee each other as wayfarers should. But thy garb is——? Philosophic, Abélard answered. No surprise is that, the Comte answered, for thou wast never without a thought for dialectics, and could put down the lute with pleasure to embarrass a man with subtle reasoning till he found himself in a quandary, and then the spirit of the lute would rise up in thee again and philosophy would be for-gotten, Pierre du Pallet. So Pierre du Pallet is now Pierre Abélard, the greatest philosopher since Plato. Which may be true or false, Abélard cried, but it is certain that thou'rt the Comte de Rodebœuf, and it ill befits me to ride beside thee when thou goest on foot. My good Pierre, it is greatly pleasing to me to meet thee in the flutter of thy good fortune, and I pray that it may never leave thee; but unless thy way be mine, we must part, for by yonder hill I have business that may mend my state. But I would come with thee and hear thy story and tell thee mine, and help thee if I may, Abélard rejoined. To help me, the Comte replied, will be an easy task, for thou'rt the best lutanist in the land of France, and my broken fingers cannot touch the strings as they used to in the olden days. Wilt play for me? Assuredly I will, Abélard said; but are the trees and the clouds our audience? Not so, the Comte answered; but let us hasten our steps and I will tell thee as we march along. There is a coach that ascends that hill-side at sunset, and if we are there before it comes the passengers will distribute largess for our songs. Of a certainty, said Abélard, I will play and sing for thee, but—— Of what thinkest thou? Rodebœuf enquired. Of the horse I am riding, Abélard replied. Thou'lt leave him at the inn, Rodebœuf answered; a good hostel lies between us and the last hill, and the last half-league we will walk together and wait in the shade of a rock, for there are no trees, till the coach comes into sight. The adventure pleases me greatly, said Abélard, and I shall listen to the story of thy broken fingers, with sorrow, of course. My fingers, my fingers! the Comte cried, thou shalt hear their story when we have collected our pence on yonder hill-side. Ride on in front of me, and when thy horse has been stabled follow the road and find me on the hill-side.

Abélard struck his heels into his horse, forgetful of the animal's temper, and the fight was a stiff one, but Abélard was again the victor, and when he walked out of the inn stables after giving instructions for the care of his horse he caught sight of Rodebœuf coming round the bend in the road, hurrying over the ground as fast as his long legs could carry him, for the Comte de Rodebœuf was a tall, hale man, with a red beard and a pleasing voice that cried: Come, come, all the haste we can make is needed. But if we hurry so, Abélard cried, we shall have no breath for song. True, thou art shorter legged than I, and as I do not catch sight of the coach on which my hope is set, let us carry our thoughts back to Erato, the Muse of light song I believe her to be, but thou canst tell me. Abélard was about to reply, but seeing the Comte bent over the dust in search of tracks, he refrained. I see no tracks, and as I gather from the undisturbed dust that we are in time, we would do well to rehearse our little concert. We will sing our old songs if thou hast not for-

gotten them, said Abélard. Not one have I forgotten—
not one of mine nor one of thine. Ten minutes, no more,
is needed for rehearsal. To it, he cried, handing Abélard
his lute, and as they knew each other's methods from old
time an excellent entertainment was ready for the travellers when they appeared. Coin after coin was thrown
to the gleemen, and when the coach horses broke into a
trot the Comte de Rodebœuf said: If we could do as
well each day as we have done to-day, there would be no
need to complain of my evil fortune. And I am glad
that it is to thee, Pierre, that I owe this little store; to
no one would I liefer be indebted. The debt may be paid
with thy story, Mathieu, Abélard answered. Let me hear
how the great Comte de Rodebœuf lost all his money and
estates and became a travelling gleeman.

Thou'lt not believe that such a reversal of fortune
could befall me or any man, and of all me, whose life
till a few years ago was successful in all things, in the
lists, in song and love story. Dost believe in evil powers,
Abélard? In the spells of the witches, and the enchant-
ments of magicians, sorcerers, and the like? In devils, of
course, for there could not be a hell without devils. But
there are evil spirits that are not in hell, and other evils.
Who does not believe in the evil eye? And there are
gems that bring evil upon those who wear them. The
opal is of evil repute, and we shrink from a man who
wears one. Worst of all, there are animals that bring
evil, as is well known. Men who have been fortunate
all their lives become possessed of a certain dog or horse,
and from that moment are followed by misfortune and
disaster. Birds have always been believed to be the
harbingers of good or evil tidings; ravens are a sign of
death, magpies cannot be seen separately without danger
if we do not turn round three times. These birds are

speaking birds, the most dangerous to man, as I know to
my cost, and the dealer who sold me Laure knew it, for of
a certainty he was of the plot to do me evil; but I know
not whether his power was on the bird or the bird's power
on him.   Let this pass: I bought a grey bird, whose
wrinkled eyelid fell over an eye that seemed to know all
things.   Thou'rt thinking that it would be easy to wring
the neck of such a bird, Pierre, and I often thought of
ridding myself of Laure in that way (Laure was the
bird's name), but I could not bring myself to wring her
neck, whether from some inward fear or some outward
fear I do not know.   Nor would it have been easy for me
to wring Laure's neck, for as soon as I approached her
cage, Laure began to meditate the harm she might do
me, and I'm not thinking of her beak, though these birds
bite to the very bone.   Let this pass, for one reason or
another I never strangled that ill bird, but let her live to
bring about my ruin.

But before I tell the haps, I will tell thee something
of the bird's hatred of me, how it flashed out of her
round, black eyes whenever I went near her.   She was
dependent upon me for all she ate and drank.   Was it for
that she hated me? I often wondered.   We cannot enter
into a bird's thoughts, but for certain Laure loved evil
for evil's sake, for if I gave her a piece of cake, she would
look round for the dog, whistle for him, and Fido would
come jumping into the room.   Laure would show him
the cake, and poor Fido, who loved cake, would go sniffing,
unsuspicious, to the cage, the wicked bird enticing the
dog on till his nose was within reach.   She would hold
on to the dog's nose, and when she released him, Laure
would look down from her perch, her round eyes full
of malice and hate.   As Fido was always getting into
trouble with Laure I put the bird into another room.   But

I haven't told that the bird was bought in the hope that she would learn some phrases of tenderness from me; and when they were perfectly remembered, my project was to present Laure to the Lady Margherita, the wife of my neighbour, the Comte Raymond de Castel-Rousillon. Thou hast him in mind still, Abélard, and our visits to his castle, thou and I, and the great tourney that was held there when I challenged all comers to meet me in the lists, and overcame all comers, wearing the sleeve of Lady Margherita? If thou hast not forgotten Raymond altogether, thou hast in mind an almost crooked little fellow, who escaped the shape of a dwarf and hunchback, but by so little that his frail legs would not bear him to the tourney. Nor was he equal to writing the humblest song or sonnet, couplet or stanza; plaint or dirge were rarely tried by him, and it was hard not to smile when he read his poems. But this can be said for him, that he soon understood that the Muses had not called him, and he often said it was fortunate that I was a neighbour, for without me his wife's beauty would remain unsung. Dost remember her, the gracious Lady Margherita? Abélard nodded, saying that her image was fixed in his memory. Thy story rouses me, he said; continue, old friend, continue. The wicked bird, I am telling, would learn no tender phrase nor song of mine; and if I persisted in my teaching the wrinkled eyelid dropped over the round black eye, and I was not sure whether Laure slept or waked. I was often much concerned to know what to do with this bird; give her away I could not, having spoken of Laure to Lady Margherita, who was looking forward to hearing the bird talk to her of me and whistle snatches of my songs during the long intervals which we had to endure lest Raymond should suspect our attachment for one another. So on my next visit to the castle I took the bird with me and gave him into the charge of my lady, for it seemed to me that even this devil would yield to the beauty and the sympathy and the charm of Margherita. But it was not so. The bird's mind was made up against Margherita at once, and she formed a hatred against her that mayhap caused her to forget her hatred of me, at which we were much surprised. Our surprise increased when the bird took Raymond into her affection, a man in whom there was nothing that might win the love of man or woman. I would not say anything ungracious of my old friend, but to speak the whole truth, Abélard, Raymond never had a sincere friend but me. So it fell out that Laure was only happy with Raymond, and we noticed that she moped when he left the room, and that her hatred of us if we drew near her was greater than ever it was when he was present; and we noticed too, indeed the sight was most flagrant, that when Raymond came in she would call to him to open her cage, and out of it she would come, and climbing up his arm to his shoulder, her head against his ear, she would talk to him privily; and we were glad of this, suspecting nothing, thinking that Raymond had made a friend at last.

Laure's attachment to him was a great joy to Raymond, and we all wished to please him. He was flattered that this bird that cared for nobody else should attach herself to him, and we often wondered what she said to the Comte, for when in the mood Laure seemed to be able to say anything; she would speak things we had never heard her say before, whilst we sat quaking, Margherita and myself, lest the bird had learnt some of our talk that would leave the Comte doubtful of our love. If the morning were wet, Laure would say: It's a wet morning, a very wet morning, Laure doesn't want to go out in the wet. Pretty little Laure, pretty little Laure, doesn't believe in getting wet. If the day was sunny she never said it was raining, but: A nice sunny day, a nice day for a walk, for Laure to go for a walk in the garden, and so forth, and there were many more phrases which I cannot remember. But very soon we began to notice that she was talkative only when Raymond was in the room; when Margherita and myself were alone with her, she sat on her perch silent and solemn, listening to us, learning what we said to each other, getting by heart all the little phrases of endearment between lovers: I wonder how it is I love you so dearly, Margherita, for thou art more to me than anything, and all my happiness is being with thee. This she could say as plainly as you or I, causing us often to quake, till one day we saw her lay her head against Raymond's ear and heard her speak some phrases of our endearments into it. Raymond rose from his seat astonished, for he had never used the words: When naked thou'rt soft and sweet as a rose. He said nothing, but his look chilled our hearts, for we could not think else than that he suspected us, and we noticed that he spoke little to us but watched us as he had never done before. Raymond is meditating something, I said to myself, trying to find courage to ask me if it is true that I love his wife. Raymond was by nature a shy, sullen man, who kept turning a thing over in his mind, but never speaking his mind to us, trusting himself only to Laure, who now spent most of the day on his shoulder. We quaked when we first heard her speak the words into his ear: I wonder how it is I love thee dearly, Margherita, and all my happiness is being with thee. It is often said that wisdom comes out of the mouths of babes and sucklings, but this time it came from a parrot's beak. Hast thou deceived me, Mathieu, or is the bird a liar? Raymond asked me one day as we rode from the castle with our falconers. I have not deceived thee, Raymond, I answered; nor is the bird a liar. She was owned by another Margherita. I had not thought of that, Raymond replied, and the gloom passed out of his face, and I was heartened when he said: Forgive me for mistrusting thee.

But that evening as we sat together, Laure began to mutter: Mathieu, I love thee dearly. Wouldst thou have me believe, cried Raymond, that this parrot was owned by another Margherita who loved another Mathieu? and he looked at his wife steadily, and the silence throughout the room was unbearable. Wouldst thou have me believe, he repeated, that this bird was owned by another Margherita and another Mathieu? Raymond, said Margherita, the parrot is no liar; we love each other dearly. But you have not sinned? Raymond asked. Whereupon the bird answered: We all enjoy a little sin, pretty little Laure. Raymond, I said, this bird is possessed of an evil spirit whose aim is to bring about our ruin. Margherita has spoken the truth, we love each other dearly; could it be else that I could live side by side in company with so beautiful a woman as Margherita without loving her? My songs have made her beauty known to all the world, and these songs could not have been written if I had not loved her and if my love was not returned. It is true that thy songs seemed to be written out of thy heart, Raymond answered, but I hoped my friend was a faithful friend. And rising from his seat, he said: I know not whether to put my trust in the bird or in you. Laure will tell the truth to me perchance. And he called the bird out of her cage, and Laure walked up his arm and laid her head against his ear. But no word would she speak. Margherita, he said, it was thy grief always that thou didst marry a man who could not make known thy beauty to the world: and that was why Mathieu came

hither, said Raymond. Then picking up the thread of
argument from Margherita quickly, I turned to Raymond,
saying: No man loves songs and music like thee, and the
Muses repay us for our many nights of toil and labour
with a woman's love, and of thee they ask forbearance.
Wilt thou prove unfaithful to the arts thou hast loved by
separating us for ever? Other knights may praise the
Lady Margherita, Raymond muttered. But none will
praise me, Margherita answered, as he has praised me. I
love you both, though my love for you both is a different
love. I love Mathieu for his genius, and thee for thy
recognition of it. By the power of tenson, stanza, ballade
and rondeau, I have been made famous in France, and in
making me famous he has exalted thee among men; thou
art the husband of the most beautiful woman in France,
and it cannot be that thou wouldst destroy with thine own
hands the fame we have built up for thee. Thou shalt
not destroy thyself, Raymond, she said; and taking a hint
once more from the Lady Margherita, I said: Whilst
thou wast with thy wife last night, sleeping side by side, I
was striving with sonnet and pastourelle, thinking amid
many difficulties of expression and action of the joy my
rhymes would be to thee. Here are the labours of the
night, and I passed several dawn songs and reverdies into
Raymond's hands, together with some serenades; and
while he read them, I watched his face, noting that he
missed nothing and loved it all. So taking my lute up
gently I struck some chords to enhance the melody, and
so well did I do this that Raymond began to soften towards
us and would have taken us both in his arms, saying: For
the sake of the art of which we all three are different
promoters I will forgive thee. He would have spoken
these words of a certainty if the bird on his shoulder
had not said: Mathieu loves Margherita, for her breasts

are white as doves and her garden is sweet in his nostrils; which was true indeed, but which roused Raymond into such a fury of passion that he tore up my beautiful songs and threw the pieces upon the fire. And after watching them burning for a while he rushed across the room and returned with a sword, with which he would have killed me if I had not fled on to the balcony. Nor was I safe from him there; the bird's screams urged him after me, and escape was no longer possible except by springing from the balcony, which I did, thereby breaking my wrist and fingers. Such is my story, and for why I am no longer a lute-player, Pierre, look at my maimed hands.

My servants found me in the morning and carried me away to my castle, where I slowly recovered. Only a partial recovery it was, Abélard, for I have never been the same since in mind or body, not since that night when an evil bird accomplished my ruin.

So that is how the world lost its lute-player, said Abélard. My life in the beginning was all good fortune, Rodebœuf answered, but the spell was cast and it was never raised. Worst of all, after my fingers, I lost my heart, to a lady less worthy than Margherita, for whom I gave great tournaments and composed much. But my songs estranged us. Thy fingers, she said, are gone; thy lute-playing is over for ever and the songs written for me are less than the songs composed for the Lady Margherita. I believed that her heart would soften, and continued to give tournaments in her honour. I gave large sums of money to the Crusades in the hope of winning back my luck. Lady Beatrice died, and my lands were sold to pay the priests to sing Masses for the repose of her soul. And here am I in a gleeman's rags, a gleeman without a patron, a gleeman without fingers, striving to pick up my living, an outcast on the road, who, if he does not find a patron soon, will have to seek his fortune in Palestine. And what hope hast thou, Abélard asked, of finding a patron? One may be found, Rodebœuf answered, in the Castle of Franchard; a Court of Love is being held there, and a prize will be given for the best song. But I can write no more songs, neither the words of the songs nor the music that follows the words. My head is as empty as my heart; but if thou wilt write a song for me I can sing it. Pierre Abélard, we were comrades long ago; save me from the Saracen. If a song of mine will save thee, I will write one; and my heart will be in it, for a song I have not written this many a day, Abélard answered. Then let us go hence to write a song together, and that we can do well in the inn yonder. Write me a song, Abélard, that will save me from Palestine, for I have no stomach for crossing the sea to fight the Saracen. But to Palestine I must go, for I have no heart to sing on hill-sides, wheedling pennies from passengers on a coach, nor for loitering at street corners strumming till housewives put their heads out of the windows. The Comte Mathieu de Rodebœuf must find a patron or die in Palestine. Come, Abélard, we are rested; come and write a song for me at the inn.

CHAP. XXII.

THE day died pale and fragrant as a flower and the night was half over when the moon rose through the orchard trees. A minstrel, eager to be heard, struck a chord and began a song, but screams and coarse laughter compelled him to lay aside his lute in despair: Music will have to wait, he said, till the low fellows and their wenches yonder have drunken themselves sleepy; till then,

let us talk. Abélard called for wine, and story was at
height among the minstrels when a black-bearded man with
Southern brilliancy and vivacity in his eyes and voice (a
Basque he was guessed to be by many) came whirling
towards them, dragging after him two unwilling wolves in
leash. On hearing that my old friend, the Comte de
Rodebœuf—— he began. Thy old friend, the Comte de
Rodebœuf, is here to welcome Jean Guiscard. Thou wast
never as other men, Jean, for a kind heart seems to have
brought thee prosperity. What wine wilt thou drink? I
will drink wine from thy flagon and sing some of my
new songs to the company, Jean Guiscard answered, but
catching sight of smiles upon all faces, he looked enquiringly at Rodebœuf. At that moment a great outburst
from the gleemen and gleemaidens in the field behind the
inn rendered a reply from Rodebœuf unnecessary, and
Jean Guiscard said: Men must amuse themselves according to their wont; and wishing that all should hear him,
he began to narrate his errand again, saying that when
tidings of the Comte de Rodebœuf came to the Castle
of Franchard, he begged permission of the most noble
Vicomtesse de Chatelleraud, the President of the Court
of Love in the absence of Eleanor of Aquitaine, now in
Palestine, that he might go to the inn and welcome his
friend, and answering him out of her well-known care for
music, she said: Yes, go to thy old friend, the Comte
Mathieu de Rodebœuf, the great lutanist of France, and
bring him here to-morrow, for I would see him. And
then we spoke of the lady in whose honour thou gavest
many tournaments, for whom thou didst tilt in many
victorious courses, and whose beauty thy songs made
known to all the world. Jean Guiscard had to press
Rodebœuf for an answer, saying, to get one: is't true that
the love of the Lady Margherita cost thee thy lands and

castle? Had she cost me no more than my lands and
castle, Rodebœuf replied, things would be better with
me than they are. She cost me my fingers, and for lack
of them thou seest the great Comte de Rodebœuf fallen
so low that he can fall no lower. To the story of thy
fingers, said Guiscard, we would hear the whole of it, for
though we cannot restore thy fingers to thee, the hope of
the Vicomtesse de Chatelleraud and of all the presidents
of the Courts of Love is to put thee back into the ease
and leisure thy songs have earned for thee. To thy
story, great singer.

And when Jean Guiscard had heard the story of the
Comte's misfortunes, he said: The Lady Margherita and
the Comte Raymond de Castel-Rousillon, both of whom
owe their renown to the Comte Mathieu de Rodebœuf,
shall be called upon to relieve him of his poverty. We
have a duty to perform towards thee; thy rehabilitation
is no less than the strict duty of our Court, now in session.
My cause appeals—— Rodebœuf began. Thy cause appeals, Jean Guiscard interrupted, to the whole of French
minstrelsy. Maybe, said Rodebœuf, it is as thou sayest,
that my songs have earned me the right to the help
of French minstrelsy. But it was not for the love of
the Lady Margherita that I wasted my substance in
festival and tourney, but for the love of the Lady Beatrice.
Then the Lady Beatrice, Jean Guiscard cried, shall be
called upon. The Lady Beatrice will be called in vain,
Rodebœuf replied, for she is amongst the gone now two
years come Michaelmas. For his care of thee, her husband will hold a place next to thee in the story of French
minstrelsy, said Jean Guiscard, and he should—— The
songs I wrote in praise of the Lady Beatrice, alas, Rodebœuf replied, did not win the same glory as those I wrote
for the Lady Margherita. Then it is the duty of the

Lady Margherita—— cried Jean Guiscard. But, good friend, Rodebœuf responded dolefully, I sang the praises of the Lady Beatrice, and in these songs—— Ah, well do I know how the rhyme runs away with the singer, said Jean. Thy case is no simple one, but the Court shall consider it, and whatever the judgment may be thy estate will be bettered. It cannot be worsened, Rodebœuf exclaimed. But thinkest that the way to escape from the horns of the dilemma would be to grant me a prize for a song? Enlarging the original sum, Abélard interjected; making it worthy of the acceptance of the great Comte de Rodebœuf, whose gleeman I once had the honour to be in days gone by.

Jean Guiscard nodded a careless approval, and without troubling Abélard with questions he allowed his mind to return to the Castle of Franchard and its many duties, telling that a judgment would be given to-morrow that would make clear the new laws of love or the old laws fallen into disuse, for one of the first cases to be heard was a minstrel's, who, when his hopes were at their highest, began to notice that his lady's face had changed from pleasure to dismay. And on enquiring the cause of the change, she answered: It is a pleasure to listen to thee, minstrel, but I love another. Whereupon his heart sank, and she said: But if ever I should cease to be in love I pray thee to present thy petition again. So overjoyed the minstrel was by these gracious words that he rode away, certain that though his present might be dark his future would be bright. But three weeks were barely gone when the news came to him that the lady had married her lover, said Guiscard; and it having been laid down by Eleanor of Aquitaine that love cannot exist in marriage, he has brought a suit against her. But how, said Abélard, will this ingenious case be decided? Without turning his head, Jean Guiscard answered that there was little doubt that the Vicomtesse de Chatelleraud would uphold the ruling of Eleanor of Aquitaine—— And call upon the lady to recompense the minstrel, Abélard interjected. As Jean Guiscard did not answer the Comte de Rodebœuf was about to name the two men to each other, but Abélard laid his hand upon Rodebœuf's arm and whispered in his ear: Remember that I am Abélard only for thee; for the company I am the gleeman Lucien de Marolle. Out of deference to Rodebœuf's friendship for his gleeman Jean Guiscard softened a little to Abélard. Thou wouldst know, he said, turning to him, the fate of the lady should she fail to redeem her promise to the minstrel? She will forfeit our approbation and pay the penalty of disobedience to our president, to be held in little esteem by all who number themselves of our company.

He put out his hand for the flagon; Rodebœuf passed it to him, and very soon it began to seem to all that the great trouvère had come to them full of wine and might be unable to tell them if he had regained the love of his lady, whose beauty he had celebrated in the loveliest songs of French minstrelsy. It was known that he had left her castle and sung the praises of another, whom he had left abruptly and devoted himself to great deeds to win Louve out of her obstinacy, for she had refused to see him. Before his arrival that evening the strangest tales were told about him; his madness or death were expected by the minstrels, and the violent drinking, to which they were witnesses, was whispered to be part of his love; no doubt it was, and in grave disquiet they watched Jean Guiscard emptying flagon after flagon, each minstrel debating how Jean might be coaxed into the confession of his folly or of his lady's heartlessness. Another flagon and he will not be able to tell us, all were thinking, when Jean Guiscard broke the silence.

It may be that you would hear the story of Louve's cruelty to me, but it's known to all the world. We would hear the story, cried many voices, and flattered by the interest in him which he read on every face, Jean Guiscard took heart. Since it would please you to hear that the stories told about me and the Lady Louve are untrue, I will tell reasons for my leaving her for a while which you, minstrels of love, will apprehend and appreciate. The company bowed in acknowledgment of the compliment, and Jean Guiscard continued: For our love to be of value we must know it, and we can only know it by contrast and comparison; and it was to make plain to myself that all is false, void and counterfeit except Louve, that I went to Marseilles and sang the praises of another lady. On hearing of my songs and judging them to be equal to those that I wrote in praise of her beauty, Louve began to hate me soon. I was thrown out of her heart, before I returned, and when I returned confident that there was no love for me but my love of Louve, I was met at the gate by lackeys, who bade me begone. Others would have been glad to receive me at their courts for the sake of the renown my songs would bring them, but my love of Louve was too deep in my heart and I retired to the forest in the hope that my miserable condition in a cave would move her to forgiveness. But Louve's heart was hard. It was in that forest that I found three wolf cubs searching for the she-wolf, killed by a huntsman maybe, or else a forgetful dam. Jean called to his wolves by name and flung them large pieces of the boar's head, thereby encouraging them to leap around him with wide-open jaws, alarming the company, whose thoughts were that the beautiful teeth could fix themselves easily in a man's throat and tear out the windpipe. Be not afraid, be not afraid, cried Jean Guiscard, see how they love me; and he told how when hunting in the forest he was led by a deer who, though unable to outstrip his wolves, kept ahead of them, leading him farther and farther into the darkling forest till at last he came upon a ruin. Into it I went, my wolves following unwilling, so frightened were they by the silence. In one of the halls we found a company of old men sitting round a table. I called to them, but they did not give me an answer, my wolves howling all the while with fear, their tails between their legs. I could not quiet them, and it was then that it became plain that we were no longer in mortal company; we were with King Arthur and his Court. On the table was a sword and a horn, and I know not how it was, but it seemed that though no words were spoken I was bidden to take the sword and blow the horn, and at the sound of it the company vanished and the castle itself. More than that I do not know; memory of all else has been taken from me. I blew a call for my wolves, who had fled from me, and rising to my feet continued blowing the call till I reached my hermitage, and therein were my wolves, who, mistaking me for a stranger, leapt upon me, but were subdued by the sound of my voice. After I had fed them we sat together, myself in meditation with a great joy in my heart, for I knew I should be rewarded for my courage in blowing the fanfare on the horn, rewarded by King Arthur, whose lot it was to sit in that ruined hall as a punishment for his sins; for even King Arthur needed absolution, as we all do, my friends, myself more than any around me need it. Like King Arthur I am waiting for forgiveness to come from my lady, and if it comes not these wolves will give me the ease that the fanfare on the horn gave to King Arthur, for I shall disguise myself in a sheepskin, and the blood of the sheep that I shall spill over the wool will guide these wolves to me and through brake and over fell they will hunt me to the door of my lady. But of what help will that be to thee or to her? Abélard asked. Wouldst, mayhap, plant the dagger of remorse in her heart? Not so, Jean Guiscard answered. If my wolves do not tear me to death before I am rescued by the lackeys, my lady will be forced to forgive and to requite me for my love of her.

Jean Guiscard called for more wine, and having emptied the tankard that was handed to him, he sat silent, and his grief was so great that none dared to break the silence of it. At last he began to speak: My lady has let it be known that she will not forgive me until a hundred lovers and their mistresses come and implore it at her feet; it is said that a hundred men and women will come but—— Thy songs, brother, will summon the necessary array of lovers from their castles, and the Courts of Love will compel her to clemency. Have good heart, brother. Without making any answer to them Jean Guiscard fell to drinking, and the company laid their heads together, certain and sure that France would not allow a great singer to be torn by wolves. The needed lovers and their mistresses would come and surround her castle. She could not refuse. Jean Guiscard brooded in goblets of wine, and the evening might have been plunged in the sadness of drunkenness if the gleemen and gleemaidens from the neighbouring field had not come down to the trouvères to ask if they might rope in a certain space for a game of blind-man's buff; and, permission being given to them, they passed a rope round the apple-trees, creating thereby a space of some twenty-five to thirty yards for the girls to run in and evade

hoodman-blind as best they could, till wantonness on one
side and trickery on the other brought a maiden into his
hands. There were courses, timorous, courageous, witty
and even chaste, the captor relinquishing his right of
search, and there were other courses in which the captor
abused his right of search, prolonging it for his own sake
rather than as a means of coming to an issue, the issue
being the name of the captured. And the game reached
its height when Jean Guiscard's eyes fell upon a girl
whose shapes tempted him into the lists. Abélard and
Rodebœuf sought to dissuade him, afraid that he would
stumble and fall and hurt himself, but he gave a good
chase, not falling too often, before he seized a leg which,
he shouted, could belong to none but Mathilde. It did, and
the pair were conducted to an arbour, serenades and reverdies being sung in their honour during their mutual enjoyment. Thou hast seen enough of this sport, I doubt not,
Rodebœuf, said Abélard; my heart is away in Brittany and
if it weren't I might be like another. So if thou'rt not
minded to try thy luck in a course, let us to thy prize
song, for if it is to be written we must write it now.
I had forgotten my prize song, he answered; let us to
it at once, else I hasten to Palestine. The riot continued
in the garden, but so intent was Abélard on writing a
poem that would save Rodebœuf from the Crusades that
he was able to close his ears to the bleating of the goats;
and he was awake at dawn struggling with rhymes, Rodebœuf unable to give or withhold his approval. Shall we
try to finish this stanza now, or finish it after sleeping?
Abélard asked, and while meditating some new versions
of the recalcitrant stanza, both poets fell asleep for an
hour, Abélard being the first to open his eyes, and seeing
his friend still wrapped in slumber he went over to him.
Awaken, Rodebœuf, to the consideration of the poem that

may save thee from Palestine. Rodebœuf roused himself, and while Abélard put the finishing hand to the incomplete stanza, he bade his friend be of stout heart. This last stanza will decide the judges in thy favour, he said, though till they reach it they have another poet in mind. It is as good, mayhap, and better than any of those I wrote in the old days, he said, whilst seeking the stirrup with his foot. I shall find a quiet room at Blois to put my rhymes and tunes in order. So let thy prayers be that my verses shall not prove unworthy of her, he cried, looking back over the heads of trouvères and gleemen going to the Castle of Franchard, or returning from it singing songs, from which to escape (for the sake of his own) he urged his nag into a canter till he came to an empty road, which seemed to him favourable to the poet or musician, whichever happened to be uppermost in him at the moment. Thou'lt be glad to see thy stable, he said, addressing his horse, and to reach it the sooner I will allow thee to ascend this hill at a walk; my stanza may be finished before we reach the top, which, however, did not come to pass, for he was not half-way up the long acclivity when horns began to sound in the woods, drawing his thoughts into imaginary hunts of bear and deer. If we are to reach Blois to-night our meditations must end at the top of the hill, he said to his horse, and to himself: To get my rhymes and tunes I must put the country behind me, and he rode all day immersed in rhymes and tunes till the great hill-side came into view, the roofs showing on a fair lemon sky. At last! he cried. Courage! thou'rt near thy stable. But there was no need to urge his horse, for, scenting the still distant town, the tired animal broke into a trot, which did not cease till they came to a hostel. Abélard pressed on up the hill-side, his horse trying to dissuade him from further search by stopping

at every sign. The Muses haunt the hill's summit, he
cried, and, obedient to his voice, the patient animal began
to climb, stopping, however, before he was asked to stop
in front of an inn that seemed to promise a fulfilment
of Abélard's hopes of board, lodging and privacy. But
whilst he was trying to come to terms with the taverner,
Héloïse's voice called out of his heart, saying: It was at
an inn by the water-side that we breakfasted together.
And at once he began to seek reasons for not coming to
terms with the taverner, whom he left growling at clerks
who did not know their own minds. The inn was here,
he said, overlooking the river behind these limes; and to
the tavener, whom the sound of hooves had drawn to his
front door: It was here that a beautiful young woman and
myself sat eating delicious shad? It was indeed in my
inn, that you, sir, and your lady partook of as fine a fish
as ever came out of the Loire, and grilled it was in a
buttered paper before a fire of dry wood. Thy words,
taverner, bring the flavour of thy shad to my mouth; but
it behooves me now to think first of quiet, for I have come
hither for the writing of songs rather than for the singing of them: thine inn is a tryst for gleemen. Gleemen
and even trouvères assemble in my courtyard, replied the
taverner, but all these are now at the Castle of Franchard, and shad is past its season. I have come, Abélard
said, to write songs for her who is on her way to Brittany,
where she will remain till her baby's birth, and I will
abide with thee, taverner, if thou hast a lute. A lute I
have indeed, the taverner replied, lifting the lid of an
oaken chest; a better you will not find in Blois. And
whilst Abélard ran his fingers over the strings he told
the instrument's story. Thy lute is to my liking, Abélard
answered, and pleased with his lodging he descended the
stairs, too tired to eat with pleasure; a draught of wine

was almost enough before seeking his bed, where, between
the fitful, shallow sleep of a man who has spent a long
day on horseback, he pursued his rhymes, longing for the
morning.

But on the morrow his rhymes were not with him, and
in search of tunes he ran his fingers over the strings.
Neither tune nor rhyme is with me to-day, he said.
Héloïse is too near for me to write about her, or my trick
has deserted me; and in growing dissatisfaction and weariness of spirit he began to consider the six months that
must pass before he would see her again, his promise to
her being not to return to Brittany till she had renewed
her figure, a command inspired by her vanity or by her
love of him.   Which? he asked himself incontinently.
Some time this summer or in the autumn I must go to
Paris, and arrange our marriage, though she thinks marriage will end my career, but a man's talent and career
are not lost if he marry, nor retained, as she believes, if
he abstain and live in celibacy.   But the state of mistress
and lover ends with child-bearing, and rising from the
table he walked to the window to watch the Loire flowing
by till a memory came into his mind of a quarrel, come
about through her wish to visit him in his room one night,
despite the danger of the Canon hearing their voices from
the stairs.   He has been at wander for several nights,
unable to sleep, he had said.   A reason there is for his
sleeping soundly to-night, she replied; I pressed the wine
upon him and he drank deeply.   It may be so, he answered, but it is better to abstain from each other for
one night more; and then if the Canon fail to sleep
soundly we will enquire for an opiate at the herbalist.
But anger broke into her face.   I pray thee to believe me
and to bear thy love in patience.   But she turned away
abruptly, leaving me to go to my room alone, asking my-

self what I had done to deserve this rebuff, and to fall asleep whilst seeking a reason for her conduct. The flowing river carried his thoughts out of the past into the future, and a long time seemed to have gone by before he remembered that it might have been her weight on the bedside that had awakened him, or some dream, perchance, of her, for she was not long sitting by him when his eyes were opened as by a command, and seeing Héloïse in tears he began to wonder at the beauty of her face, now more beautiful than he had ever seen it before. I have been weeping, she said. For how long? he asked. Since I saw thee last. And how long is that? Three hours, she answered; and no longer able to bear my grief, I could not do else than disobey thy dear command, given, I know, for my safety. He stretched his arms to her, and placing the lamp on the table without blowing out the flame, she dropped her garment and glided down by his side, her face glowing with anticipation of the pleasure she could not withhold herself from any longer, nor long endure, but must escape out of into the nothingness of a swoon so deep that he could not awaken her. So heavy did she lie, almost without sign of life, beyond words or even kisses, that only a sigh could he get in answer; and if he tried to lift her, her eyes opened for a moment only and she dropped into swoon again. A swoon that may be death, he said; and every moment our danger is greater, for should the Canon's sleep be broken we are undone.

But though he spoke in her ear he could not rouse her, and at last, knowing barely what to do, he carried her out of his room, through the company-room, to hers, stumbling once in his haste, so loudly did the stair-head creak under their double weight. After laying her in her bed he would have escaped back to his room, but she, afraid of nothing, detained him; and, wrapt in admiration of her pale grey eyes, luminous in bluish white, set so far apart that the word noble rose unsought as the epithet most worthy of her, he sat listening as none had listened before, for none had even heard before a woman speak of love as she did, and not only of her love of him but of the poets who had loved before them. To listen to her was a spiritual intoxication, and he forgot the danger of the Canon, who might at any moment come up the staircase. But he did not come, and they continued to tell each other till daybreak of the verses they admired, she quoting three or four lines, sometimes ten or twelve, and when her memory failed her he was often able to prompt her. Now it was Ovid they were reciting, and then Virgil; afterwards a poet whom she loved better than he did, Tibullus, for being at heart a pagan she liked to read of the worship of the old Gods in ancient Rome. But he, being a Christian, was sometimes perturbed by the paganism into which his life was falling, all things slipping away from him, even his Christianity, while he was with her; and now that he was away from her, she in Brittany and he by the side of the Loire, the sense of his slavery frightened him, and he asked himself if the words: frightened him, were the ones to choose when speaking of her. No; frightened he was not; but this he knew of a certainty, that his life, hitherto a triumph, would change—for better or for worse he knew not which, but it would change. He had come to a parting of the ways. She would have him become a prelate, an archbishop, but knowing or rather feeling that he must have her as his wife, he would as lief return to Fulbert and make an end of the separation he was enduring: if she remained his mistress and not his wife these separations would continue, becoming longer, and their meetings

briefer, till life lost its savour—philosophy leading him
no longer, songs and tunes and poems and their music
appealing to him no more. And it was in such uncertain
mood that he stood watching the river flowing by; the
green country stretching all the way to the ocean, the
thought pressing him sorely that nothing on the earth or
in the heavens above the earth mattered if Héloïse were
lost to him, all things having turned to one in his mind.
The miracle is within me, and not without, as all things
are, in God; and at forty, at the height of my renown, I
find myself helpless, without protection, my learning un-
availing, a girl of seventeen having captured my life,
leaving nothing but herself between me and nothingness.

He wandered from the town to watch the angles by the
river, and though there were no hawks in the air, nor a
heron, he saw the three birds still battling, for all he had
seen and heard with Héloïse was for ever fixed in his
memory. When she was with him all the world was wonderful, and now that she was absent the world interested
him no more. Wherefore if any man be in love, he said,
applying the apostle's words to his condition, he is a new
creature; old things have passed away; behold, all things
are become new. Such is my condition, he muttered, not
knowing whether he was glad or sorry. And then the
words of the evangelist coming to his aid, he said: But
the water that I shall give him shall be in him a well of
water springing up into everlasting life.

And as the words of John were dying out of his mind
he came upon Jean Guiscard walking in front of the inn
amid his disciples, talking loudly, his head thrown back,
staying his steps, however, for a moment to tell Abélard
that he did not remember a prize having been granted to
Rodebœuf. No; he did not remember having heard
Rodebœuf's poem. He appealed to his disciples, but

none remembered that Rodebœuf had sung before the Court. No; he did not remember. The heaviest sum of money was granted to a poet who had never written so well before, of that he was sure. The master sought for some verses of it in his memory and, finding none, turned again for help to his disciples; and Abélard was perplexed, for the poem that they tried to recall seemed not unlike his own poem. But he held his peace, and accepted Jean Guiscard's almost command to join his company at supper in the inn yard.

As none suspected that Lucien de Marolle, the gleeman, was Abélard, the philosopher, he might sing and play in competition with all and sundry, thereby escaping from his too insistent self for a while, and laying aside the lute he was screwing up into tune, he gave his ear to Jean Guiscard, who was waiting for the complete attention of the company. After a last glance round to make sure that all eyes were upon him he began: We must not forget to-morrow in the pleasure of to-night, for many things will be debated at Franchard of great import, and questions so subtle will be put that the philosophers of old time would be obliged to collect their wits before answering. It will be asked to-morrow at Franchard if Aristotle would take the view that the husband's right to beget children could not be denied. The question will bring Plato into the debate, whose views, though not doubtful, cannot be stated briefly.

Jean Guiscard put out his hand for the flagon, and the wine that he drank seemed to awaken in him concern for the prospects of to-morrow's disputation, which was afraid would soon overflow its banks and entangle them sooner or later in contradictions, some vociferating views the very opposite to those they had set out in the beginning to uphold; for we are not all Platos and Aristotles, he cried, reaching out his hand again for the flagon. Aristotle's view, so you have said, Guiscard, would be that the husband's right to beget children could not be denied, but you have not said that Plato would side with or against him. Abélard waited for an answer to this question, which he already regretted having put, for disputation with Guiscard would profit him nothing. Plato, Jean Guiscard answered—in a tone more amiable than that which he had yet adopted towards Abélard—would begin by reminding the assembly that the Court was called into being for the purpose of considering the soul rather than in hope of devising a wiser ordering for the material world than that which prevails at present. Is it true, Abélard asked, that Plato would overlook the bed, so essential in matrimony, and omit to speak of the model or archetypal bed laid up in heaven, and, rating the soul as he did above all things would fail to see that children could not be begotten without concourse of lovers? If I have to answer all Lucien de Marolle's questions, cried Jean Guiscard, I shall not be able to tell the company of the many curious points the Court will have to decide to-morrow. I will ask no more questions, said Abélard, for we would hear the cases to be decided, and when we have heard them there will be time to expatiate in the views held by Plato and Aristotle.

In the questions we shall be called upon to decide, I shall range myself with Aristotle, Jean Guiscard said, holding that in a necessarily imperfect world a middle course is wiser than a counsel of perfection. Abélard would have liked to intervene again on behalf of Plato, but he could think only of Héloïse, and for the first time elected to remain outside a discussion; and he was glad he had done so when a hiccoughing gleeman interposed, saying that there were many who would wish to hear how a lady may protect her mouth from her husband, sudden and coarse incursions into the wife's chamber being common in married life. A kiss snatched from a sleeping lady is not a kiss, Jean Guiscard answered; for a kiss to be a kiss involves a mutual clinging of lips, and a lady, if she wishes to save her mouth, can do so with her hand and with her arm. She can do this much—— Well then, continued the caviller, another difficulty arises: If, while abandoning her body to her husband, her senses should awake, shall she be considered to be an unfaithful mistress? Our senses are beyond our control, sir, Jean Guiscard replied, and the Court will recommend that a lady who would escape a sousing husband would do well to thrust a book of prayers under her pillow before lying down, recourse being made to it immediately the door opens, for in certain moods a husband does not care to hear prayers; holy names baffle his ardour, and the lady will be left to sleep unsoiled, repeating, perchance, the songs in which her beauty was woven into verse. This is a question, Guiscard continued, that will be put to-morrow: and the view will be held, I hope and believe, that a lover's prerogative should be to rise above his instincts, ceding the grosser parts of the woman to the husband and finding his sufficient delight in her kiss, the gainer thereby, for desire dies in attainment, as she to whom my life is dedicated has often said, checking me when wanton passion was about to overcome wisdom, and saying well: The mouth is the joint author of our wit, for it is through the mouth that the mind speaks; without our tongues we should be as animals, knowing naught of each other's souls. It is when lips meet that the soul rises up in the eyes, and it is at the parting of lips that a mistress, guessing her lover's heart, says: What concern is it of our love that my husband possesses me from the knee to the navel, since my eyes, my hair, my bosom, my hands, and of all, my mouth, are for thee and for thee alone? The rest of love is naught but residue and lees.

Again a memory of Héloïse restrained Abélard from answering the obscene drunkard. Hast no answer, Marolle, for our friend Jean Guiscard? asked a gleeman. Abélard was about to answer, but some gleemaidens, entering suddenly, diverted the attention of the company from him, and not wishing to find himself again among scenes of a great unseemliness, he retired to his bed, to fall asleep in the thought that next day he would leave Blois for Franchard to seek Rodebœuf, who, he learnt on his arrival at the inn, had not yet left the neighbourhood. He wanders in the forest, said the innkeeper; and we hope he will return to pay his bill. He will pay it, Abélard answered, and giving his horse to the innkeeper he turned into the woods to ramble, nowise displeased at not having come upon Rodebœuf immediately. We shall meet soon enough, he muttered; and he rambled on, thinking of Héloïse, for now nothing else seemed worth thinking about. Realism and Nominalism, songs and lute-playing, were forgotten in remembrances of the light as it fell upon her clear brown face, of her laughter with a touch of sorrow in it always, of her fragrant fingers, of the lighting up of her face as a thought came into her mind—such thoughts as never came into a woman's mind before. In the woods of Franchard she was so near to him that he often looked up, almost expecting to see her: nearer, he continued, than when we were together in the false world that we call reality; to reveal her to me a few leagues were needed, and he vowed that when they met his love would be more worthy of her than it was in the past. And his thoughts breaking away suddenly, he asked himself if death would reveal the significance of our life to us. For the past being a mirror, he continued, death may be a greater mirror. The sound of water gurgling through the reeds accompanied his thoughts till he heard his name spoken, and looking up from the water he was watching he saw Rodebœuf himself. Good friend, said Abélard, I have come from Blois, where I spent a week writing poems, the best—— But I may not praise my poems, since the poem I wrote for thee failed to gain the prize. Thy poem, Rodebœuf answered, gained the prize; but I lost it. Thou speakest in riddles, said Abélard. One that is easily unriddled, replied Rodebœuf. One of the poets heard me learning thy poem, and becoming possessed of the music and the words he could not help himself from singing it, I not being present in the hall to protest, and it was whilst walking in the garden with a lutanist appointed to accompany me, studying how each phrase might be enhanced in the singing, that the story of my ill luck was broken upon me by the crowd coming from the hall bearing the false poet in a litter, crowned with the laurels that rightly belonged to me. It even behoved me to see him crowned with laurels and to hear him sing my poem to the crowd, for verily I believe he looked upon it as his own, so great is the power of self-love. Some of it was mine; but that many of the lines were thine robbed me of all power to claim it at the moment, and the ruling of the Vicomtesse de Chatelleraud was that my claim should have been made on the day of the competition. My disgrace is such that I must hie to Palestine without further delay; some great deed may blot out the memory of a disgraceful incident, and if that deed be not accomplished, why then death—— A sad story, good friend, and one common enough in this world, the false always being accepted rather than the true, and small satisfaction it is to us that the truth shall prevail in the end, Abélard said. looking up from the long, flowering grasses in which he was lying. A sad and humble countenance Rodebœuf wore, and Abélard was sorry for him. A dejected figure, he stood in the sunny landscape, already on his way to Palestine in his imagination, where the sky could hardly be bluer than the sky above the stream at whose edge he stood. A great eel wriggled its way from beneath the stone on which Rodebœuf was standing in the stream, and it and the silence and the shadows of the reeds in the water, and the birds coming to drink and going away again, perplexed them. A fish leaped, all was still again; but their hearts were not still, and the world began to seem a mockery to Abélard and Rodebœuf. But if that be so, God himself is part of the mockery. And while Abélard paused to consider this sudden thought he was startled by a step coming through the wood, and on looking up he saw an old man standing amid its fringes, whom he judged to be an inhabitant of the place, belike a hermit, though in many little ways he differed from the hermit who forsakes the world to meditate on the nature of the soul that God has given him and the nature of God.

Although an old man, he was of erect carriage, full of vigour and health, and his staff was not of the rough-and-ready kind that hermits make for themselves out of some dry branch, but shaped with craft, polished, ivory-headed. And Abélard tried in vain to associate him with some religious community, deciding quickly that he was not a Benedictine nor a Carthusian; and, rejecting the Carmelites, which next rose up in his mind, he fell to a closer examination of the intruder, perceiving him to be a tall man with sloping shoulders, inclined to bulk about the hips, one whose face was long, of the horse kind, but redeemed by an amiable forehead and lit with pale, ironical eyes that hinted a smile even when they ceased to smile. Abélard waited for a word from him, but he did not speak, and the twain began to take pleasure in his appearance, which was not disagreeable after the first glance. His quizzical eyes began to smile again, and it became a question which should speak first. Abélard and Rodebœuf held their tongues by mutual consent, it seeming to them that the duty of finding the first words fell to the hermit, since he was a denizen of the woods and cliffs and they were but casual passengers; and while waiting for him to break the silence their thoughts were: With what phrase will he break it, and what will his voice be like? An engaging tenor voice was not expected, yet when it came it seemed the only voice that their hermit could speak suitably, and they were asked with much grace and courtesy if they were comers from the Court of Love which was now in session. At once Abélard began to speak of a great miscarriage of justice and was pointing to his friend, the Comte de Rodebœuf, when the old man said that he had not come from his cell to give ear to a case of injustice, but in the hope of hearing news of the Lady Malberge.

But you wear a puzzled look, good sir. As well I may, Abélard replied, for my friend and myself mistook you for a hermit come to live in a quiet wood that he might better meditate on the nature of his soul. Your guessing does you credit, sirs, the hermit answered. It was for naught else certainly that I came hither. None deserts the world but to come to terms with his soul. But the wood, good hermit, is not an hour's walk from a Court of Love, Abélard interposed; nor is this the whole of the paradox; the Christian hermits flee from the world to escape from thoughts of women, and do not leave their cells at the sound of footsteps and voices to enquire for news of them. Your views of hermits are narrow, said the old man, raising his hand some five or six inches higher up, thereby gaining a more picturesque attitude. If the Lady Malberge should be the hermit's soul, would you have him flee from the Court of Love in which she presides? The Lady Malberge the hermit's soul! Abélard muttered, and Rodebœuf awoke for a moment from his despondency. You will easily apprehend my philosophy, or that science of life which I have come by, the hermit said. Hearken! If we have a fair image in our minds always, the world passes away from us and a great part of ourselves; only what is most real in us remains. Rodebœuf would have moved on, for he was in no humour to listen to such discourses, but Abélard's religious curiosity obliged him to put further questions, and he asked the hermit what great spiritual crisis compelled him to live apart from the Lady Malberge, whom he understood to be none other than the Vicomtesse de Chatelleraud. But I do not live apart; she is always with me and that she should never be far from me is my reason for having withdrawn myself from her. It was not fear of hell nor desire of heaven that drove you hither? said Abélard. By no means, good sir, the hermit answered, but that I might meditate upon the nature of my soul. But if, continued Abélard, becoming more and more interested, you are careless of heaven and hell, as though they concern you not—— I am afraid I do not understand you, good hermit. That may be, good sir, for you are unaware that I am Gaucelm d'Arembert, whose soul is well known to be the Lady Malberge. I cannot call my love of her anything else, for it abides when all other things have passed, and day by day it grows clearer to me and nearer to me, and the soul, we have always been told, is what is most essential in us. If that be so, and who will say it is not, Malberge is my soul, for nothing is essential in me except her.

Without her I should not have been myself, and were she taken from me I should be nothing; therefore I say, and not without reason, it seems to me, that the Lady Malberge is my soul. Or my love of her is my soul, if your mood, sir, is to split hairs. But, said Abélard, the soul is all spirit. My love is all spirit, Gaucelm answered. Was your love then unfleshly? Abélard asked. By no means; it was in my lady's bed that I came to know myself. I was nothing before I entered it, merely a man given over to vain commerce with every woman that took his fancy. And you have never wavered from your love? Abélard enquired. Wavered from my love? You might as well ask if I have wavered from my senses. All I see and hear is my Lady Malberge. She is the bird that sings within me; she is the fruit that I taste—— In memory, Abélard interposed. Memory is the truer reality, Gaucelm answered. She is the flower that I meet upon my way and that I gather, and for each flower I gather another springs up in its place, the same flower sometimes or else a more beautiful flower than the one I have gathered. And you are satisfied to live alone in this hermitage? Abélard asked. Why not? Gaucelm replied. My friends bring me food, and the birds and the beasts of the wood bring me entertainment. I have friends amongst them all. They share my meals with me, and when I am not with them I meditate, which reminds me that I must bid you good-bye, for the hour of my meditation has come. But, said Abélard, we regret to interrupt your meditations, but your knowledge of life is so instructive that we would wish to hear you on this subject to which you have dedicated your life. To which, Gaucelm answered, I would devote many lives, had I many for giving, for all that is not Malberge is death. Many of us live without suspicion of the real life. It was so with me; for twenty years I was without it, living on rinds and shucks and husks, but when I met Malberge I began to live the essential life. For ten years I have lived with her in what is known as reality, and ever since have been living it in a memory which is even sweeter than the reality. But how, good hermit, did this good fortune come about? Abélard asked. There were twenty years—— That I was without knowledge of Malberge, the hermit interrupted. Yes, if we begin to count our life from the eighteenth year, for I was thirty-eight before my eyes were won by her beauty and my ears ravished by her voice, for Malberge's voice is—— Good hermit, tell us, Abélard intervened, of how you met the Lady Malberge. At a tournament it was, good sirs, in which another knight was to carry her colours; but after a few words with me her fancy changed, and she said that I should wear her colours; and when it was pointed out to her by her first husband (Malberge has been wedded twice), that she could not put aside the knight she had chosen, she answered him, saying: The tournament is given in my honour, therefore my mind may change as it pleases, and I will not sit on the balcony and watch the knights charging each other in the lists if Gaucelm d'Arembert does not wear my colours; here is my sleeve for him. And she cut her sleeve from her gown and gave it to me, and all were amazed. But she would have her way, and her sleeve pinned upon my arm gave it such great favour that I overthrew all. That day none could withstand my prowess. And next day when I went to the Lady Malberge to return to her her sleeve, she raised her face to mine, and when our lips met in a kiss all my nature took fire, and the flame that was lighted that day shall never be quenched.

The fire still smoulders under the ashes of many years; stir it and it will flame again. Your questions bring it all back to me, and that is why I have not sent you away and retired into meditation of the great benefits I have received from my dear lady. But how, good hermit, did it fall out, Abélard asked, that on the death of her first husband, or divorce, whichever happened that separated them one from another, you did not wed the Lady Malberge? Our wedding was often in our minds, but I felt, and Malberge shared my belief, that love could not exist in marriage, and I said to her: Malberge, if I wed thee thou wilt hate me in six months, but if we are wise and stint our desires to blessed adultery, our love shall last to the end of our lives. Ponder well before thou choosest another husband; and to the best of my power I did advise the Lady Malberge in her choice, and the Vicomte de Chatelleraud has proved worthy of the confidence that I placed in him.

For two years during the life of her first husband I lived in the memory of my last meeting with Malberge, and each time I entered the Lady Malberge's bed it seemed to me more clear than the last time that it was not a mortal woman I lay beside, but divinity, Venus herself, and our union was, or seemed to me to be, which is the same thing, a sacramental deed, in harmony with the universe and part of it. You will think me mad, good sirs, but that is a matter for your concern rather than mine, whose only care now is to discover the truth about myself and the Lady Malberge—my foible, and the last one. A pleasure it is to speak of her to you, for I am without any company except the birds and the beasts of these woods, and the castle servants, who bring me presents of food from Malberge, and the peasants from whom I buy it, therefore I thank you for having allowed me the privilege of speaking the truth to you. Does Malberge come to visit you here in your hermitage? Does she sit and talk with you of the days when you loved each other? Abélard asked. Malberge, the hermit answered, speaks very little of the days when we loved each other, and methinks she cares little to hear me remind her of them; but she comes to see me and I possess her affection, and there is little that I might ask that she would not do for me. And never during all those years did another woman tempt you? Rodebœuf enquired, feeling that he had been for a long time like one forgotten. My good sir, he who has enjoyed divinity turns aside from merely mortal woman. And was Malberge as faithful to you, sir, as you were to her? Rodebœuf asked. Eighteen years lay between me and Malberge. She was twenty when I was thirty-eight, and her imagination was as mine was in my youth. Men captured her imagination as women captured mine. Thou wilt not chide me if I spend part of to-morrow with a certain knight? she said to me. And I answered: Malberge, I hear thee with a certain sorrow, but thou canst not be else than what thou art, and if thou wert else I might not love thee. So be thyself. My prudence was rewarded, for after a very little while she quitted the new knight. It has fallen out that Malberge has wept naked in my arms, telling me that I must help her to obtain some man who had caught her fancy, reminding me of our long love, her tears flowing on her cheeks. Thou wilt help me, she has said, for I must have both of you. One is not enough, I must have both, I must live with both of you; and on these words she surrendered her beautiful body to me and her tears were forgotten. A strange lady was thine, good hermit, one such as we have never heard of before, cried Rodebœuf. And now, said Abélard, you have set up a hermitage in her domain, and she holds a Court of Love at Chatelleraud. Yes; and sometimes I mingle with the crowd and

catch sight of her, and sometimes a whim brings her here
to me, and I look upon my life as it has come to me
through Malberge as a perfect gift. My death, which
cannot be far away now, only affects me in this much, that
I shall not see Malberge any more; and not seeing her,
I shall be indifferent to all things after death as I am
during life, indifferent to all things but Malberge.

And on these words Gaucelm d'Arembert turned away,
thinking that he had said enough. But Abélard detained
him still and said: You, who have found a perfect answer
to the riddle of life, may counsel me in my distress, which
is a sore one. Better counsellor than you I shall never
find, good hermit. Not so, good sir, no man can advise
another; wisdom is a gift that we bring into the world,
and what we bring with us we may not pass on to another.
If we could, we should be angels by this time. Return to
your business, whatever it may be. If poet or philosopher, return to poetry or philosophy, or to both, or to
wedded life, or to adulterous if you be a lover. You have
detained me long enough; my meditations, too long delayed, must be begun. Good-bye, sirs.

CHAP. XXIII.

A FEW minutes after his dismissal, Abélard and Rodebœuf returned through the wood seeking Gaucelm's hermitage, and when they came upon it they cried: Will you,
good sir, delay your meditations a few moments to hear
a great miscarriage of justice at the Court of Love pre-
sided over by the Lady Malberge? And Gaucelm answered: Any story that concerns the Lady Malberge I
will listen to willingly and with gratitude. Abélard then
told how a valuable prize had been given, not to the man
who wrote the poem and composed the music, but to a

man who had learned it from another as a parrot learns. Gaucelm listened with an attention and interest in the story that persuaded Abélard he would use his influence with the Lady Malberge to have the decision of the Court reversed and the prize taken away from him who had stolen it. But in this he was mistaken. Gaucelm was averse from Abélard's plan that he should go to the Court and tell the story to the Lady Malberge herself, or at least say that he believed the story to be true, and that a test might be put which would discover the truth. The rival singers might be asked to add a verse, and in the added verse the true authorship of the poem would appear. The test that you propose to me is ingenious and has my sympathy, good sirs, but I have removed myself from the world, and to see the Lady Malberge among the great assembly would be painful to me and distract my thoughts from herself. For she has no real being except in me; she is here, and nowhere else, and the hermit pointed to his heart. Abélard heard Rodebœuf sigh and move away, for with the hermit's refusal to intervene he knew that his last hope of gaining the prize was lost. Your words, Gaucelm, leave us no hope, but the trouvère who was once you would like to hear the song. And Gaucelm signifying that he had no reason for not listening for a few moments longer, Abélard said: My friend has moved away into the wood, and I have no lute. There is one in my cell, the hermit said; I will fetch it. Thank you, Gaucelm, for your lute, and now I will sing you the song that gained the prize.

The first preliminary chords called forth a few words of praise from the hermit, who said: I hear plainly that you are among the first of lute-players, good sir. And Abélard answered: I was thought to be such when a gleeman in Rodebœuf's service. Abélard continued playing a little while on the lute and then began his song, which Gaucelm listened to devoutly, religiously, for he was listening to words and music that had charmed the Lady Malberge. Whatever the song was he would have admired it for that reason, enough reason for him, and in consideration of the pleasure that it had given him, he asked Abélard why he had abandoned lute-playing. For philosophy, my good sir, I laid the lute aside; I am Pierre Abélard, of whom you have heard, no doubt. But Gaucelm's face told Abélard that he had not heard the name before, and to pass over an awkward moment Abélard began to tell of his love for a girl whom he had left with his relatives at Tours. She is with child by me, he exclaimed, in the hope of capturing the hermit's attention. But Gaucelm was too deeply engaged with his own dreams to hear him, and with an absent-minded air he asked, after a long silence, what Abélard's reasons were for abandoning music for dialectics. I heard, he said, the word philosophy and also the word gleeman, and from your lute-playing and your singing I judged that you were on the way to becoming a trouvère. You should have been content with your lute-playing and left dialectics to others; they are the web that the spider weaves to trap unwary flies. In reply to another question—why did he leave Rodebœuf's service?—Abélard answered that though at first Rodebœuf and himself seemed to be at one with regard to music and poetry, in the second year of his service differences arose, for whereas it seemed to Abélard that the business of the melody was to express as far as possible the meaning of the words, the taste of Rodebœuf, who was more musician than poet, was to adorn his tunes, not only his own tunes, but mine, said Abélard, with grace notes, appoggiaturas and slurred intervals. At first our differences were slight, and it amused us to wrangle over an art that was dear to both of us; but in the second year we wearied of our differences, and one day, owing to his insistence regarding devices which seemed to me useless, if not ridiculous, we came to words, and exasperated beyond endurance I rode away from his castle, angry with myself and poetry, my thoughts returning to dialectics, which for two years I had almost forgotten.

Abélard waited with some curiosity for the hermit's answer, but Gaucelm could not abstract himself from his thoughts, and his absent-mindedness was so apparent that Abélard began to wonder if the story he had told of the reasons which prevented him from remaining in Rodebœuf's service was already forgotten. Not quite forgotten, he gathered, for after excusing himself for his dreams, Gaucelm sought in his memory, and discovering therein the name of Rodebœuf, he said: have you re-entered his service? The great Comte de Rodebœuf is without lands, and having failed to gain the prize with his poem, will join the next Crusade, Abélard answered. And yourself? Gaucelm asked. You wear a mask of youth, but masks never quite shut out the truth. Good health and good living and abstemiousness hid the forties for a while from me, but my eyes begin to descry your years and they put them at thirty-eight. Two years short of my years, which are forty, Abélard replied, too old to start a trouvère's life again. A trouvère's life does not include many years beyond thirty. It is true my years were thirty-eight when I met the Lady Malberge the first time, and despite my age our love was prolonged till her mother began to say that Malberge was no longer as young as she used to be, said Gaucelm. Was it for words spoken by her mother that you ceased—— I have never ceased to love Malberge, Gaucelm answered, and if I

remember her mother's words it is for that they were
spoken at the close of my forty-eighth year, when I was
no longer young in love as I used to be. And one more
question I would put to you—did you never wish to wed
Malberge? Many times, Gaucelm answered; but held my
tongue between my teeth. And Malberge? Abélard asked.
Only once did she speak of marriage; it was, if I remember rightly, soon after the death of her first husband,
during the first week of her widowhood, and for answer
I took her hand in mine and said: Wouldst sacrifice our
love, Malberge? And so that the thought might not
trouble her again, I spoke to her of all the men we knew,
discarding them one after another, till at last a name
came up, and we agreed that here was the husband
decreed for her. Nor did my judgment fail us, for her
marriage is spoken of around the beautiful country of
Chatelleraud as the most admirable in Touraine. We
were the wise ones of the earth, we knew that love does
not exist in marriage from the beginning. She has laid
to heart your teaching, noble hermit, Abélard replied,
and he told of the lady who had promised her love to a
knight should she ever find herself out of love; on her
marriage she had fallen out of love and must recompense
her swain. Such, good hermit, was the Lady Malberge's
ruling at the Court of Love now in session at the Castle
of Franchard, said Abélard.

CHAP. XXIV.

HE had not left the hermit's cell many hours before he
was overtaken by a sense of resentment against this hermitage; and the hermit's colloquies, his polished staff of
rare wood, his lute, his theories and doctrines, became

suddenly abhorrent. The sham, the fraud, the falseness! But after all, he said, stopping in the middle of a glade, all they say and do is their truth, so why am I angry? It may be that Gaucelm did well to turn aside from marriage. But I am not Gaucelm; and with clouded countenance and angry mien he crossed the glade hurriedly, finding a path on the other side that led him out of the wood into the beauty of a summer day.

The sun has not yet gone, for there are shadows and lights, but my heart tells me it must be near the sunset, for there is no hour of the day or night when we are possessed of such peace as now. In this persuasive hour our enemies are indifferent to us, almost forgotten, and our friends are far away, like the clouds. Like the sky, life is serene, inimitable; and the rich country of the Touraine, full of trees and corn and vines, lies before me league after league, watered by the great river hidden from my eyes now, but which I can see with my mind's eye driving its straight, shallow course towards the sea. The Loire winds less than any river, he said, and now it is blue in the sunset and the swallows flit over the great sandy reaches under the arches of the bridges, and thousands are high in the air. A land of corn and sand and wine is this country, and of Héloïse, he cried, for these things would be nothing to me without her. And he recalled those grassy islands she would pass by, filled with drowsy cattle brought over in boats to feed, the river growing deeper on its way to Nantes, where it became an estuary. As he walked his thoughts passed from Nantes to Paris, to Fulbert! before whom he would have to appear sooner or later. At the thought of the meeting from which he could not escape, the beautiful evening, lighted by the long rays of the setting sun, darkened, and, with all the summer landscape, was blotted

from his eyes, with the hermit in the wood, Rodebœuf, the
Court of Love, even Héloïse, for he was unhappy in his
own heart; and the world is naught but ourselves, as the
oldest philosophy tells and the newest.

He went his way, but with a drop of poison in his
heart. Sometimes the poison was active, sometimes dor-
mant, but it was always there; and nothing could set him
free but Fulbert's death, which was not to be counted on,
and his reason told him that the sooner he went to Paris
the easier would be the encounter. But his instinct was
more powerful than his reason, and he stayed in the pleasant country of the Touraine, putting off the inevitable
hour, finding some relief in the thought that the spell of
circumstance would propel him to Fulbert. It is pleasanter to be propelled than to come to a decision, he said,
smiling at the vein of inconsequence he had come upon
in his character. To escape from himself he composed,
and sometimes a whole day passed without a thought of
Fulbert coming into his mind, and it was not till the end
of September, towards the close of the summer season,
at the moment of the great stillness when Nature seems
to prepare herself for her long winter sleep, that he rode
a tired horse from a village distant about ten leagues
through the half-rural, half-urban district known as the
Lombard, past gardens and through lanes, the fields
breaking into view with white oxen ploughing towards
the headlands just as of yore. He would never forget
how his tired, listless horse, on approaching Paris, pricked
up his ears and began to trot, scenting a stable. Or
maybe he recognises the bells of Saint-Germains-l'Auxerrois and Saint-Gervais, said Abélard. Anon the bells of
Notre-Dame came into the ear, with the bells of the left
bank answering them, sweet, reciprocating chimes: Abélard knew them all, far and near, distinguishing the

deeper resonances of Notre-Dame from the chimes of such late castings as the bells of Sainte-Geneviève. The bells in the east are the bells of Saint-Victor, and those in the west are the bells of Saint-Germains-des-Prés. How beautiful is the reverberation in the still morning air, he said, and fell to thinking of the many churches on either bank of the Seine, enumerating fifteen as he crossed the Little Bridge, saying to himself: in Paris at last! It is good to depart, else we should not know the pleasure of return, he continued, reining up his horse that he might hearken to the different cries. Wake up, gentlemen, cried the bathkeeper, and come to your baths; the baths are ready, gentlemen. Jackets and cloaks to be sold, cried the tailor, he who lacks a cloak is cold to-day; fur cloaks mended, winter will soon be here again. Candles brighter than a thousand stars, cried the chandlers. Good wine at thirty-two, at sixteen, at twelve, at six and a half ha'pence a quart, cried the wine merchants. How pleasant it is to be in Paris again. Ah, if it were not for Fulbert——— Abélard muttered, and rode on again.

Again his heart failed him, and he rode his tired horse round the city so that he might reconsider what he would say to Fulbert, when a well-known voice hailed him. About so early, Mangold, he said, and the disciple, laying hold of his master's stirrup-leather, walked alongside of him, telling him that the heat of the night had kept him awake for hours, and that an unneighbourly neighbour's dog barked all the morning. So I betook myself from my bed, saying that I would at least enjoy the new-born day, and have been recompensed, as you see, sir. But whence have you come? A long way, judging by the horse you ride; poor beast, he can hardly put one foot before the other. I will get off his back, Abélard answered, it is painful to see him, so tired is he; ten leagues

to-day was his faring, and on other days seven. We have
come from Tours. Let us to your lodging, master, for
you would doubtless hear the news from me, and it is as
well you should hear it. Hast bad news for me, then?
Abélard asked. Of the news you will judge yourself,
master; let us hasten. But we're here, cried Abélard, and
giving his horse to an ostler he bade him take great care
of him, saying: He deserves it, having carried me from
Tours to Paris in five days. And then, laying his hand
on Mangold's shoulder, he said: It is of Fulbert thou
wouldst speak to me? Mangold answered: In Latin,
when the doors are closed. So serious as that then? Abélard answered. And returning from the door, he said:
Tell me. When Fulbert returned from Soissons, Mangold
said, and found his niece gone, he was nigh to losing his
wits in grief, and has been good for little else since. For
so much I can vouch, for I have seen and passed a few
words with Fulbert, but the stories that are put about
may be inventions to work you ill, master; we are quick
to answer: these stories are lies, but the gossips answer
us: where is he? Why—— So it is well that I have
come back to silence my enemies, Abélard interposed; and
to do this well let me hear what the gossips have to say
against me. What is said to-day, master, may be truth,
Mangold answered, but the gossips are busy fabling the
story that during Fulbert's absence at Soissons you and
Héloïse and the servant Madelon rode away together over
the Little Bridge in the direction of Orléans. How the
story came to be put about, we don't know; it may be
false that you—— It is not false, Abélard answered,
but relate the story. What is said is that Fulbert returned
from Soissons in a peaceful and happy mood, stopping to
view the shops, passing on till he came to the river, turning the corner, for, you see, his house faces the river—

I know it well, Abélard said, continue—unsuspicious of
what had befallen him till, seeing his door open and children playing within his threshold, he began to wonder
how such disorder had come to pass.   The children
could tell him nothing, and it is said that he wandered on
from room to room, finding at last a letter from Héloïse
telling that she had gone to Brittany.   They are six days'
journey ahead of me, he is reported as saying; and catch
them up I cannot, horse-riding being unsuited to my time
of life.   But whatever his thoughts were at first, they soon
began to leave him, and it is known of a certainty that
he came out of his house like one daft, whose senses had
left him.

It is the wonder of all that he did not walk into the
river, for it was many hours before he knew where he
was going, and would never have known had he not been
met by friends who led him home and cared for him, for
the man was by turns desperate and silly.   It is said
that for many days he did not know what he was saying,
but sat mumbling like one whose wits have gone, he cannot
tell whither, but though it is certain that he was without
his wits for a while, it is true that he is as sane to-day
as you and I.   One thing I have forgotten, that his grief
for Héloïse, his niece, is not greater than his grief for
Madelon, a servant devoted to him for twenty years or
more, and that the words most frequently in his mouth
are: Had Abélard left me Madelon I might have forgiven
him the theft that love urged upon him, for love is a hard
taskmaster, as all men know, but when the belly suffers
the heart is hard.   Such is the gossip of the city; but I
doubt if it be more than folk-wit, for another story is
about that he has been seen in converse with the old
assassin of the mountains to whose orders all the cut-
purses of the city are obedient.   Indeed I have heard as

much as that he was remarked waiting at the corner of the rue Coupe-Gueule.

Abélard listened without speaking, and when Mangold ceased speaking he rose to his feet and paced the room. So it is well indeed that you came early in the morning, Mangold continued; and that I met you, for I have told you all, omitting nothing, and it is for you, master, to pick and choose and devise means of escape. This much of the story is certain, said Abélard, that Fulbert is brooding revenge. He is brooding a plan of revenge, Mangold answered, and how he may get his niece back again, for it is said that he intends to send to Brittany hirelings who will break into whatever house Héloïse may be hiding in, and carry her off to some place chosen and devised by him. The money to do the deed will come out of the coffers of the Church, so it is said. The Church is on his side, Abélard answered, for he is Canon of Notre-Dame, and even my faint adherence to the accursed doctrine is spoken of as heretical. In these days whatever doctrine one sets forth, Abélard continued, somebody is ready to declare it a heresy. But Héloïse must not be robbed from me, and I thank thee, Mangold, for thy words, for they are as a sword in my hand. To know who are my enemies, and their plans, is the way to victory. I thank thee, Mangold. But do not leave me; we'll eat together in an hour's time. Now I must write a long letter to Brittany, telling that I have just heard of Fulbert's project to send a force of men to carry off Héloïse, and that it might be well to hide her in the forest over against Clisson: in those caves known only to ourselves, mayhap. But stopping suddenly, he said: No, I will not write, for the messenger may betray me, if I should find one. A better plan will be to go this very hour, before resting and eating and drinking, to Fulbert. What thinkest thou, Mangold, that

I am putting my head into a noose, or taking it out of one? Mangold seemed unwilling to answer, and Abélard had to press him to do so. I am not sure, he said; and when one is not sure advice is more than ever useless. Not sure, Abélard answered, that I would save myself from the assassination which was in my mind just now? Hast forgotten the tryst at the corner of the rue Coupe-Gueule? Such talk, Mangold replied, was repeated so that you should know all, master. Did I not say as well that it was but the chatter of the folk going to and fro about their business, hardly knowing what they were saying? Abélard replied: But where there is smoke there soon will be a fire. Why not quench the smouldering thought, and by doing so gain for myself that which my heart most desires—Héloïse? A plain imagination, and I await thy answer. Since you press me for an answer, master, there is one ready. The light that God called, a light such as yours, belongs to all the world; for a thousand years the world has waited, since Plato and Aristotle, and now you would throw God's gift aside for a girl's face! My good Mangold, Abélard said, in a chastened tone, even though all thou sayest be true, and I have come to speak a truth that will set many ignorant centuries behind us, for ever behind us, how, I would ask thee, would my marriage affect the truth? Not for me, master, nor for the few who love the truth for itself, but how many truth-lovers are there in this world of ours, and the celibate has always had more power than the married. Why that should be I know not, but is it not so?

Abélard rose to his feet suddenly, and walked to and fro without speaking, Mangold's eyes always upon him, for the disciple saw that the master was perturbed. Mangold, he said at last, if it should be as thou sayest, if men should prefer the appearance to the reality—— Jesus had no wife, Paul had none, nor had Buddha, but Socrates had, cried Mangold, and we know the trouble and the ridicule she brought upon him and perhaps his death, for she made him seem contemptible. Abélard remained deep in his thoughts for what seemed a long while to Mangold, and then, coming to a sudden decision, his instinct breaking through his reason, he said: My heart tells me the truth; I must go and claim her who belongs to me by right and only to me. God did not create this unity for nothing. Mangold, thy judgment of me comes out of a different experience. Thy youth—thou art still in it—has not passed like mine in repression. Thou goest from one girl to another joyously, with niches in thy heart for all, but in my heart there was only one niche, and I will go to her uncle to claim her, so no more. I shall find thee here when I return, and we will take food together then; and I will tell thee of Fulbert, how we met and how we parted and on what terms.

He left the room abruptly, and looking from the window Mangold saw Abélard hastening along, the passengers saluting him as he passed, recognising, as Mangold's heart said, the philosopher of all time. But Abélard had no thought of philosophy in his heart, which was full of Héloïse, and he hastened on, answering the salutations as he crossed the island, keeping out of sight of the ecclesiastics whom he saw collected around the church of Notre-Dame. Before it is known I have returned I must see Fulbert; should he be away from Paris I must follow him. So did he speak to himself as he hastened down the rue des Chantres, his heart beating quickly on reaching the doorstep, his voice agitated when he answered the servant: Tell the Canon that I am bringing him news of his niece and he will see me. On hearing this, without asking leave from her master, she let Abélard into the house, and knowing it well, he ran before her and threw open the door of the room in which he expected to find Fulbert, saying: Sir, I have come with news of your niece and to ask your forgiveness for not having brought it before, the journey being so long from Brittany.

Fulbert started at the sound of Abélard's voice and his face enflamed with hatred, and Abélard had need of all his courage to face the old man who sat looking at him saying nothing. Sir, though I have been in Paris but an hour, I have heard already of your grief, and I find you bowed in affliction. But your niece is well; she is safe with my people in Brittany. With thy people in Brittany, Fulbert answered, starting to his feet, and thou darest to come hither to ask my forgiveness for the seduction of my niece. I believed thee to be a continent man, who would teach her philosophy; a learned companionship I foresaw, and was deceived. All that you can say, sir, is known to me, and it has been a great grief to me during the journey to Brittany, and the journey back from Brittany. A grief to thee, Abélard? Add not hypocrisy to lechery, the Canon answered. Lechery there is none, sir, for the love that I bear for your niece is as pure as any man ever bore for woman. And all my erring, though I would not condone it, seems to be condemned somewhat harshly, men having sinned since the beginning of time, men and women together, each as culpable as the other. Even though, the Canon said, the seducer be forty and the girl be sixteen! Thy crime, Abélard, will stink in the nostrils of all men, and it is to beg me not to make known thy shame and hers that thou art here, for no better reason. But there is no better reason, or worse reason; get beyond my house at once, cried the Canon. I pray you, sir, Abélard answered, as he went towards the door, to believe that I love your niece purely as a man loves a girl who is going to become his wife. The Canon remained silent, and Abélard stood watching him, wondering of what he was thinking. I have come to ask her hand in holy wedlock, Abélard repeated. Her hand in holy wedlock! the Canon said, starting out of his reverie. My hope is that by this marriage I may obtain your forgiveness, sir. Fulbert rose to his feet and crossed the room, thinking, and then coming back he stood looking into Abélard's face, and Abélard, mistaking his scrutiny for lack of belief in his sincerity, began to fear that he would not be able to convince the Canon that he had come to him with an honourable proposal. Your face tells me, he said, that you do not believe me. But why should you disbelieve me, knowing your niece as you do? In what other woman should I find her qualities, her wit, her learning, her beauty?—for she has beauty. But it is not for me to praise her charms. I have come to ask her hand in marriage. Thou hast come, the Canon replied, with fair words, which I find hard to believe at this moment, for I have in mind and intensely at this moment, the deception practised on me in this room. There is no need to ask me to remember, sir; it is not likely that I have forgotten anything. But I have come to ask you for your niece's hand in marriage. And Abélard watched the Canon's face, not liking it but too absorbed in his own thoughts and interests to read it truly. I cannot give thee an answer now, the Canon said at last; come back to me in a week's time. There is one condition, Abélard interjected. Ah, there are conditions, the Canon said. There are stumbling-blocks in every treaty, Abélard replied. Treaty? the Canon repeated; I do not like the word. You know, sir, that my pupils and disciples will not look upon my marriage favourably, for celibacy has always been looked upon as the natural state of philosophers and teachers, and the one condition that I would make is that our marriage shall remain secret. A secret marriage, the Canon said. For how long wouldst thou have the secret kept, Abélard? We cannot pry into the future too closely, we must leave the future to decide the things of the future for us, Abélard answered. But I would like to meet you on that point; let it be Héloïse herself who shall decide when our marriage shall be made public. Thou hast come to me, Abélard—I say it again —with a fair proposal, and I must put aside my own feelings and distrust of thee. I must act as reason tells me I should act. Thou wouldst wed my niece. It is a pity that thou didst not do so before, but, as thou sayest, regrets are vain, and I must not allow my natural anger to interfere with her fortune. She loves thee, and therefore would marry thee, and no more remains for me to say than that, it being thy wish and her wish, my consent will not be withheld. But I too have a condition to impose, and it is that we enter into a pact before witnesses. Thou shalt bring three of thy friends here and I shall bring three of my friends. Would it not be better, Abélard said, that this promise remain secret between us two? My niece, Abélard, is a charge that I have received from my dead brother, Philippe, and he speaks through me; and I believe now that, despite the past, thou comest here as a brave and loyal man, but my brother whispers: a bond, a bond! Thy friends will not reveal the marriage, nor will mine, for if it were known, as thou sayest, thy position as a philosopher and teacher would not be the same as that of a celibate. The Church in her wisdom has made priests celibates for no other reason than that the world in its instinct believes the truth, that the married man is always implicated in sensual interests. Therefore thy marriage shall be kept secret till my niece desires to make it known. In my turn, Canon, I say that you meet me with fair words; and nothing will be said by you or done by you to injure my position during the months that must elapse before we are wedded. Months! the Canon said; why should months elapse? And Abélard answered: we are now in autumn and the road to Brittany and back is a journey of many weeks. That is true, and if she be with child—— Yes, sir, she is with child, Abélard said; and now, sir, you will not refuse me your hand? We will take hands when we meet here next week to enter into a covenant, Fulbert answered, and Abélard, feeling that nothing more remained to be said, bowed acquiescence and returned to Mangold, and related all he had said to the Canon and the answer he had gotten. Is a marriage ever secret? Mangold asked, and Abélard said: Now, Mangold, there is no other way but the secret marriage. On one side I am threatened with assassination if I do not marry, and on the other with the loss of all I have worked for these many years if I do marry. Thou wilt come to the meeting, and after it thou wilt be better able to judge the Canon. I will come to the meeting, Mangold answered.

CHAP. XXV.

A FEW days afterwards the Canon's three friends and Abélard's met to draw a covenant between Fulbert and Abélard, and the terms of it were that Fulbert should give his niece in marriage to Abélard, and that the marriage should take place in Paris, in a church chosen by Fulbert himself, at the beginning of the next year, as soon as Héloïse was able to travel; and that if any of the six witnesses present were to die in the meantime, the

five or four or three that remained should nominate others
by mutual agreement; and that the marriage should be
kept secret, and that the twain should live apart, without
seeing each other, Héloïse with her uncle, and Abélard
in his lodging as heretofore till such time as Héloïse
should think meet for the advertisement of the marriage,
and that till that day and afterwards Canon Fulbert
should keep himself from any act or word that might
prejudice Abélard in the eyes of the world, and speak of
him always with deference and courtesy.

After the signing of the covenant Fulbert and Abélard
embraced, promising fealty to each other, and the friends
delayed at the street corner to rejoice together that their
efforts had been successful, saying that a great scandal
had been averted and a great philosopher preserved to
the world. The belief of all was that Abélard would
respect the covenant and would go to Brittany to bring
back Héloïse and wed her according to the terms laid
down; the doubt, for one loitered in their minds as they
turned to go their different ways, was the wisdom of a
secret marriage; each of the six witnesses was certain
that he would not betray the secret, but none was sure
that Fulbert would overcome the temptation to harm Abélard, which he could do after the marriage more easily
even than before. The success or failure of their enterprise lay in the character of Fulbert himself, and who
could foresee so deep into a man's character? He had
signed the covenant in good faith, but would he think the
same after his niece's marriage as he thought before it?
A riddle to himself and to others is every man. And it
was with these thoughts in their minds that the six witnesses watched Fulbert's conduct during the winter of
eleven hundred and eighteen and the spring of eleven-
nineteen.

It proved itself to be all they could wish for, as much as they hoped and even more, for Fulbert spoke no word against Abélard, whose success in the cloister during the winter was greater than ever, students coming to him from all parts of Europe, adding to the perennial question: Was Abélard greater than Plato and Aristotle, the still more interesting question: in what part has he hidden Héloïse, some averring that he had taken her away to England, others saying that she was in his own country, Brittany; and into these inventions a curious folk-tale was embroidered, it being said that Héloïse, having received instruction in Nominalism, was teaching the new philosophy in Brittany, and for so doing was to be burnt at the stake; the fact that she didn't know the Breton language (though often pointed out) was easily slurred till the explanation came that she had learnt Breton from a Breton nurse.   But the Parisians could not discover any clue to Fulbert's attitude towards Abélard, to the courtesy with which he spoke of him, and his admiration of his talent.   Paris could not do else but expatiate in wonder, for the love adventure was a plume of finer shape and hue than those that Abélard had worn hitherto so gallantly.   So when at the beginning of spring he disappeared suddenly without telling anyone whither he was going, the gossips began afresh, telling, whenever two or three came together, that Abélard had gone, forsooth, to fetch Héloïse out of her hiding, to bring her back his wife; and the jealous answered: who then will care for him and his philosophy?

And Abélard himself as he journeyed through the Orléans forest, accompanied now by a guard of six hirelings, often bethought himself of what Héloïse had said to him, that there was no advancement for a man outside of the Church.   But if he were to take Orders, his life would no longer be a chain of madcap, happy adventures, which it had been till now, but mere developments and analysis of received opinions, and he hated to think of himself as an animal at tether, moving circlewise, always equidistant from the centre, never able to project himself even a few feet farther into the unknown. Already the tether rope was taut; he would wed Héloïse in disappointment, for there could be no further advancement for him except in the Church, she thought, and he recalled her comely head and her grey, spirit eyes that always seemed to be looking into thoughts and dreams rather than at things. He was not a man for her, despite her passion, but an ambition; and if he had not met her his life would have continued to be an ever-swirling adventure. But in every life there is an adventure that sums up the lesser adventures, and Héloïse was this summary, this abridgment, this compendium of life. His life would have been but the waving of a flag without her, and he could hardly doubt that she was thrown across his path for a purpose, a divine purpose mayhap.

And secure in the watchfulness of his guard, Abélard rode through the forest in meditation, his men choosing shorter roads and paths than those he had taken a year ago. Héloïse had come into his life when he was thirty-eight! Until this last year his life had been in his own hands, directed by himself, but in this last year he had lost control of his life and it was now rolling down a steep hill, carried along swiftly and more swiftly by its own weight—whither? Into some valley, in whose quiet his life would continue in that content which comes to every man and every thing in the end. On looking still further into his mind he began to perceive that no more than a seat in the runaway carriage was allotted to him; he did not wish to steer to the right or to the left, or to stop; if he wished anything, it was to increase the pace that he was going: to be happy in Héloïse's arms if he could, or to be unhappy, no matter, but to be in her arms. He began to count the days, and broke off short in his count, for it was by no means sure that she would love him, robbed, bereft of his ambition, for, rightly or wrongly, that was how she would view his marriage, saying again, as she had said before: outside the Church there is no advancement. But is there any real advancement within the Church? She would tell him that with marriage his career was ended, and that knowledge might kill her love. The word kill recalled his danger; Mangold's words were that Fulbert was plotting to get his revenge and might get it through assassination, and this fate he had only escaped by covenanting that he should marry Héloïse. Strange it was that in this covenant Héloïse had never been considered, not even by him, who knew that her wish was that he should enter the Church; and he asked himself in vain if his fear of falling by the hands of Fulbert's assassins compelled him to accept Fulbert's terms without adding: if they be agreeable to Héloïse. It was not fear of his life that had induced him to forgo such proviso; what was it then? Abélard asked himself. How different, he cried, is this journey from the first journey, before we were afraid of Fulbert! We are not afraid of him now! it is of ourselves that we are afraid.

It would have been almost a relief to him to learn that some internal commotion of the earth had diverted the sand in the river disadvantageously, and that no ship could pass Blois, for then at least it would not be his hand but the hand of God that stayed his purpose. But alas, a ship was unfurling its sails when he arrived at Orléans, the skipper speaking of unfavourable winds, and Abélard said: the wind that took us to Tours was favourable throughout. And they had barely passed Meung when the ship drifted on a sandbank, and at Beaugency the wind blew up the river with such force that they had to lie by. Two days later they reached Blois. After Blois was Tours, after Tours was Nantes. In a few hours, he said, I shall be in her arms, and happiness will begin again, for nothing matters but Héloïse. The words sounded in his mind like an oracle, and he asked himself again and again if he were speaking the truth to himself. For was he sure that his career had lost, if not all, some of its attraction? Was he sure that he had ever put philosophy above minstrelsy? But of what use, he said, to torment myself with questions that I cannot answer and that time will soon answer?

His thoughts broke off suddenly, for it had come into his mind that it would not be well to speak to Héloïse at once of the covenant. Not, he said, before some days, at the end of the period, the week of love that I have promised myself, and to which I have looked so eagerly. On the morning of our departure the words should be spoken: Héloïse, thou must come with me to Paris to be wedded, for—— Now what reason can I give for this wedding to which she is opposed? Not the threat of assassination, for that would be a faint-hearted argument to use to convince her. The child, he said, must have a father; he cannot remain a bastard; and thoughts of his child blended with the familiar aspects of the road, every turn of which he knew, with the size and shape of every field, each tumbling wall, every wood, almost every tree, with the walls and towers of the city he was born in. At the next bend of the road they will appear, he said, and he waited for the sight of them with a growing irritation in his heart, for Brittany was instinctively alien to him, and he remembered once again how he had made his lands over to his brothers and sisters in the hope that he might thereby escape from Brittany for ever. Is it not strange, he said to himself, that what I love best in the world should bring me back to the country most antagonistic to me and my ideas, and reining in his horse he pondered in front of the city on hatred and love, asking himself which was the deeper feeling. But the stout towers and walls of Le Pallet were not favourable to abstract thinking, and he was very soon among the early days of his childhood, when Le Pallet was ravaged by the Normans and great clearances of forest were made by the Bretons to avoid being surprised by their enemies. The great round tower of the castle showed against a strip of reddening sky, and he called to mind the house in which he was born, the market-place, the streets in which he had played as a child, and the walls, every stone of which he knew, riding by Le Pallet, however, without knocking at its gate, his thoughts set on the valley farm, on the few dozen elm-trees that sheltered the stead from the west wind, and of all, on the great well, a hundred feet deep or more, into which the serving-women let down a bucket by a chain. The grey-green stones, the dim water below, his fears of falling down, and his admiration of the men who had built this mysterious well, were still quick in his mind. The very taste of the sweet, cool water was on his tongue, and he remembered the small russet-red apples that he used to gather in the garden and eat under the gooseberry bushes, though the taking of fruit was forbidden. A few minutes after the grey-walled garden came into view with a figure bending over the garlic or onion bed— his brother-in-law or a serf?—he was still too far to be sure; nor did he care, for Héloïse was in his mind and too intensely for any other things. No need, he said to himself, to call for help, and he walked into the great kitchen, leaving his horse to wander or to wait for him, not caring which.

At last, she cried; at last! But why these words? he asked. Have I delayed by one hour, by one day, by one week, than the time appointed? Are not the words at last those that should be always on the lips of a mistress waiting for her lover? she replied, recovering a bare sufficiency of speech to tell him that she had borne him a boy. I knew that I should bear thee a boy, she said, but we must not wake him, and they stood by the cradle hushed. Abélard dropped on his knees so that he might hear his son's breathing, and after listening a little he took Héloïse in his arms, this second embrace by the cradle telling a man's gratitude to the woman who has borne him a son; and when their embrace relaxed Abélard's arm lay still about Héloïse's shoulders, the gesture telling better than words their appreciation of the mystery of birth. But mysteries are only for a little while, and we are glad to pass back from them to the prattle of daily life, to babies, their health, our own meals, and such like. A good baby, the best of babies, Héloïse said; I believe that there was never so good a child, and would that thou couldst see his eyes, Abélard, for he has thine own. Our voices have awakened him. The child showed no wish to close his eyes again, but seemed glad at the sight of the world. A step was heard, and his nurse said: he may be feeling hungry, madame, let me give him the breast; and she retired to a corner of the room where she could suckle him at her ease.

I have been happy here with my baby, Héloïse continued, looking forward to this day, to seeing what I have seen, for he seems to recognise thee by instinct; it cannot be doubted at least that he welcomed thee, and I love him better seeing that he loves what I love. Again she fell

into her lover's arms, and remained on his shoulder hushed
in her happiness. Dear wife, dear wife! he said, overcoming the suffocation of the moment. Thy wife? Thou
wilt never be my husband, but always my lover, she answered. Our child yonder has changed the mistress to
the wife and the lover to the husband, Abélard replied.
Abélard, thou knowest that I cannot be thy wife; not for
the sake even of our child can I do that. And Abélard,
guessing what was passing in her mind, said: Again the
vanity of my renown is troubling thee. But it is no vanity, she answered; a child might be born to thee of another
woman, and a child might be born of me by another man,
and these children might be no better and no worse than
the great tide of children that pours over the world day
after day. But when thou wast born to the world something more than a child came with thee, a great teacher,
a philosopher, the greatest—— Ah, say not those words
again, Abélard cried; I am weary of them. To hear me
praise thee—— she began, but he interrupted her again:
We are in the presence of something greater than my
philosophy, whatever that may be worth; in the presence
of a human life given to us by God. That thou gavest
to me, Abélard. That God permitted me to give, Abélard
answered, and that thou didst ask for, saying: partial
love satisfies me no longer, I will take the hazard. Thy
words were prompted by the wife in thee, the wife that
I have come all this way to claim. Abélard, Abélard, I
love to hear those words from thee, for I covet thy love
more than all things, more than all except thy renown.
Thy promise hast been given to me; thou art to enter the
Church, for—— Héloïse, I have a story to tell thee;
come let us sit on these stools and let me tell it, for
stories are told better sitting than standing.

　　And when the story was told, she said: but, Abélard,

what reason was there for that covenant? Abélard told
her that Fulbert was beside himself with grief, and he
continued for a long time trying to persuade her that
Fulbert had done right, and could not have done else,
for, as thou hast told me, Héloïse, he fears his brother's
spirit and may have had a message from him that marriage
must be exacted. But master of words though he was,
his words fell dryly on Héloïse's ears, and she may not
have heard half of what he spoke. Then thy promise to
me to enter the Church counts for nothing? she asked; we
shall be judged ill in other days and hours; and I shall
take my place among the many women who have brought
ruin upon men. But this shall not be, Abélard. Ask all
else of me, but ask me not to ruin thee and to make
myself a shame during all time. Héloïse, thou wilt not
hear, and the woman whom he had always seen meek he
now saw raging through the room to and fro, unable for
her passion to hear him. Thou wilt not hear! he cried.
And when she stopped before him to tell him in a sudden
calm of mind that the philosopher is never the married
man, he knew that there was right on her side. Hast
forgotten St. Paul's words? she asked, just as he expected
she would: Art thou free from women? if not, it is better
that a man should marry than that he should burn, and
quickly St. Jerome's words were hurled at him: Fornication is a refuse heap, marriage is barley, chastity wheaten
flour. And Cicero? she said, breaking back to classical
antiquity for proof that Abélard's work would dwindle
and end in the materialism of married life. When Cicero
was asked to marry Terentia, he refused to do so, saying
that he could not give his mind equally to woman and
philosophy. Art thou less than Cicero? Remember, Abélard, the words of Seneca, whom we have read together:
we must neglect everything for philosophy, life is not

long enough, and all interruptions rob us of the fruit.
Jesus did not condemn marriage, but he did not take to
himself a wife, nor did Buddha. But Mohammed, Abélard replied, seeking to escape from an argument in which
he was being worsted, was a married man, I believe. But
he was a warrior, not a philosopher, Héloïse answered
at once; and they began to talk of the Koran, without
either knowing whether it contained a philosophy comparable to the great creed of nothingness taught by
Buddha. We are talking, Abélard said at last, of what
neither of us knows anything about. If we know little,
Héloïse answered, of Buddha, we both know that Socrates
was married, and that the sufferings of his married life
should cause the most thoughtless to ponder; and to
escape from the violent mood which his proposal of
marriage had awakened in Héloïse, Abélard asked her
if she remembered the storm of abuse with which
Xanthippe assailed Socrates from the windows of his
house, and the filthy fluid poured upon him from above,
and how he had answered, while wiping his head clean:
thunder always brings rain. Come, he said, let us look
at our child again, who, poor darling, has provoked
our first dissension. And they watched a sweet, good-
humoured child who, having taken enough milk from the
breast, was looking round vaguely interested in the
strange world into which he had come. Already, Héloïse
said, thoughts are stirring in him. He wants thy ring,
Abélard; give it to him. And Abélard gave the ring,
saying: a hostage I will claim when we return to Brittany.
Shall we ever return hither, she said, if we leave it?
Héloïse, Héloïse! Abélard cried, for he feared that the
argument between them was about to begin again.

CHAP. XXVI.

AND the argument might have begun again had not
Denise and her husband come into the room and Abélard
gone out with his brother-in-law, leaving Héloïse with
his sister, who would have liked to hear of the meeting
between the lovers. But Héloïse did not care to share
her mind with anybody, and the evening passed away
amid family talk of relations and friends, and at nine
o'clock they all went out to view a poor stricken cow
that had been turned out into the field after calving and
was now dying. It was painful to watch her agony and
they returned to the stead, Denise and her husband
thinking what they might do to relieve the poor animal's
sufferings, undecided whether it would not be better to
kill her that night. Abélard and Héloïse looking forward
to a fresh disputation as soon as they might find themselves alone, each stubborn, each determined to carry his
or her point. Side by side they lay divided, Abélard
appealing (treacherously, Héloïse thought) to her love of
him. But my love, she cried, is powerless to make wrong
right; Abélard, thou art mine and I am thine, but thou
art part of the world's heritage and thou canst not surrender it. Art thou the guardian of this world? he asked.
A cruel answer, she replied, and anon he heard her weeping. She threw her arms about him, and body catching
fire from body, voices softened for a while, and having
taken their joy of each other, each lay listening to the
other's breathing till shallow sleep came, and starting out
of an evil dream, she heard his voice in the darkness
saying suddenly: Thou art afraid lest in time to come
thou shouldst be accused of having sacrificed me. Even
so, she replied; is that a fault? He did not answer,
for he felt that he had spoken harsh words. As they

lay divided their thoughts turned to the cow dying in the byre, and at last they began to talk of the cow, and fell asleep while talking of her.

The news next morning was that the cow might recover after all, and the lovers were invited to the byre to mark the improvement. But the sight of the choking cow was still painful to watch, and leaving the byre Abélard and Héloïse walked to Le Pallet, for Héloïse was minded to go thither with him to see the house he was born in, and follow with him the winding course of the Sangeuse under the bare poplar-trees. It was under these trees that the argument began again: Abélard, thou hast made a covenant with my uncle, but means of escape can be discovered from thy bond. Whereupon Abélard could hold his secret no longer to him, and he told her all that he had heard from Mangold, that his life hung upon his marriage with her. Why didst thou not tell me that thy life was in danger? So to save thy life I have to destroy it, she said. Thy thought is the same as it was overnight? Abélard asked. The same, Héloïse answered, but now enforced by reason, for now I understand that my uncle is but a tool in the hands of the Church. The Church would have thee married lest thou shouldst enter the Church and rise from priest to bishop. Only by keeping thee out of the Church can the Church conquer; and it has conquered, for to save thy mortal life, Abélard, I will wed thee. To-morrow we go to Paris, for the breaking of the covenant would cost me thy life. To break it would be like flinging thy life into the air like a coin. But it is part of the covenant that our marriage is to be kept secret, Abélard rejoined, Héloïse answering him quickly that Fulbert would not keep the secret. For why should he? she asked, and the twain stood looking at each other abashed, Héloïse breaking the pause, her

words: Ah, the intrigue is woven skilfully—the Church
rids herself of a stumbling-block and Fulbert gets his
revenge, rising up in her mind without premeditation as
if she were possessed of foreknowledge of the future.
Abélard's soul was affrighted, and they walked on in
silence through a windy evening, watching great clouds
gathering in the dusk, a portentous sunset alarming
Abélard, who barely knew whether to yield or to continue
to oppose her. Now that he had said that the price of
his life was reckoned at marriage he could not draw back,
neither could she; and they walked on till it was almost
night about them, and they were startled from their
reveries by Madelon, whom they overtook a quarter of a
league from the valley farm weighed down by the weight
of a large basket of live chickens. I will carry these for
thee, Abélard said; Madelon resisted, but Abélard took
the basket from her, and Héloïse began to tell of their
immediate departure, blurting out the whole story that
Abélard stood in danger of his life if he returned to Paris
without her. A story in which there is no surprise for
me, Madelon answered, and like Héloïse she saw clearly
that Fulbert's promise to keep the marriage secret was
no more than a blind. Why marry if nobody is to know
you're married? was her common-sense, and was Denise's
common-sense that night when the story was told after
supper. We start in the morning, Héloïse said, and more
talk only weakens and embarrasses the mind. But the
baby? The baby will be well looked after, Denise answered. Have no fear, Madelon said, for the baby; do
the best you can for yourselves, and whenever anybody
is going to Paris he will bring a letter to you. Have no
fear for the child. But it is hard to part with him,
Héloïse answered, and next morning when the horses
came to the door she was not to be found. She is after

her baby, Madelon said; I was the same when——
Héloïse returned with traces of tears in her eyes. Alan
and Denise were accompanying them to Nantes; Abélard
rode a little in the rear and when, turning in their
saddles, they asked him of what he was thinking, he answered: the wind is blowing from the east, which they
understood to mean that the journey to Orléans would
be a long one.

Abélard thought they might take the constant wind for
a sign, but he did not speak his foreboding as he stood
with Héloïse watching their monotonous, almost doubtful
progress from bank to bank, steering now on the short,
now on the long tack, gaining a little every time, but
so little that it seemed that the four days' journey would
be prolonged to fourteen. At Tours the wind dropped;
the oars had to be got out, but it was hard to make way
against the current, and, as the skipper foresaw, they
had to lie by. At Blois the wind was west by south and
it enabled them to reach Orléans, where they were advised
not to take the same road through the forest that they
had come by, and this advice was accepted willingly, for
neither cared to return to Paris along the track of their
dead happiness in suppressed and seldom talk. Alan has
taught thee to ride, Abélard said at last, that is plain, and
he added: we shall not spend so many days riding to
Paris as we did in riding from Paris, regretting the words
as soon as they were spoken. Unhappiness is reached
more quickly than happiness, she answered, and the days
they had spent at Saint-Jean-de-Braie, at Étampes, at
Chécy, rose up in her mind; and it was difficult for her
to keep back her tears, but she kept them back, wearing
as cheerful a countenance as she could during the journey,
which filled several days, each seeming bitterer than the
last till they drew rein at the Little Bridge, and knew

they had come to their parting, Héloïse going to her
uncle's house in the rue des Chantres, and Abélard to his
lodging. She threw him her horse's reins and turned her
head to see him ride away; and that was all till they met
next day and were married in the presence of the witnesses that assembled in the rue des Chantres for the
drawing of the covenant. And all was according to the
covenant, husband and wife separating after the marriage,
Héloïse returning disdainfully, so it seemed to Abélard,
who on his way back to his lodging began to understand
that Héloïse's instinct for the truth was surer than his
own. He had already abandoned hope that the marriage
would be kept a secret, and as he sat in his room alone
he asked himself again and again why he had consented
to this marriage; not only consented, he said to himself,
but forced the marriage upon her. Assassination would
have been better for me than this, but not for her. Unhappy fortune, thrice unhappy fortune, he said, and his
thoughts melted away. When he returned to himself it
was to remember that their return to Paris would set all
the gossips talking and that Fulbert, despite his wish to
keep the secret (if he entertained such a wish), would
have to confess the marriage to his fellow-canons. And
from the Cathedral the tidings would spread rapidly over
the city. All this he foresaw, but not that Héloïse would
deny the marriage, thereby exciting her uncle's rage
against her. If Madelon were here—— he said, as he
sat chewing the new story of Fulbert's cruelty. If Madelon were here—— he muttered, as he paced the floor,
thinking how Héloïse's escape might be contrived. The
door opened. It was she. Abélard guessed her errand,
and when he heard her story he took her hand, saying:
Thou wast right in Brittany, thou art always right,
Héloïse. Marriages are broken, she answered, whenever

it suits Rome to break them, and the Pope may break
ours to retain thee for the Church.

The Pope's care, Abélard answered, is for emperors
rather than for philosophers, and the truth of his words
appealing to her understanding instantly, she replied:
Thy father and mother wearied of the world and entered
the religious life, breaking thereby the marriage bond.
But thou'rt not minded that we should do likewise? If
I escape to the convent of Argenteuil, she said, thou'lt
be free to enter the priesthood. If, Abélard cried, thou
takest the veil. Yes, Abélard, if I take the veil, she
replied, and that I will do, for by taking it I shall give
a philosopher to the Church. The Church needs no
philosopher, and I cannot sacrifice thee; my life is with
thee, O resolute, indomitable Héloïse. But Pierre, thou
wilt not lose me but gain me; and he stood looking into
her eyes, her meaning becoming slowly clear to him.
The heart of the Prioress is a simple one, he said, and
having known love herself she turns a kindly ear to the
stories of lovers, but—— But, Héloïse intervened, she
need not, indeed she must not, know of our meetings;
nor need there be any, thou must not come to Argenteuil
before ordination. But, Abélard answered, we must meet
and swear that by one common accord we are moved to
embrace the religious life. As a priest the convent will
be free to thee, she answered, and the abstinences imposed
upon us will keep our love from fading. We shall never
become common to each other, as might befall us in wedlock. As she spoke she loosed her girdle. This is the
last night we shall spend together for many a day, she
continued, with a trace of fever in her voice. Be not
afraid, Héloïse, he will not dare to come hither with hirelings to put us apart, for God has said: those that God
hath joined together let no man put asunder. It will be

better, she said, for me to go to Argenteuil without delay.
But he cannot claim thee, said Abélard. I shall be safer
in the convent than here, she answered. In such talk
and restless sleep the night went by, and at dawn they
passed without noise from the house and up and hid
themselves by the Little Bridge to wait for a cart going
to Argenteuil. And they were not long hidden when a
rumble caught the ear. If it should be on its way to
Argenteuil—— Héloïse said. Then we are indeed fortunate, Abélard replied. A bit of a round Argenteuil
will be, the peasant said, but no matter, I will take you;
and moving up the bench from which he drove, he made
room for them. When thou'rt a priest thou'lt come to
see me? And Abélard answered: Let this be our covenant: that I remain away till I am ordained and thou'lt
wait in the convent for me. I'll wait faithful, she answered, but we shall meet again, for the Prioress will
send for the Bishop of Paris. I will see him this day,
he replied; and their talk was continued in abrupt Latin
sentences, till at last, as if unable to bear the strain any
longer, Abélard said: we are now within a mile or two
of Argenteuil. And without more words he jumped from
the cart and disappeared round a bend in the lane.

Thy good man be in a hurry to leave thee, and he goeth
like a man that hath a heavy load of business on his mind;
that I can hear, though I have no Latin. Héloïse answered the peasant: Thine eyes tell thee what thine ear
heareth not. Faith, lady, he said, your good sense puts
you into the way of my mind; and for the rest of the
journey he was telling the story of his horse, bought at
a fair some two years back for half of his value, the
peasant chuckled. The very horse, everyone was saying,
for a nobleman's coach; and he would have gone for a big
sum of money. But standing behind the horse, I saw that

one of his quarters was lower than the other, a thing
that mattered not at all in the animal's work, and not
much in his appearance, for the droop could only be seen
when standing directly behind him, and the horse at ease.
Come, says I to the man about to buy him, canst not see?
See what? says he. Well, the droop, says I. Lord!
thou'rt right, cried he, and he shoves all his money back
into his pocket. After that the sale was spoiled; nobody
would look at the horse, and in the end, rather than
take him home unsold, the owner let me have him for
half the price. And a better horse, the peasant chuckled,
was never between the shafts. Always stand behind a
horse—me feyther's very words to me. And the peasant
continued his giggling chatter about his father, who was
a farrier, and the best in the country, without noticing
that Héloïse's thoughts were far away among the seven
years of her childhood spent in the convent which she
was waiting to see. At last it came into view, looking
like a line of low buildings rather than a single one,
grey stone walls and red roofs rising at right angles to
one another, with a squat bell tower, the sight of which
reminded her of the many offices that its tolling enforced.
The bell was always tolling for some thing or other and
at every moment of the last mile of her journey she
expected to hear its clanging tongue. At last it began,
and while waiting till Mass was over she remembered
how dependent her life was once upon that bell, and
how again she would become subject to it for all her life
long, till it tolled for her funeral. From daybreak till
dusk it would toll out her life, its first tolling beginning
at six for Urban's prayer, and not long after it would
be tolling for Matins, Lauds, Prime, Tierce and Mass.
It would toll at the Consecration, and for Sext, for None
and for their meal at eleven, and again at noon for

Urban's prayer; for Vespers, for our meal, she added, at the fifth hour; for Compline, and for silence at sunset.

CHAP. XXVII.

I WILL tell the Prioress you are here, but you'll have to wait a little while, for she is busy now. I shall not mind waiting, Héloïse replied, and following the portress to the parlour door, she said: You know my name, Sister Agatha? Know it, Sister Agatha answered; what can you be thinking of? And you here with us for five years. my word! For six, Héloïse replied. Six, was it? I'd forgotten. And the sister paused to think the matter out; but remembering suddenly that the Prioress would be wanting to know who the visitor might be, she said: I must run away with the good news. But what an hour you have chosen to come, she cried back, from the end of the corridor, to Héloïse, who was about to re-enter the parlour, a room once of great importance in her life, for when she was summoned from the classroom and told that she was wanted in the parlour, she knew that all the fruits of the season awaited her; besides fruit, Madelon's basket often contained a cheese, and it helped her to forget the convent fare, somewhiles trite and commonplace. She was glad, moreover, to see Madelon, to hear of the rue des Chantres and her uncle, who, alas, never came to see her. It would have been, in those days, a little triumph for her had he come to Argenteuil, for the pupils were judged by the rank and wealth of their parents and friends who came to see them. Madelon sometimes forgot to put on her best gown, and Héloïse remembered how one day, while walking with Madelon in the orchard, a pupil had caught sight of them, and asked her afterwards with whom she was walking. She had yielded to the temptation to lie to her fellow-pupil. With my aunt, she said, for to lie seemed better than to confess that her visitor was her uncle's servant. She had dared it, for the pupil was many yards away, too far to notice Madelon's stained and worn gown. The memory of this lie often threw a doubt on her own essential character, as she hoped it was and believed it to be; and now this bygone lie pierced her more sharply than it had ever done before. A mean spirit once dwelt within me, she said; it is in me still, though subdued, perhaps conquered. As she stood waiting for the Prioress she bethought herself of the cake that Madelon had brought her, of its great brown crust as much as the exquisite crumb, and how she had shared it with the pupil in the convent parlour. On the table before me, she said, we opened the hamper; and then to escape from an unpleasant memory she looked round the room, saying: Nothing is changed. The table and six chairs are all in their places, that one still unmended, broken, not by Madelon, though she was charged with the breaking, put away in a distant corner for safety; and the books, too, piled one upon the other, just as I last saw them. The floor was polished last Tuesday, she added, drawing her feet along the shining surface, the beeswax giving forth a faint odour. I could tell the room by the smell, though I were blindfolded. The last time she was in the parlour she was summoned from the illuminating-room: a lay sister came to fetch her: Héloïse is wanted in the parlour, and she had run thither thinking of cake; and the sting of her disappointment on not seeing a basket on the table was still in her mind, and the sound of Madelon's voice saying: I have come to fetch thee back to Paris, so make thy bundle quickly or we shall be late for supper. To fetch me to Paris for always or for a few days? she asked, and Madelon answered: That is just as his humour may fall out. Two years ago, about this very time of year, Héloïse said; almost the same hour of the day. Two years have passed, and in those two years is the stuff of my life: Abélard, Astrolabe and marriage. Yet in spite of all my fate is to return to Argenteuil. In a few days I shall wear the habit. How extraordinary! It requires courage, she said; but I feel that I shall not lack courage if I keep my thoughts fixed on the end; and if the waiting outruns two or three years Astrolabe may be sent for. For why not? she asked, and her thoughts returning to the years gone by, she remembered Clothilde, who, being the Prioress's daughter, was never beaten, the exemption seeming reasonable to all, for Clothide's mind did not retain much of what was put into it, so what use to beat a child for being as God made her?

One day, in answer to a question: Why has the Prioress got a daughter? I thought nuns never had children, she was told that the Prioress was a widow and entered the religious life in consequence of her husband's death, Comte Godfrey de Châtillon, who went to the Crusades and was buried in a place well known to the Prioress; for during the first year of her widowhood her husband's ghost often came to beg her to enter a convent and dedicate the rest of her life to praying for the release of his soul from purgatory. Such was the story the pupils whispered among themselves, and if a pupil turned to a nun to ask if it were true that Godfrey appeared before the Prioress to beg that as soon as his soul was called into heaven his body should be sought on the field of battle and buried in Jerusalem in the Church of the Holy Sepulchre alongside that of Godfrey de Bouillon, the pupil was told that the Prioress entered the religious life with the intention of devoting herself to the liberation of her husband's soul.   And for that very reason she was elected Prioress.   But there was another reason; Héloïse often heard it mentioned with lowered breath that the management of the convent would be safer in the hands of a widow than in those of a spinster, which was true in a way, but she was not altogether certain that the nuns did not feel that a noble name would add to the fame of the convent.

It was the custom of the convent for the pupils to visit the Prioress in her room occasionally, and Héloïse dwelt on the emotion she experienced one day on being bidden thither, the dread she felt while mounting the stairs almost forbidding her to lift the latch of the door. Her knock was still clear in her memory, and the answer to it, and the great fat woman sitting in her chair writing at a table covered with papers.   The Prioress's veil was thrown aside, and Héloïse caught sight of a large bald patch and a few straggling grey hairs before the Prioress had had time to readjust her veil.   The moment fixed itself upon her mind, and she had often recalled it, thinking of the Prioress as exceptionally of her race and country.   For although a large woman of commanding presence, her face was small, rather short than long, with round, intelligent eyes, and her nose when she was a young woman must have been of great beauty, for it was beautiful in her decline, lying low upon the face, well shapen, with clear-cut nostrils.   Héloïse remembered her mouth, large but well-shapen, and the chin's deflection, giving to her face in conjunction with her eyes an expression of great kindliness.   She had read in it pity and compassion, if not a liking an amiable toleration for human weaknesses; and a proneness to discover reasons why they should be overlooked, condoned and forgiven in others. When one of her nuns came and opened her heart to her she imposed no heavy penance, Héloïse was sure of that; and the story of Sister Paula's baby was rising up in Héloïse's mind, with a suspicion of the Prioress's sympathy, when the Prioress herself opened the door and came forward with so ardent a face, and one so eloquent with welcome, that Héloïse was ashamed of herself for having indulged in a momentary condemnation, if her charity could be rightly called a condemnation.

The Prioress had aged in the last two years; she was now an old woman with her middle age behind her; her gait was feebler, she tottered, but Héloïse could read some of the ancient grace in her hands when she sat talking, her hands laid on her clumsy knees, long, delicately shaped hands, that told of an ancestry free from kitchen work. There was charm in the Prioress's low and affectionate voice when she began to talk of Héloïse's father, Philippe, who was killed in Palestine. The lay sisters were waiting for their orders in the passage, and at last they took heart and rapped. But they were bidden to wait, and were clean forgotten—put out of her mind by memories of Peter the Hermit, who was from her own country. My father, as you know, Héloïse, was the Comte Guy de Puiset, and Abdère was the village in which Peter was born, not many miles from the castle where I was born, six miles from Amiens. He often came up to the castle, and touched by his piety and desire to see the Holy Sepulchre, which seemed to absorb the whole of his life, we gave him money for the journey (not all the money but the greater part of it), and I remember his thanks to us on the castle steps before he went away.

A year or eighteen months passed before we began to

think of him again, and the news we got was that on arriving at Jerusalem he was shocked by the indignity with which the pilgrims were treated and the cruelty often put upon them, so much so that he was heartened to undertake a journey to Rome, where he caught the ear quickly of the good Pope Urban II., who promised him his aid in the persuasion of Europe to unite and go forth and win back our Lord's Sepulchre from the Saracen. You know the story, but it is pleasant to go over it again. After persuading the Pope to come to his aid, Peter crossed the Alps and preached from town to town, towns and villages emptying before him. He was of small stature, a dark, pleasant face, with long white hair, and rode upon a mule from whose tail his followers plucked hairs to keep as cherished relics. The Prioress's voice became graver when she began to tell how the mule kicked out and broke a man's ribs; but Peter, turning round in his saddle, raised his hands and invoked the power of the Lord, whereupon the man was made whole again, and, falling on his knees, he gave thanks. Nor was it long after, she said, that Urban II. came to France to hold a great Council, and when the Council was over and Urban preached to the multitude, passing from the Latin language to the French, a thing he was able to do, for he had not forgotten the language of his youth, a great shout went up: Deus vult. The Pope appealed to the knights standing by, asking how it was that they were busy in these fateful times shearing their brethren like sheep, and quarrelling one with the other. Fallen knights, he said, descendants of unconquered sires, remember the vigour of your forefathers and do not degenerate from your noble stock. As the voice of the Pope died away, there went up from the multitude once more: Deus vult! Deus vult! And with eyes raised to heaven Urban stretched out his hands for silence and began to speak, this time in terms of praise. Still forgetful of the lay sisters, the Prioress commenced her relation of the crusade. Héloïse had heard part of it, at least, for the nuns never wearied of telling it, but she had not heard it before from the lips of the widow of Godfrey de Châtillon; and in listening to the old nun she forgot her physical infirmities, her age, her bulk, and listened with reverence to the tale of the sufferings of the knights as they strove through Hungary—how the Huns, having been but lately converted to Christianity, did not welcome the Crusaders and the army; and that when the Crusaders saw the arms of their vanguard hanging in derision from the walls, they poured a thick flight of arrows into the city. The story she told was captivating, but it began to seem to Héloïse as if the Prioress would never come to the end of it, and she would have liked to remind the Prioress of the lay sisters waiting in the corridor, but she dared not; and so it befell her to hear that the Crusaders seized a deserted fortress called Exerogorgo, soon to be besieged by the Sultan of Rhum, and there being no drinking water they drank the blood of the horses to assuage their thirst; and the next thing Héloïse heard was of the capture of the sacred city by means of a wooden tower on wheels pushed alongside the wall, invented by Godfrey of Lorraine, and having thereby one part of the wall, a breach was made through which the Christian army poured, destroying the Saracens, killing men, women, and children, relinquishing their destruction only when they were moved to go to pray at the Holy Sepulchre; and their prayers done they rose up again and continued to extirpate the enemies of our Lord.

But thou'st heard me tell all this story before. Héloïse,

and hast not forgotten any of it, maybe. But I have forgotten the nuns waiting in the corridor for orders, and
have not welcomed thee as I should have done, allowing
myself to be drawn into the old story before asking by
what heavenly design thou'st been led back to us, though
it be but for a visit. For more than a visit, dear Mother,
Héloïse answered; for I have come to enter the religious
life, the life of the world not seeming to us enough.
The hand of God I see in this, the Prioress answered,
and rising from her chair she took Héloïse in her arms.
Let us kneel down together, she said, and thank God at
once for His great goodness. He is good indeed, so good
that we cannot measure His goodness. After having said
a prayer the two women rose to their feet, and the Prioress
said: We have praised God, and now, Héloïse, thou
deservest a word of praise; for we work together with
God. Grace is given to us—— But you must hear my
story before you praise me, Héloïse said. I am sure, the
Prioress answered, there is nothing in Héloïse's story of
herself that will withdraw my love from her. I am sure
that you will listen kindly, dear Mother, as kindly as
Jesus did to the woman of Samaria. The Prioress bowed
her head at the sacred name, and at that moment the
door opened and Sister Cecilia came into the room,
stopping abruptly in the middle of the floor to apologise
for her intrusion. So overjoyed was I, dear Mother, at
the news that Héloïse had come to see us, that I forgot
that you and she would have much to talk about privily,
and she turned to go, but Héloïse cried: don't go, Cecilia;
don't go. Forgive me, dear Mother, Héloïse said, turning to the Prioress, but I have been so long out of the
convent that I forgot to ask if Cecilia might not remain
to hear my story; and waiting for the Prioress to answer,
Héloïse sat gazing at a tall nun, whose long and round

upper lip had always reminded her of a goat, a practical, managing woman, whose talent in the illuminating-room was a source of profit and renown to the convent. Am I to go or stay? Cecilia asked, and the Prioress answered that if Cecilia wished to stay and hear Héloïse's story she might stay. But thou'st not heard, Héloïse, that my dear Clothilde, whom thou knewest in the novitiate, has departed from us and is now with God. We say so almost with certainty, for there are some souls that pass to heaven without delay in purgatory, sinless souls, and Clothilde was surely one of these. We must believe that some go straight to heaven. Peter the Hermit—— Forgive me, Mother, Sister Cecilia interrupted, I forgot to tell you that the lay sisters, Apollonia and Marcella, are waiting to see you. I will see them presently, the Prioress answered: but we have first to hear the story Héloïse has come to tell us.

And the nuns listened unabashed to Héloïse's relation of her life with her uncle in the rue des Chantres, her meeting with Abélard, her flight to Brittany, and the birth of her baby. And to think that living within six miles of Paris we should not have heard of this before! cried Sister Cecilia. We have put the world behind us, Sister, the Prioress answered, for she had begun to think that the story they were listening to would prove a loosening in the convent discipline, already too lax. But she could not summon enough courage to dismiss Cecilia now, and with a heart full of misgivings and fears she gave ear to Héloïse, who told a moving story of how Abélard and herself were resolved to enter the religious life (it being in their case a necessity), thereby breaking the marriage yoke, which she admitted was not accepted by them with Christian humility, but as a sort of penance for the original sin. We should not be happy if we were to lose our souls in the end, she said. For of what does it profit a man to gain the whole world if he lose his own soul? the Prioress murmured, and then, raising her eyes subdued in awe, she asked if there had been a manifestation. I mean, did an angel warn you that your marriage was a mistake and distasteful to God? We both began to feel that we could not continue in married life, Héloïse answered. And to whom was it first revealed that the religious life was the only way out of your difficulty? the Prioress asked. To me, I think, Héloïse replied; but Abélard knew that I spoke his truth as well as my own.

A beautiful story, said the Prioress, and then, speaking like one in a dream, she continued: it may be that I'm speaking heresy if I say that God in His divine goodness may use sin as a means of bringing the souls He most needs nearer to Himself. I am afraid I am, for does not the Church teach that sin is employed only by the Evil One to capture the souls he covets for the hell in which God has placed him? And though an angel be the messenger we are not sure he comes from God, for angels come from under as well as from above the earth. As no angel appeared to thee it must be that the order came from God. And Abélard being of the same mind I should have said I hold it to be certain that the hand of God is in it as much as it was in the inspiration that took Peter the Hermit to the Holy Land, for wife and husband have never before been called apart from one another in a few days. A few weeks, dear Mother, Héloïse corrected; and the talk wore on, Héloïse telling as much of the story as she dared, repeating that Abélard and herself had agreed to part, though loving each other dearly. He to the priesthood and I to the cloister, she said, hoping that she had chosen words that would remove all doubt from the Prioress. But the nun did not answer, and Héloïse began to doubt that her story found acceptance; a mistake, however, this was, for the Prioress's silence did not proceed from her doubts, for how could the story she had heard be thought of but as a rare and beautiful incident of the grace of God descending upon two human beings, taking them out of the danger of earthly life, and at the same time setting their feet on the way to the true life that lies beyond the grave? So did the old nun feel and think, and when she awoke from her dream of God and His providence, she said that the convent would be glad that Héloïse should remain with them if it were her husband's wish. My husband, Héloïse said, will come here to-morrow, and we shall make the declaration which will free us from the marriage bond. It was at that moment that she began to understand that her end could not be reached except through a maze of lies, and forthright she accepted lies as part of her life's business, saying to herself that it was hurtful to lie, and of all, to the Prioress, but to waver in the pursuit of that thing which seemed to her the only thing worth striving for was unworthy.

A treacherous scruple could not enter a mind already aware that in marrying Abélard she had discovered not only a great passion but a career and an ambition, and she was filled with contempt for herself for the faint hesitation with which she had lied to the Prioress; and vowing to be more resolute in future, she spoke with enthusiasm of the life in the convent, of the new nuns that had joined, adding anxious enquiries for pupils with the view to deceiving the nuns. Thy return to us is indeed a gift of God, said the Prioress. But here comes an old friend of thine, Sister Tetta, and Héloïse rose to greet a small nun, small and withered, like an autumn leaf

seemingly ready to detach itself from its stem, to flutter
down into the earth. But though very little was left
of the original woman, Sister Tetta still retained her
funny running little gait and her pleasant, almost joyful,
voice. Why, it is Héloïse, she cried, come back to us
at last, at last. We have all been wondering if you had
forgotten us; it must be more than two years, nearly
three, since we have seen you.

Héloïse has been married, the Prioress said, and has
left husband and baby to join us; and Abélard, the great
philosopher, her husband, was moved by the grace of God
to forget the vanities of this life, else she could not have
come hither. And is not this story which Héloïse has
just related to me and Sister Cecilia an extraordinary
manifestation of God's goodness and His unending providence? Two or three years, Sister Tetta answered, of
the life of the world is enough for those in whom God
has implanted the instinct of heaven, and I think I always
felt that one day Héloïse would be returned to us. But
how long has Héloïse been away from us? Sister Cecilia
asked, and the three nuns were agreed that it must be
about three years since Madelon had come from Argenteuil
with a letter from Canon Fulbert saying that Héloïse
was to return home. But at what season did Madelon
come with this letter? Sister Cecilia asked, and the
Prioress and Sister Tetta were not agreed, the Prioress
holding that it was in October, Sister Tetta holding by
August as the date of Héloïse's departure. But why this
dispute about the date, since we may find it, for you
all remember the first page of the missal that is going
to-morrow to the Bishop of Lichfield. It will be a great
adornment to his cathedral, Cecilia continued, for it is
the best work we have done. You cannot, Mother Prioress,
have forgotten that we stood by this very table wondering

at the beauty of the page? Sister Cecilia opened the missal, and pointing to the two knights fighting, she said: you cannot have forgotten this, Héloïse? Here are the two knights, one on the ground bleeding, the other leaning on his sword, and the cat scrambling through the tendrils and leaves of the bower carrying away the privy member that the knight has just lopped from his rival's body. Thou canst not have forgotten, Héloïse, for these leaves are thine and nearly as firm in line as anything in the missal. We shall be glad of thy handicraft again if thou hast not lost it, which cannot be in so short a time. Does not the cat recall to thee the old brindled fellow, Satan, that used to watch us, sitting on the table beside us as we worked, a little bored, sometimes taking the pencil from our fingers?

Héloïse looked into the missal, and the nuns talked on a little, forgetful of Héloïse, who was too tired to listen to them. Her eyes closed from time to time and she opened them quickly, not unmindful of the politeness she owed to the nuns, and every time she did so she heard the same argument—that another Peter the Hermit must be sought and found who would rouse Europe again to go forth to repel the Saracen. But we are forgetting our visitor, the Prioress cried. My dear Héloïse, thou'rt falling asleep and weak with hunger. Héloïse protested. But obedience to the Superior is the first rule, the Prioress said; thou'rt too tired to eat, but a glass of milk shall be sent to thee and some food, a slice of bread and butter and a fruit or two; and I, too, will disappear, but to return again later in the afternoon.

CHAP. XXVIII.

HER sleep deepened hour after hour, and when the opening of the door awoke her she could remember nothing, and sat staring at her visitor, a pleasant, open-faced woman, thirty or thirty-five, of medium height and good figure. I hope that I have not disturbed you, she said, and Héloïse answered: No, for I was near to the end of my sleep. How long have I been asleep? It doesn't matter in the least, the sister answered; return to sleep if you are so disposed. No, do not go, Héloïse cried, unwilling to part with the nun's pretty forehead, curved eyes, and the face coming to a point, her long, shapely hands and winning smile, a smile so intimate that Héloïse already felt a longing for the nun's friendship beginning in her. My name, she said, is Hildegarde, I am the novice mistress, but Hilda is the name my friends know me by, and I hope you'll soon be one of them. Héloïse answered that she felt she was already one of them. But you were not here when I was a child, getting my education from the nuns? she asked. I was not, the nun answered; I have been here only two years. You must have come soon after I left to go to live with my uncle in Paris, said Héloïse, and Mother Hilda answered her that it is always coming and going from the convent to the world, and from the world to the convent. You've just been married, yet I hear that you and your husband have decided to enter the religious life. God's grace comes suddenly and inexplicably, Héloïse said, sorry to look into the nun's beautiful face with a lie upon her lips. And to escape from further lies she began to tell of the Prioress's willingness to chatter of Peter the Hermit. She never wearies of that story, said Mother Hilda; nor is there any reason why she should. The husband she loved truly was killed fighting for the possession of the Holy Sepulchre, and his spirit appears to her. Her husband's ghost was a good reason for her to come hither, Héloïse replied; she could not leave the poor soul lamenting in purgatory. Did many of the nuns in this convent lose their husbands in the Holy Land? she asked. I lost mine, Mother Hilda answered; and she told that she had been compelled from the world into the convent for the same reason, or very nearly the same reason, as the Prioress. My husband was killed in the Holy Land fighting for the Holy Sepulchre, and I came hither to think of him more securely than I could do in the world, afraid, she said, that in the world temptation might find me out, and the poor dead require all our thoughts, for they live in us and are only really dead when we cease to think of them. Do you think the beloved dead die when we die? Héloïse asked. If no one is left to think of them, Mother Hilda replied, they die; and that is why, it seems to me, that men will sacrifice all things for glory, for by the achievement of great deeds they beget memory that will keep them alive for centuries. So you think, Mother Hilda, that the Crusaders go to the Holy Land to rescue the Holy Sepulchre to save their own lives? In a measure, yes, the nun answered; Jesus lives for us as long as we think of Him, and the more we think of Him the more intensely he lives. But, Mother Hilda, Jesus is God. Jesus is God, of course, Mother Hilda replied. I was thinking of how He lives in us, not how He lives in heaven. Men do not know, she said, pursuing her thoughts as if she had forgotten Héloïse, why they sacrifice themselves in battle, retire into caves, fast and pray; why they write books or build churches. They act in obedience to an instinct. Only the shallows of our lives are agitated by reason, instinct controls the depths, and

our highest instinct is of our immortality. It begins here
on earth—— You do not think then, Héloïse interrupted,
that we drink our immortality from the same cup? From
the same cup, perhaps, Mother Hilda answered, but not
the same draught. At that moment a tall, slim nun entered, and Héloïse's heart sank, for Sister Angela closed
the door and came over to join in the conversation, seemingly the least likely person in the world to understand
or appreciate spiritual confidences; such was Héloïse's
reading of Sister Angela's round, almost foolish eyes,
her dragging mouth and drooping chin. In her face was
the simplicity of the deer, and not even the nun's habit
could hide the gracefulness of her long arms and slender
hands. Héloïse expected a stupid woman to reveal herself, but an intelligence began to appear—a fitful, dis-
connected intelligence that broke into the conversation
and then left it as abruptly, putting thoughts into Héloïse's
mind of animals she had seen at one moment eager to
claim human companionship and then, wearying suddenly
of it, returning into themselves without apparent reason.

Mother Hilda turned to the second Crusade, which was
being talked about, and after listening with a look of
contempt on her face, Sister Angela said: It is not by
hacking the Saracens with battle-axes and stabbing them
with halberts that we shall win the Sepulchre, but by
prayers for their conversion. But do you think, Héloïse
asked, that if all the monasteries were to offer up prayers
together for the conversion of the Caliph, he would re-
linquish the errors he was born into? If we were to
devote our lives to praying for the Caliph, he would not
be able to help himself, said Sister Angela; but our
prayers are thwarted by the prayers of monks asking for
more battle-axes, and the Sepulchre though won from
the Saracens may fall into the Infidels' hands again, for

the Saracen warriors are not the barbarians they are represented to be, but poets—troubadours indeed. And the talk of the nuns turning from troubadours to the great men of the past, to Socrates and Plato, Sister Angela then held that men who lived virtuous lives were sure of heaven, not perhaps as sure as any Christian, but still sure. It seemed to Héloïse that Mother Hilda listened approvingly when Sister Angela began to advocate one of Abélard's doctrines, that heaven was not closed to the great Pagans. But this belief was called into question by a new-comer. Whereupon Sister Angela rose to her feet, saying: Now I must be going, and left the room abruptly. I hope I said nothing to offend her, said the nun who had dared to impugn Angela's orthodoxy. Mother Hilda answered that Angela was always sudden and unexpected. We always say that one side of Angela knows nothing of the other side, and in support of this appreciation Héloïse heard that Sister Angela had been engaged for some years on a great work. But if we ask her, said Mother Hilda, what the great work is about she cannot tell us, for as I have said one side of Angela is a stranger to the other.

The door opened. It was the Prioress come to ask Héloïse if she would like to take the air on the green sward. I thought that if thou wert not tired—— I am quite rested, Héloïse replied. And thou must come with us, Mother Hilda, said the Prioress, and addressing Héloïse, she added: our novice mistress. Mother Hilda pleaded that she had been away from the novitiate too long, and hoping that the Prioress would excuse her she left them. A most successful novice mistress, the Prioress said, and thou'lt like her as much as the others do. For to-morrow I shall be in the novitiate, Héloïse replied, and she sat silent, afraid that her voice had betrayed her. In three or four months we'll give thee the white veil; and the habit is a great help. The Prioress continued talking, and Héloïse sat rapt in thoughts of Abélard's ordination, and was glad when the sun-litten windows interrupted the prosy Prioress, reminding her that summer was not yet over. A beautiful summer, she said; I have yet in mind the fine days breaking slowly after a wet spring, for in March it seemed as if God wished to punish us; such stupid thoughts often come to me, so thoughtless am I of all that God does for us. We all forget Him but He never forgets us, as this evening testifies. I have known beautiful Junes and Julys and beautiful Augusts, too, but never a September like this one. Look up, Héloïse, didst ever see such clouds? And Héloïse was uncertain what colour to put upon the clouds, for they were neither red nor yellow; a red-yellow, she said, making the blue between bluer than any flower. We must not compare the abode of God with the abode of man, the Prioress replied. I started in the dusk, said Héloïse; when not a leaf was stirring. And not a leaf is stirring now, the Prioress answered; a beautiful day has gone by. I am glad, she continued, that thou hast come to us on an evening like this one. In the world we forget quickly, but we remember our childhood, and I am glad to think that thy childhood was passed with us. Mother, I remember everything. Well then, come and see the things that thou dost not remember—our little improvements. Here we are in the orchard, where thou hast walked many times. The gravel of this broad path is familiar under my feet, Héloïse answered, and the smell of the orchard brings the years back to me. But what an abundance of fruit you have; the trees are loaded. They are indeed, Héloïse. But the waste of the fruit breaks my heart, for we cannot eat it all nor sell

as much of it as we wish; we store the apples along
numberless shelves. I know them, Héloïse answered.
We have put up many more during thine absence, dear
child, and in this way we keep our apples sound till
Christmas; but after Christmas decay begins. If we walk
a little farther thou'lt see a low wall built along the
river's bank and this wall is one of our improvements.
It gives us greater privacy, and it is not too high to
shut out the view of the river and the towing-path on
the other side. From the windows of the illuminating-
room thou'lt see the barges sailing, coming up from Normandy laden with food, returning in ballast, a beautiful
sight. Mother, I have never seen anything more beautiful than the great plain along which the mists are now
rising. The silence seems to unite earth with heaven,
and the moon rising up behind yonder poplar puts me in
mind of a tall altar candle. Lighted for thee, the Prioress
answered. But, Mother, God would not take notice of
anything so small as I am. My dear child, God knows
all things, and is everywhere, in all things, behind things,
and in front of things; all is permeated with God. The
smallest life, as well as what seems to us the greatest,
are all the same in His eyes. I say this in truth, for His
hand must be everywhere or nowhere.

CHAP. XXIX.

A LITTLE whirling wind blew up from the river; a
presage, it seemed to the Prioress to be, of winter,
mayhap of a bronchial cold, and she drew her feet more
quickly through the loose gravel and sand, to Héloïse's
admiration, for she did not think the old woman could
walk so fast, throwing the pebbles from side to side.
She was, moreover, weary of the Prioress's pious talk,

and thinking that she could not endure it another five minutes, she confessed to a great longing for bed, for you see, Mother, I was out of bed at daybreak. Thou shalt be in it within the next few minutes, the Prioress answered, and Héloïse was scarcely at length before she was asleep. I must have dozed at once, she said, when the Mass bell awoke her.

Her breakfast was brought to her in the parlour; and after Mother Hilda, her first visitor, many old friends came to see her. Sister Paula was amongst them, and her fresh, girlish face—she had changed but little, if at all—drew Héloïse's eyes to her; and, her thoughts crossing ever back and forth between Brittany and Argenteuil, she bethought herself of a little outing, she and Paula going to visit the woman who was looking after Paula's baby, she had forgotten the child's name. But to arrange for this excursion she must have some private talk with Paula, and while she was thinking how this might be managed, Sister Cecilia asked Héloïse to come to the illuminating-room and sit there with her. Sister Josiane proposed the library, and Héloïse answered: For a whole year in Brittany I have not seen a book. In Brittany? cried several voices. Yes, Héloïse replied; I went to Brittany to have my baby; but as soon as I have cast a look over the shelves and returned from a little walk in the orchard and kitchen garden, you may expect me. But do not forget, Sister Cecilia, that I have not put my hand to painting since I left here, and you can entrust me only with the simplest work. I am glad, answered Sister Cecilia, that you have not forgotten the convent. So well do I remember it that I am going to become one of you, Sister Héloïse replied. A miracle our Prioress declares it to be, and a miracle it must be, for none of us thought to see you again. But why a miracle, Sister

Cecilia? asked Héloïse. That grace should have come
to you both, and at the same time, and you only a month
wedded, is indeed miraculous, the nun answered; and
Héloïse shrank from Sister Cecilia's examination of her
motives in returning to the convent, and changed the
matter of their talk by a mention of the beauty of yester
evening by the river. We must get rid of our pigs, Sister
Cecilia said, or keep them in sties. You will not forget,
said Sister Tetta, to walk down to the river and see the
wall we have built there, for you'll find a long, low
wooden seat that has been put up since you were here;
we sit there in our evening recreation and look out on
the world. I have already admired the wall in the
Prioress's company, but I will admire it in yours, Tetta.
But first I must look up and down the bookshelves. In
this you have not changed much, Héloïse, for a book was
always the best thing in the world for you, and having
opened the library door for her, Sister Tetta said: You
will stay here just as long as you please, dear Héloïse.
It is your last day of liberty; if Abélard comes to-day
and you sign the declaration, you will re-enter the novitiate to-morrow.

In the novitiate to-morrow, she repeated to herself,
climbing the steep way to Abélard's fame, my happy lot.
On these words her eyes turned from the shelves, and
when they went back to the shelves she began to ask
herself of what she had been thinking. Virgil's name
distracted her thoughts from herself, and she recalled
the window in the rue des Chantres overlooking the
river, the town springing up on the right bank, the fields
between the houses in which the white steers laboured
and the ploughman bent over the stilts, a landscape
nearer her heart than the landscape before her, for it was
at a window overlooking the Lombard quarter that she

had read Virgil, Tibullus, Horace, Cornelius Nepos, Sallust, Seneca.   It was in the rue des Chantres that she had spoken to Abélard of the *Academics,* Cicero's book putting a thought of another book in Abélard's head, *Sic et non,* in which he would show the Fathers contradicting each other just like the Philosophers.   Boëthius! A high official whose book on the consolations of philosophy was written whilst waiting for execution; and whilst waiting for Abélard she might have to rely on the consolations of philosophy.   Her curiosity was caught next by the *Thebais* of Statius, a writer of whom she had never heard, and taking down his book she began to turn over the pages, reading here and there till her attention was fixed by the story of the blaspheming Capaneus, who threatened to storm Thebes in spite of Jupiter's lightning and was struck down by a thunderbolt.   And then she came upon some works by Aristotle—the *Categories*— which she returned to their place on the shelf for a future occasion.   She passed over a translation of Plato's *Timœus,* and on taking down its neighbour, the translation of Dionysius, the Areopagite, on the heavenly hierarchy, by John Scotus Erigena, she remembered having heard Abélard say that the Pope was not sure that this work ought to be translated, but did not condemn it, for Dionysius was a saint, the patron saint of France, and one that could not be easily condemned.   She continued to think of him while opening and shutting books filled with stories of Troy and Alexander, and these seemed to contain many things not in Virgil or the historians. One of these days when I have a bad cold in the head—— she said, and turning to the next shelf, she found it filled with the works of Jerome, Ambrose, Augustine and his disciple Orosius, who, she had heard Abélard say, set himself to prove that the whole history of the kingdoms and republics of the world was a calamitous history. After reading a few pages she closed it, saying: A dismal book, but needed at the time to reply to the heathen, who declared their misfortunes were due to Christianity. It was not, however, a book with which to break her long fast from literature, and she sought along the shelves for something more tasty. For beauty I shall have to go to the ancients, she said, and Ovid's *Art of Love* seemed to her suitable to her circumstance; for it will remind me of the love that I put aside, and which I may forget in this convent if his ordination be retarded unduly. But one doesn't forget, she added; and she read on and on, as much for the sake of the subject as for the elegant Latin in which the poet conveys his teaching. The Latin was often so apt that it set her thinking (she had not read Latin for more than a year) that Virgil was not a greater poet than Ovid, and to set her mind at rest she sought for the *Metamorphoses,* and finding it fell to admiring the strenuous narrative flowing on without break. A wonderful imagination, she said, but not so near to the heart of poetry as Virgil, whereupon the *Metamorphoses* was laid aside, and after reading the *Georgics* a little while she breathed a happy sigh and sat quite still, rapt in meditation, saying: He loved life as life has ever been, as it will always be, bringing the earth in its holiness before us, the fields and all the shows of the seasons. She picked up the book and sat reading, laying it aside from time to time so that she might enjoy her old admirations, and returning to her book after a long dream she read on, forgetful of her promise to visit Cecilia in the illuminating-room.

You must eat and not read so much, the lay sister said, for Héloïse did not put aside her book and apply herself to the platters but read while she ate, the meal seeming a tiresome interruption to her. She was still reading when the Prioress came into the room an hour later abruptly and a little fussed, saying that Abélard had arrived with Hubert, the Archbishop's chaplain, who has come, she said, to find out from thee if it be thy wish to enter the religious life (as if thou wouldst have come hither and asked to be admitted if it were not thy wish). Am I to go to him now? Héloïse asked, and the Prioress answered: Yes; and when his scruples are satisfied we will join you, myself and the Mothers and Stephen, our chaplain. Héloïse rose and walked down the passage, stopping a moment to consider how she could answer the questions that would be put to her, and the Prioress, who was watching, said: she is not certain of herself; I'll run and offer up a prayer in the chapel. And while the Prioress prayed Héloïse passed into the parlour, to meet there a small, thin, bony, olive-coloured man, with bright, intelligent eyes and an alert voice. His eyes are full of enquiry, was her comment, and I must be upon my guard; and checking the impulse to talk, she listened to him without a sign of interest or appreciation on her face while he told her that Abélard had called yesterday on the Archbishop to tell him that he wished to enter the religious life. Héloïse's coldness checked the priest in his amiable mood, but as she did not speak he was obliged to continue talking, telling her that years ago the ecclesiastics of Notre-Dame hoped that Abélard would enter the religious life; but last winter the rumour ran through the city that Abélard intended to go to Brittany in the spring to fetch you back and make you his wife. So Fulbert was already preparing the announcement of the wedding even before it took place, Héloïse said to herself, and she crossed her hands and looked demure, for she was determined to reveal little of herself to the Archbishop's chaplain. Hubert waited for her to speak, but she kept herself from speaking till the silence became so irritating that he found himself again obliged to break the pause. It was a surprise to his Grace to hear that you had decided to enter the religious life. Again the priest waited for Héloïse to speak, and this time feeling that she must say something, she said: his Grace's surprise was most natural; and so that she might not seem wilfully reserved, she added: we were surprised ourselves. You left your uncle's house last spring and have been in Brittany ever since? said the priest. Living at Le Pallet, Héloïse answered. Your baby was born in Brittany and you have left him? the priest rejoined, and Héloïse replied: my baby is but four months old; we could not bring him with us. A long journey for an infant, Hubert said. A long journey for anybody, Héloïse replied, and feeling that the moment had come for her to be garrulous, she began to speak of the dangers of the forest, it being infested with robbers; and the journey by ship from Orléans to Nantes is a long and tedious journey, she said, if the wind be not blowing from the east. The priest shuddered and Héloïse smiled faintly, saying that the east wind is welcomed by those who are going to Nantes, cursed by those voyaging from Nantes to Orléans. She spoke of shallows and sandbanks to gain time, saying to herself: Abélard and the Prioress are waiting and his Grace's chaplain knows it, and the more I tell him of the journey the fewer questions he will be able to put to me. She began a relation of the inns of Meung and Beaugency, and the grand flight of hawks they had witnessed from their ship, till the priest was forced to intervene, saying that although all she was telling him was of great interest (for himself contemplated a journey to Brittany), he must remind her that several people were waiting to witness the signing of the deed, and that what he had come to enquire out was when her vocation for the religious life was revealed to her. None can explain God's grace, Héloïse answered, but whosoever receives it cannot be in doubt that he or she has been led by the hand. There is then no doubt in your mind that your renunciation of your married life is a manifestation of God's grace? Can it be else? Héloïse answered; the devil would not lead me hither, it would be to his purpose to leave me in the world, where I might succumb to temptation. A house that is divided against itself, Father—— You cannot tell me why God chose you, the priest intervened, Héloïse thought rather testily; but you can tell me when all doubt was removed from your mind. It seems to me, she replied, that I was always conscious of sin, but sin was so delightful in the beginning that I could not withhold myself; but as I continued to sin I became more and more conscious that—— Héloïse hesitated, and the priest said: conscious that you were losing your soul, that the devil's hand was extended to grip you. I don't know that I thought about the devil, Héloïse answered. But, said the priest, we are conscious of sin because we believe in hell. But should we not be conscious of sin, Héloïse replied, even though hell and purgatory were not? And then, feeling that she was on very delicate ground, she said: Atonement, Father. We atone by confessing our sins to a priest and performing the penances imposed upon us, he answered. We do indeed, Father, for such is the law of the Church. But you loved Abélard, and you have a child by him; these ties are strong, and you have not yet told me how the conviction grew in you that it was God's will that you should enter the religious life. After my marriage I was unhappy, Héloïse said. But, my dear daughter, the priest interposed, marriage should have soothed your conscience. I was unhappy, Héloïse continued, for it lay with me to say when my marriage should be made public. I denied my marriage to those to whom my uncle was proclaiming it, and my obstinacy was so great that my uncle came to believe that I had lost my wits when I related how I had striven against the marriage in Brittany. And why did you strive against the marriage in Brittany? the priest asked. I can give no other reason, Héloïse answered, than that it was the will of God I should come hither. You are sure of that? As sure as one can be, she replied, of anything in this world. As there seemed to be no issue to my trouble I left my uncle's house one night to find Abélard in his lodging and told him of the great change God had operated in me. Let us kneel down together and pray, Abélard said, and we knelt and prayed; and when we rose to our feet he took me in his arms and said: Héloïse, I too have been striving against God's will, but God's will is stronger than we.

The priest did not answer but sat like one overcome and overawed, and Héloïse, seeing that he believed all she had told, rejoiced secretly. It seems to me, daughter, said the priest at last, that you have spoken out of your heart. As well as I know how, she answered. Miracle upon miracle! said Hubert; Abélard the headstrong has submitted to the Church. He always opposed the Nominalism of Roscelin, Héloïse answered dryly; his Nominalism was his own and you know how he expressed it—— Yes, yes, said the priest, I know that he has striven to draw fine distinction between the ultra-Nominalism of Roscelin and the ultra-Realism of Champeaux; but Abélard himself and the Prioress are waiting, and this is not the moment to discuss his philosophy. You wish to enter the religious life? Héloïse answered: I do.

The priest rang a bell and a few seconds afterwards Abélard, the Prioress, the two Mothers, Mother Hilda and Mother Ysabeau, and Stephen, the convent chaplain, entered. You have talked together, and I hope that Héloïse has satisfied you that she wishes to enter the religious life? the Prioress said. Héloïse has answered all my questions, Hubert replied, and I am satisfied that our dear daughter has been brought hither by the grace of God. Then let us thank God, the Prioress said, dropping upon her knees, and the others, men and women, could not do else but fall upon their knees, join their hands, and pray, or simulate prayer. It seemed to Hubert that he would be lacking in courtesy if he did not ask Stephen to pray aloud, which he did, and when their prayers were finished they rose to their feet; and it seeming to Hubert that they had yielded mayhap unduly to their emotions, he said, abruptly, addressing the twain: Ye are aware of the meaning of this act? It has occupied your thoughts, and you have considered it? Héloïse and Abélard answered that they had; a pen was handed to them, and they added their signatures to the scroll of parchment, and stood waiting while the witnesses appended their names to the deed. And then, addressing Stephen, Hubert, the Prioress, Mother Ysabeau and Mother Hilda, Héloïse said: If it seem to you good my husband and myself would like to confer together before we part. We have a child in Brittany, Abélard added, who has been overlooked in the strain of these days, and we crave a few minutes together to speak of our child's welfare. A few minutes in the orchard, said Héloïse, if it please you to grant us this brief delay. The unexpected request seemed to embarrass Hubert more than it did Stephen, but to refuse to allow the wedded to speak a few words privately before they parted seemed ungra-

cious. Before we part, Abélard said, to meet for ever
in the blessed communion of saints and angels—— The
Archbishop will offer up a Mass that you may be given
strength to persevere, Hubert interjected, and on these
words Abélard took his wife's hand in his and led her
away.

Dost think, Abélard, that the request of a few last
minutes together put a thought into their minds that we
are playing a double game? And she told him the answers
she had made to the priest's questions. The Prioress
suspects nothing, he answered, but we must not delay
long. Abélard, Abélard, it is hard to part from thee, and
even now we can ask for the scroll if—— I know how
small and mean is the life of nuns, but I shall be able
to bear it and adopt all subterfuge and trickery needful. Where lies and trickery, subterfuge and deceit
prevail, where snares and nets are set about us, we cannot
do else than use the same weapons against our enemies
as they use against us. And God knows, Abélard said,
that snares have been set for me often enough, and if I
have not fallen into any it is for that my enemies did not
set their snares cunningly. Champeaux and Anselm——
We have but a few minutes to speak, Héloïse interrupted;
thou'lt not raise up difficult questions in Paris, but wilt
lean to the side of the Church? Ah, said Abélard, now
thy finger is set on the spot that may bring our enterprise
to naught, for no man can make himself different from
what he is, and were it possible for me to become a
Champeaux or an Anselm, it would avail me nothing,
for as thou knowest, Champeaux, when he began under
pressure of my argument to abandon the outworks of
his defences against Nominalism, found himself alone in
his school, deserted by all but three or four faithful
adherents in the benches, his power gone from him. One

thing and one thing only interests the world at this moment—— Nominalism and Realism. Were I to yield a point, the Church would no longer fear me, and I shall receive nothing from the Church except through fear. We must not shrink from the means whereby we are to attain our end, she said; a great enterprise is always set with snares, and my business is to wait till thou returnest to me, a priest. But should the convent have its own way with thee, he said, and mould thee to its own idea? I have thought of that, she answered: we are always changing, but I shall not fail thee and do thou not fail me. Thou'rt free now; I am no longer a hitch, a hindrance, a stumbling-block, and having won so much as a simple cleric, as a bishop thou canst not fail to win all: Bishop of Lyons, of Paris, of Toulouse, she said. If great victories await me in any one of these bishoprics, how much greater would my victories be were I Pope. Thy genius, Abélard, would be wasted in the papal chair. Once thou didst speak differently, Héloïse—— Yes, in my childhood, she interjected quickly, I said I wished to see thee in the papal chair, but now I am a woman and understand things better. Thy gift from God was philosophy, and popes are not philosophers but administrators, and philosophy and administration have never yet been joined in the same man. And when didst thou come to think like this? he asked. At this very moment, she answered. Bishops are often philosophers, Abélard replied, and, as thou sayest, a pope is but an administrator. But how knowest thou these things? I know them, she answered, for I love thee, and all that concerns thee is clear to me, though the rest be dark.

Here I remain, Héloïse said, as they walked from the river up the broad path between the orchard trees, watching the peaked roofs of the convent and a sky full of sunny blue, with great white clouds ascending, but without threat of rain. I remain here, Abélard, waiting for thee, she said, her voice quiet and subdued, it seeming to him that she was absorbing all his will and that he could not do else but obey. I wait for thee, it may be two or three years, no matter; I shall wait, and my heart will not lighten till tidings reach me of thy ordination; and then—— We will not look further into the future. One thing more, she said; we leave a child in Brittany, and my life here will be at times hard enough to bear, so thou wilt spare me any anxiety regarding our child? Go to him, Abélard, if thou canst find the time, and if not send Madelon a letter. And now, farewell, for if we remain talking together any longer the delay will put suspicion into the minds of those whose minds must be free from suspicion.

CHAP. XXX.

EVER since her marriage, before it in Brittany, almost from the moment when she turned from the baby's cot at the sound of Abélard's footsteps and voice, she had been at struggle, but not with herself, for the course of her life and her fate became clear to her during the months she spent in Brittany; in her mind's eye she saw her life winding like a road breaking out in different places, leading to what mysterious bourne—to Abélard's victory? For nothing less would she have surrendered Abélard, for nothing less would he have surrendered her. At that moment something seemed to break in her mind suddenly, and afraid that she was about to lose control of herself and might speak without judgment or yield to the temptation of some extravagant act, she rose from the bench at the end of the broad walk and turned into the orchard, and upon a heap of dead leaves abandoned herself to the intoxication of her dream, rejoicing in it from within, admiring it from without, seeing herself always contrite, humble, and even meek, three masks that she must wear in turn. Never must she be seen without one of them, neither by nun nor by priest, till Abélard was returned to her, in one, two, or maybe three years. A long waiting it will be, she said; but we have to wait many months for the smallest seed to rise out of the ground; and two or three years are but a little while to wait for his ordination: ten years but a moment if his teaching prevail.

The inner vision faded and the outer rose before her— Abélard returning bearing tidings of his ordination so plainly in his eyes that words were not needed; and so intense was the vision that she swooned in imagination in his arms, the darkness growing dimmer till the dream scroll was again unrolled, and she became aware of the thick atmosphere of groined roofs and pillars, windows like rich jewels, gold vestments, white surplices, the dusky flames of the candles and heard the Mass chanted amid choir and banners and the swinging of censers till at last the throng divided, and in the centre of the nave Abélard appeared, a gold mitre on his head and the shepherd's staff in his hand.

The multitude passed away; none remained, and in the silence of stale incense she waited for him to come from the sacristy. But he did not come, and when the cathedral melted like a cloud, it was in an avenue of clipped limes that she waited, tremulous, for in front of her was a dark figure who could not be else than Abélard coming to her with the joyful tidings that the reign of reason was nigh—and himself triumphant, equal to Plato and Aristotle. Yes, it was he coming towards her with slow step,

loitering in the patterned path. Her heart seemed to
stand still lest he should stop or return whence he came.
A dream it was and no more, she knew it, but in her
waking life his lips never procured a tenderer mood of
pleasure than she enjoyed now upon a heap of weeds and
grasses in a corner of the convent orchard, and she prayed
that no straying sister should come to interrupt or ruffle
her dream. None came and her ecstasy continued hour
after hour, weakening a little towards evening, till she
returned to herself fully and lay with her eyes open, seeing a large, tumultuous sky with an opening in the clouds
forming a sort of silver shield, which she was prone to
accept as a sign from God and to associate with Abélard,
who, in her eyes, was a knight going forth in quest of the
soul that the Church had buried in a dungeon long ago.
But, though in chains, the soul never dies, and when the
great silver shield in the sky disappeared she was walking
through the orchard saying to herself: to-morrow I shall
wear a habit and shall be cold in it; and again her
thoughts took flight, and she walked on exalted by the
vision of the great philosopher missionary going forth, a
silver shield on his arm. It was then that a long trail
of fragrant smoke swept across her face and she spied
an old peasant raking dried leaves into a distant corner,
throwing them upon the smouldering fire without drawing
any thought from his seasonable work, living as the
husbandmen lived in the *Georgics,* a shadowy figure in
the evening landscape. We are all gathering dead leaves
for the burning, she said, and to soothe her aching mind
she walked straight to the convent library, and thanked
God that it was empty.

And while thinking before the shelves how much more
precious would be a letter from Abélard than any book
she might take down, she opened Seneca, and her eyes

lighted on a passage in a letter written to his friend,
Lucilius: You write to me often, and I thank you; you
bring yourself before me as best you may; and whenever
I get one of your letters we are together again. If the
portraits of our absent friends soothe us, if they quicken
remembrance, vain and deceptive consolation, and lighten
the regret we feel at their absence, how much dearer to us
are the letters that bring the very hand-writing, the sign-
manual of the absent friend? How true, how true, she
sighed, and was moved to send the words to Abélard; so
full were they of kindly affection that they could not
do else than bring him to a table and compel him to write
to her, so it seemed. But the pen she picked up fell from
her hand, and she sat remembering that it was agreed
she would remain in the convent, giving no sign till
she heard from him. Why, therefore, should she break
the covenant? Her letter might fall into other hands,
and not even quotations from Seneca's letter to Lucilius
were safe, for how else could the quotation be interpreted
except as an invitation to correspond: write to me, for
I am hungry and thirsty for the sight of thee, and since I
may not see thee, write, for such tidings as a letter
brings soothe.

She must not write, nor even ask for news of him,
and she wearied of saying to herself: no news is good
news. As day passed over day almost reproaches against
Abélard and against herself began to arise, with memories
of the words she had spoken to him as they walked down
the orchard path by the very seat she was now leaning
on. And now all that she had said seemed lies, yet she
had said nothing that was not in her heart at the while.
How hard it is to speak the truth, she said. It escapes
like water that we would hold in our hands. I told him
that I must remain in this convent so that he might

become a priest; I wished for his advancement and I wish for it still, for fameless Abélard would not be Abélard. So said I, and to-day am no longer sure that Abélard would not be Abélard to me, the master of my heart and body, on a desert island forgotten by all men. That is my truth to-day; to-morrow's is hidden. It may be this: let Abélard be given back to me and common man dwell in the dungeon he built for himself. Never did I seek in Abélard anything but himself, without thought that a ray of his glory might fall upon me. It was his will and not mine that I had at heart always and sought to gratify. I would have preferred the name of mistress, of concubine or light-of-love, to that of wife; and never would have consented to that fatal marriage had it not been that I was afraid of the hireling's dagger.

It was not later than three months after he had left her that the black thought came into her mind that she was a dupe perhaps, for it might be he had accepted her proposal to enter a convent so that he might rid himself of her. She had, it is true, spoken of the convent as a way out of the difficulty in which her marriage put them, a marriage that she had opposed to the last and only consented to lest a refusal should make her seem less worthy in his eyes. It was always to show him he was first in my thoughts that I spoke of this convent. But now I can see he never loved me; it was not love, but lies. For now he has no thought for me, not even enough to bring him to a table to write a letter, and she watched the river flowing and the passing boats, till, awakening from a vague sense of sorrow, she asked herself what Abélard would think of her, and how unworthy he would deem her, if he knew the thoughts that were passing through her mind. For why should I suspect him of treachery? Why, indeed? Is it because I love him beyond all things that shameful thoughts cross my mind? Life is a strange thing, for here sits a suspicious woman, as different as may be from the woman that sat by him on this bench a few weeks ago.

Sister Héloïse, are you not cold siting here in this bleak wind watching the craft going up and down the river? Héloïse uttered a little cry, and turning she saw Mother Hilda. We have been looking for you, Mother Hilda continued, for news has come of Pierre Abélard. News of him? Where is he? cried Héloïse. In the monastery of Saint-Denis, Hilda answered. In the monastery of Saint-Denis! Héloïse repeated, and she stood looking into Mother Hilda's pretty, pointed, freckled face, lighted with round, kind eyes. Yes; we know for certain that he is with the monks, but why does it startle you to hear that he is at Saint-Denis? I was not thinking of a cowl, Héloïse said, for there is no monk in Abélard, but a great prelate who will be an honour to the Church. Mother Hilda looked enquiringly into Héloïse's eyes and then answered: He may have gone to the monastery to prepare for his ordination. A retreat, Héloïse said, and seeing that her presence was needed Hilda sat by her and took her hand, saying: Héloïse, why are you overcome like this? and Héloïse answered, hardly aware of the words she was uttering: a priest, yes, but not a monk. Mother Hilda repeated that most likely Abélard had gone to the monastery of Saint-Denis for the retreat that is usual before ordination. You would not lose him, she said, though you are separated you are not divided; your interests are still his. You would see him a great prelate but not a humble monk. Do you blame me, Hilda? No, I do not blame you; maybe I should feel as you do if I had married a great man. You are feeling better now; let us walk together, for it is cold sitting here, and you will

tell me of Abélard's philosophy and the great service his
ideas will be to the Church, much troubled now by the
rival schools of Nominalism and Realism and the licentious
lives of troubadours in the south and the not less licentious
lives of trouvères in the north, and Courts of Love, whose
only virtue is the singing of a song correctly, lute-playing,
and fidelity to another man's wife.   Abélard's aim,
Héloïse replied, is to show that neither the Realists nor
the Nominalists are altogether right, that the true path
lies between the extreme of Realism as taught by Champeaux and the extreme form of Nominalism as it was
tought by Roscelin, who has submitted to the Church.
We shall be less likely to meet any of the sisters if we
walk this way, Sister Héloïse, less likely to meet Angela
or Cecilia, for either of these will be glad to join us, and
three cannot talk out of their hearts.

Héloïse would have welcomed an interruption from
Angela or Cecilia, for she was afraid that the impulse
to open her heart to Hilda might overcome her, and once
she had spoken the truth she could not remain in the
convent.   Abélard was the law that was over her and were
she to break this law the mainspring of her life would
be broken; she therefore hardened her heart and talked
to deceive Hilda as best she could that day and the next
day and all through the winter, news coming from time
to time to Argenteuil of Abélard's great success as a
teacher, of the number of pupils that came to him and the
fees they paid.   A good thing for us are these fees, Sister
Angela said, one windy day in March, to Héloïse; for
these monks are always complaining of their poverty and
casting covetous eyes on the lands we hold on lease
from them.

The watermen were casting cargo into the river to
lighten the barge, and Héloïse did not hear Sister Angela

till she said that Abélard had left the monastery of Saint-
Denis. Do you think, Sister Angela, said Héloïse, that
our love for one another has ceased? It is true, she
continued, that I am now his sister in Jesus Christ and
that he is my brother in Christ. But we cannot separate
ourselves from our earthly life, and Abélard's misfortunes
are still mine. So he has left the monastery of Saint-
Denis, and for why? Tell me, Sister Angela, all the
news you have of him. All the news I have, Sister
Angela answered, is that he blamed the abominations of
the Abbot Adam, and became obnoxious to the monks,
who were jealous of him. Of Abélard? Héloïse interjected. Yes, of Abélard, Sister Angela answered, and
they welcomed his disciples when they came to beg him
to resume his teaching, which he has done, establishing a
school at Maisoncelle on lands belonging to the Count of
Champagne. You say he has opened a school at Maisoncelle? Héloïse said. Yes; and students come from all
parts of the country. His theological lectures attract and
win many over to his side, and his lectures on Latin literature many more. The world, it would seem, asks for nothing better than to listen to him. But what are the abominations that caused him to leave the monastery, Sister
Angela? Wine-drinking and lute-playing, Sister Angela
answered, and where gleemen go they bring gleemaidens
with them, and singing boys too, whom the monks prefer
to the maidens, their love being more ardent, so it is
said. Yet these same monks seek to defame our convent,
spreading stories about Sister Paula (you were with us
when her baby was born), and about Sister Agnes, who
left us last year for a minstrel. His wont was to sail up
the river in the summer evenings, anchor his boat under
the reeds yonder, and sing; his singing won her away
from us. Whither was she rowed? Héloïse asked. We

never heard of her again. I do not know why I asked
for news of her, Héloïse replied dolefully. Tell me about
Abélard. We hold these lands on lease from the monks
of Saint-Denis, Sister Angela answered, and the lease
goes far back, two or three hundred years. I've heard it
said that the monks have lost any rights they may have
had. But for some while they have been pressing their
claim, and to gain sympathy they try to defame our
convent, spreading stories of our convent chaplain and
the school children. Against Stephen! cried Héloïse.
Such calumny cries to heaven for punishment, Angela
replied, and I should be no wise astonished to hear that
fire descended from heaven on their monastery. It was
to stay the calumny and the rumours they set going against
us that our Prioress wished to strengthen the rule, but we,
myself among the dissidents, said: we will obey the rule
we have vowed to obey, but not new rules. The rules are
severe enough, and were made by men; monks go back
and forth from their monastery, they follow the Crusaders
to Palestine, but we are here always, and life is harder
upon women in religion than on men. You were telling
me, Sister Angela, that we hold the lands of Argenteuil
on lease from the monks of Saint-Denis. Yes, that is so,
Angela replied, and I have often wondered what would
become of us if the monks of Saint-Denis were to succeed
in breaking the lease we hold and possessing themselves
of our property. We should have to seek other convents,
and if none would take us in I suppose many of us would
return to our parents. But would our parents welcome
us? Would they even let us inside their doors? We
should have to go away with trouvères, who like nuns, it
is said. One liked Sister Agnes and she is at least as
happy with him as she was with us. She was not happy
as a nun? Héloïse asked. I do not think any are happy

here, or only those who pass on from the school to the novitiate before they find their sex, Angela answered.

My sister, she said, breaking the pause, used to sit half asleep among women, but when a man came into the room she awoke, and I often wondered at the change, for though I was the elder I was at that time without sex. Your sister is married? Héloïse said. Yes, Sister Angela replied; but I didn't know I was a woman till I was four and twenty and now I am eight and twenty, and the last four years have been a torment to me. That is why, Sister Héloïse, it is hard to understand how you twain, each possessed of the other's love, could have been so ruthless. Ruthless, Héloïse replied. Yes, Sister Angela answered quickly, if our lives were given to us that we might live them; and has not our Lord said that in heaven there is neither marriage nor giving in marriage? But, Sister Angela, it seems to me that despite your chastity, perhaps because of it, you fail to understand that love has a spiritual side. In the end, no doubt, but in the beginning love is but a chance, Sister Angela said. . . . My meeting with Abélard seemed to be but a chance, Héloïse answered, for I know not why I turned into the city instead of crossing the Great Bridge to seek the violets that were coming up in the woods. The springtime was in your feet and sent you forth in search of love, said Sister Angela, to which Héloïse replied that she could not love any other man but Abélard; and Angela answered her with a courage born of long abstinence: It pleases you to think that, Sister Héloïse, but if there were no Abélard, if he had never been born, you do not think you would have descended into your grave a virgin, do you? If Abélard had never been born! As well ask me if I had never been born. But things being as they are, I could love none but Abélard. You will

answer me that question again when you have been some
years in the convent, Angela replied cynically, and
Héloïse felt that she hated this nun, and vowing that
she would not speak intimately with her again, she fell
to thinking that it was strange that chastity should
look into the heart of love so clearly and judge it to
be lust.

CHAP. XXXI.

MY marriage, she said, and fell to thinking of the dismal
swamp it had led her into, and from which there seemed
no hope of escape.   It was the Prioress's voice that
awoke her: Dear Héloïse, thou'rt too given to brooding,
and without just cause, for we know that he must be
preparing for his ordination at Saint-Denis.   But, Mother,
if he were preparing for his ordination he wouldn't have
left Saint-Denis to establish a school at Maisoncelle.   And
his teaching, whatever it may be, will make it difficult for
him to find a bishop to ordain him.   Then why should he
have returned to Saint-Denis? the Prioress asked, taken
aback.   I have sought for a reason, Héloïse replied, but
haven't found any sufficient one.   There seems to be
something behind this of which we know nothing, dear
Mother, for though God may have commanded him to put
on a monk's habit, so that he may forget me, God certainly
did not command him to leave me in trouble, in pain, in
grief, when a few simple words sent hither would relieve
me. His silence is strange, of a certainty, said the Prioress,
and it seems to me that I should be justified in allowing
thee to leave the convent for a few days; three would be
enough to set thy mind at rest, or shall I send our peasant?
Abélard knows where I am, Héloïse answered, and if he
has not sent a letter it is because he deems it well to keep

silent. He knows where I am; it would be wrong of me
to write, dear Mother. It is the lot of men and women
to suffer in this life, women perhaps more than men; so
God in his supreme wisdom has settled it and we must
obey his decrees. Nothing can be changed; things cannot
be else than as they are.

Héloïse hid her face in her hands, and hearing her sob
the Prioress withdrew from the library; and Héloïse
wept, for she remembered that she had known from the
first that marriage would bring about his ruin. Almost
from their wedding day their ruin had begun, and her
device to break the marriage seemed of no avail. Our
plight, she said, was never worse than it is to-day, for
while I am waiting to receive the veil, Abélard wears the
cowl. I am led blindfold; all is darkness about me. And
in her despair she began to consider how she might appear
a creditable human being to the mothers and to the nuns,
diverting their suspicions always, representing herself
as a true daughter of the Church, whereas there was
nothing true in her except her love for Abélard, whom
she would follow into the gulfs of hell rather than live
in paradise without him. A vain and lonely place paradise woud be without Abélard; shadowy as the world she
saw about her when she left the library and walked into
the open air. All things seemed to have receded, and in
the void Abélard was. At every hour of the day, even at
the sacrifice of Mass, she was thinking of him; ard
like the clouds of the air her thoughts disappeared and
collected again, always different and always the same,
beginning from the point at which they ceased three weeks
before, curling and going out as before. She had parted
from him in the belief that her next news would be his
ordination and she now heard that he was wearing a
monk's cowl in the monastery of Saint-Denis. But is

it true? It cannot be that he has entered a monastery
without telling me. For why should he? For why, dear
God? Say why. He knows where I am, yet he does not
write. He knows that I suffer in this silence, yet he
lets me suffer. But he does this for some good reason.
Therefore I will keep the troth that I plighted, and
though false in all else I will be true to him, remaining
here till he comes.

My recompense will be greater for what I have suffered,
and her thoughts melting suddenly, she sat, forgetful of
all things, absorbed in a vague sense of sorrow. Once a
priest, she said, he will be able to impose his will. The
first bishopric available will fall to him, and my name at
least will not appear among the list of women that have
proved to be the scourge of genius. A warning in Proverbs
against women rose up in her mind: now, my son, hearken
to me and be attentive to the words of my mouth; let thy
heart not be drawn into the ways of woman, lose not
thyself in her paths, for she has tripped and overthrown
a great number; the strongest have been killed by her,
her house is the way to hell, and she leads to the gulfs
of death. And again: I have pondered everything with
the eyes of my soul and have found woman bitterer than
death; she is the net of the hunter; her heart is a snare;
her hands are chains; he who pleaseth God escapes her,
but the sinner is her prey.

She remembered too that from the beginning the first
woman brought about the banishment of man from paradise, and she who was created by the Lord to come to
his help was the instrument of his fall. The man whose
birth was announced by an angel was brought to naught
by Delilah; it was she who gave him up to his enemies,
and he was brought to such despair that he buried himself
and them under the ruins of the temple. Solomon, the

wisest of the wise, lost his reason through a woman, who
roused him to such a fury of mind that he, whom the
Lord had chosen to build his temple in preference to
David, his father, fell into idolatry and remained in it
till the end of his days; his heart closed to the worship
of the true God, whose glory he had celebrated by written
and spoken words and whose teaching he had made known.
It was against his wife that Job, that holy man, fought the
last and hardest fight of all; the cunning tempter knew
this well enough, having learnt the truth through experience that men found always a reason for their fall in
women. With Abélard it was different, for he lost by
marriage what he had not lost through lust, the devil
accomplishing evil with good, not being able to do evil
with evil. Meditation followed upon meditation, ending
always in a yearning discontent, in a cry of weariness:
has he forgotten me, who can never forget him? And very
often the words: who can never forget him, threw her
backwards into such memories of the love they had shared
together that she could not do else than write the tortures
her love of him put upon her, in the hope that they might
be lessened by translation from the flesh into spirit. But
why do I talk of the evil one? I, a prisoner in this
convent, put here by his will and by my own, but more
by his will than by mine, for there is no repentance in
my heart for the sins that we have committed nor any
acknowledgment to the Church that I have sinned, nor
could hell, were it opened before me, force me to regret
my sins, if they were sins. Is there then no forgiveness
for those who love outside the bonds of wedlock? None.
For those who have loved truly may not regret. All this
I know full well, for my own heart tells me that this is
true. The joys of love that Pierre and myself have
tasted together were so sweet that the remembrance could

not be displeasing to me, however much I may be brought Godward, even unto God himself. Whichever side I look, memories rise up before me, and I am taken again with the desires that they awaken, fallacious images that leave me no peace even in sleep. Nor even at Mass, for at the solemn moment of consecration, when prayer should be pure and at height, licentious thoughts rise up unbidden and will not be put away, and I sigh and tears start to my eyes that Abélard is not by me that I might sin once more with him. The hours and the places of every act and deed, together with his image, are engraved upon my heart, and so clearly that I am transported to these places and back to the hours, committing again the same acts, the same deeds, even in sleep, in sleep more intensely than in waking. The very movement of my body betrays the thoughts of my soul, and the words that I said in his ear are spoken again by me.

After writing a few pages she remembered that she had promised to abide by his will, and the thought stopped her hand. He knows where I am and if the words I have written were to fall into the hands of his enemies my letter would be cited in testimony against him and our lot would be worse than before. He has not forgotten me, that cannot be, so there is a cause for his silence, though I cannot guess it; something has befallen him. But what can have befallen him? And with this question before her constantly, almost vindictively, she was sitting in the library when the opening of the library door awoke her; and Héloïse, weary of her thoughts, welcomed the Prioress's intrusion—it was almost one, for this corner of the library (a little room in itself) had come to be looked upon as almost privy to Héloïse. Art busy, my dear child, with thy writings? Busy, dear Mother? What matter if I were, and what could be my business? Our thoughts and the control of them are our business always, the Prioress answered. A reproof this seemed to Héloïse, and her face darkened, causing the Prioress to regret her words, for she was the bearer of ill news and had come to the library thinking how she might break the news lightly; and in her dread of having pained Héloïse unnecessarily, she stumbled forthright into the heart of her story, omitting all preparations, saying: Héloïse, my dear child, I am the bringer of serious news. He is not dead, Mother? Héloïse asked, her cheeks blanching. No, he is not dead, the Prioress replied. Some injury has befallen him? Héloïse interjected. The Prioress's face changed; a look of pity passed over it, but she recovered herself quickly and answered that Abélard was well. What then has happened? Héloïse cried. Something has happened; thy face tells me thou'rt the bearer of evil news, so speak quickly, dear Mother. My dear, I would have broken the news gently to thee. O Mother, tell me quickly. Abélard was summoned before a council assembled at Soissons and was ordered to throw his book into a fire in the market-place, reciting the Athanasian Creed from a scroll like a little child, as if he did not know it by heart. But he defended himself? said Héloïse. He did indeed, and his defense was worthy of his genius; the Pope's legate, Conan, was for an acquittal.

But O, it is a long story, Héloïse, and I am not gifted to tell it as it should be told. He will defeat his enemies in the end, Héloïse cried, and there was a note of joy in her voice, for she knew now that Abélard could not write to her in the midst of a trial for heresy. I would hear the whole story, Mother, from the day he entered the monastery of Saint-Denis. But if his enemies triumphed, however short-lived their triumph may be, a punishment has been meted out to him. What is that punishment? Héloïse asked. Besides the burning of his book he was condemned to a term of imprisonment in the monastery of Saint-Médard. A term of imprisonment, Héloïse muttered. But why did he become a monk, and why did he leave the monastery? I cannot tell thee, the Prioress answered, why he became a monk, but he left the monastery of Saint-Denis at the request of the Abbot and the brethren, whose vices he had spoken against in public and privily, and at the request of his disciples, who begged him to set up a school of philosophy, saying that students would come from all parts of the world to hear him, which was no more than the truth, for when he set up his school at Maisoncelle the neighbourhood was not large enough to contain them all. He taught theology, cried Héloïse. He did. But it was his lectures on the poetry of Virgil and Ovid and Tibullus that emptied the rival schools, the Prioress answered. I cannot tell the story fully and do not know how it began to be put about that he should not be allowed to teach theology—— Because he was not a priest, Héloïse interjected. It could not have been else, the Prioress answered, for it was proved that he taught nothing contrary to the teaching of the Church. But, Mother, the term of imprisonment. The term of imprisonment, the Prioress repeated; I am afraid that no term was mentioned. No term mentioned! cried Héloïse. The words were: perpetual seclusion in a monastery, the Prioress answered, and Héloïse stood staring like one daft, her thoughts upset, her mind and face awry, recovering herself a little when the Prioress said: but the legate, Conan, will remit the sentence. It is understood that it cannot be longer than a few months; it may not be longer than a few weeks. But, my dear child, had I known the news would affect thee like this, I would not have told thee. Take heart;

the sentence is merely nominal. Sister Josiane will return presently and she will tell the story better than I. Methinks now that I should not have ventured into it at all. Stephen—— It was he, Héloïse interrupted, who brought the news? The Prioress answered that it was, and that all France was speaking of the sentence. But the nuns will not speak of it to thee, only Sister Josiane, who can tell the story better than anybody else. He made a great defense? Héloïse asked, and the Prioress answered that the excellence of his defense irritated the Council, and he was advised to withdraw it.

CHAP. XXXII.

I HAVE just learnt, Sister Josiane, that Pierre Abélard, once my husband, now my brother in Jesus Christ, was condemned at Soissons to throw his book on the Trinity into the flames whilst reading aloud the Athanasian Creed. He is now a prisoner in the monastery of Saint-Médard, so much I have learnt from the Prioress, but it appears that there is hope that the papal legate, Conan, will release him soon; perhaps at once. You can imagine my grief, Sister, so begin the story, which the Prioress says nobody will be able to tell as well as you—not even our chaplain, who brought the news.

Sister Josiane laid her book aside and the two women stood looking at each other, Héloïse thinking that she read annoyance at the interruption in the tall Breton's flat face, lighted with round, pale, wandering eyes, in whom she seemed to trace a likeness to Madelon; which was strange, if it were true, for no women were more different in shape, Madelon being short and round and Sister Josiane tall and thin, the nearest thing that Héloïse had ever seen to a plank in a human being, in front like a plank and behind nearly as flat; a rumpless, bosomless woman, with thin shoulders and long thin arms, and untidy brown hair often slipping from underneath her coif. Héloïse was never sure whether she was attracted or repelled by Sister Josiane, for she was both by turns. A sour, evil-visaged woman, she would say, and again she was won by the kindly nature of the sister, which responded at once to the claim of physical suffering—Héloïse herself had been ill once or twice and other nuns had been ill, and Sister Josiane attended upon them all, never making complaint. She responds to human suffering, Héloïse often said to herself; she is gentle and kind in front of it and obdurate only in ideas. She would watch by my sick-bed hour after hour, but if it were to save my life she could not concede that Abélard is a master philosopher. She almost laughed in my face when I compared him with Plato and Aristotle; it would have been better if she had, for laughter is not cruel like contempt; and Héloïse bethought herself how contempt lingered about those thin lips and that horrid little perky, insolent, lumpy nose. Two minutes after Héloïse had laughed at her anger, saying to herself: Josiane is hard and narrow in her ideas, inflexible in them; but we like her as we like a surly dog who will not make friends with us. But if you would read his books, Sister, Héloïse remembered saying, you would—— Agree with you, Sister, Josiane answered, that he is greater than Plato and Aristotle? Now you are sneering, Héloïse replied. But though we may not compare the present with a past so far away, you will admit, I think, that Abélard is the greatest philosopher that has lived since antiquity.

There lived in France three hundred years ago a philosopher to whom all the world is indebted, the one original mind since Plato and Aristotle and equal to them,

Sister Josiane had answered sharply. Who may that one be? Héloïse asked. John Scotus Erigena? Sister Josiane's sour face lighted up at the sound of the name, her face became pleasant to look upon and Héloïse learned from her that John Scotus was an Irishman who left the barbarians at home and came to France and taught at the Court of Charles the Bald. Sister Josiane took down his *Treatise on Predestination,* and after reading to Héloïse for an hour, she began to expound the master, saying: I will make plain the master's thought, which is not for everybody. To be among the goats, as it is said in our language of images, which is not the language of pure intellect, only means living the happy life of human beings according to nature, and the teaching of the master is that to live the separate life is not to forfeit the eternal life; for all things return to God ultimately, all things being of God; nothing is lost; but deification is not for these livers of the separate life, but for some men and some angels only, as we are given to understand from the parable of the wise and the foolish virgins. The foolish represent those who seek only natural goods; by the wise are signified those whose thoughts turn to the identity of all things with God. A master mind is surely plain in these lines, and at some other time I should like to read to you *On the Division of Nature,* the master's great work, thrown into a dialogue between master and pupil, and when you——

Héloïse remembered rising to her feet thinking she would never speak again except on plain matters of business to Sister Josiane, whom she suspected of forcing her, by the deliberate repetition of the word master, to acquiesce in the belief that Abélard was not an original but merely a secondary mind. But the love of conquest brings us back to the surly dog that will not accept our

friendship, and Héloïse found it hard to sit in the library
reading without ever exchanging words with Sister Josiane, even when she needed her help, which she often did
of late, for she knew little of philosophy and was puzzled
by the idiom; and when the reconciliation, which could
not be long delayed, came about one day in the library,
Héloïse could not help smiling at the words spoken
behind her: so you are reading the master? It was Sister
Josiane, who had come in without Héloïse hearing her,
so buried was she in the master's great work. The
master is sometimes hard to follow, said Sister Josiane, but he is worth following, and the recompense helps
us to forget the pain that we have endured. The voice
sounded so friendly in her ears that Héloïse brightened
and broke into speech suddenly as a bird will into song.
For the word master offended her no longer. She began
to like to hear it on Sister Josiane's lips, and soon after
she began to be attracted by Josiane's stories of the
master, and to see him in her imagination in great rages
in his classroom at the Court of Alfred the Great, where
he was stabbed and killed by his pupils, who could not
bear with his evil temper; such was their excuse for the
murder. A wonderful and symbolic death, she said, for
is it not so always? Children devour their fathers. Sister
Josiane did not answer, and Héloïse guessed her thoughts
to be an aversion for the story told of the master's death.
I cannot but think, Sister Josiane, that if you had lived
three hundred years ago you would have loved John
Scotus. For we women, she added, are attracted by men's
minds; and waited for Sister Josiane to answer, but she
did not answer, nor even raise her eyes.

And now as the two women stood looking at each other,
Héloïse anxious to hear the reasons for the burning of
the book on the Trinity from Sister Josiane, the words

were remembered, and Josiane's heart was again softened
to Héloïse.   Tell me, Héloïse said, the story of his trial
at Soissons.   The Prioress has sent me to hear it from
you, for you, Sister, more than any other in the convent,
can tell it, so she says; and I know that you would have
suffered if *On the Division of Nature* were burnt publicly
with or without the recital of the Athanasian Creed.   I
should indeed, Sister Josiane answered, and it pains me to
hear the story that is told of his death; I hope it is not true.
True or false, it is a long time ago, said Héloïse.   Does
that make any difference?   Sister Josiane asked gently,
and Héloïse had to ask her again to tell the story of the
trial at Soissons, how it came about and who provoked it.

His popularity provoked it, Sister Josiane answered; if
John Scotus had had as many pupils as Abélard, he too
would have been persecuted.   But what, said Héloïse,
were the charges that were brought against Abélard's
teaching, for charges there must have been.   That is what
I am craving to hear, and none but you can tell me.   Our
chaplain—— Sister Josiane interposed.   But his telling
would be prejudiced or might be, his interest being in
religion as it is taught rather than in true religion as it
exists in the mind, interrupted Héloïse.   It may be that
Stephen is more attached to dogma and doctrine than I
am.   Abélard, Héloïse answered, is more concerned to
make plain the truth that we can only believe in what
we understand, and that it is absurd to teach to others
what we do not understand ourselves, and that in saying
as much he is taking his lesson from our Lord himself,
who blamed the blind for leading the blind.   That is his
teaching, neither more nor less, and it is one that all
reasonable people must approve of, for who is there who
would confess himself to be unreasonable?   But man's
passions are a valley between him and reason, Sister

Josiane answered, and Abélard's success has brought him
many enemies, Albéric and Lotulfe. Yes, it was these who
began the attack ever since the death of Anselm and
Champeaux, Héloïse answered. They have watched
Abélard, seeking ever an occasion for his undoing. Their
school at Rheims, Josiane said, lost many pupils, and
their complaint to Raoul, Archbishop of Rheims, passed
unheeded at first; but they continued their attacks, despite
lack of success, and, wearied out, it appears that Raoul
called to his aid Conan, the Bishop of Préneste, the Pope's
legate in France, and the scandal becoming greater every
day it was at last decided to call a Council together at
Soissons and to invite Abélard to bring his famous book
and defend it if he were able to do so. He lost no time,
for though to defend oneself against heresy is nearly
impossible, Abélard accepted the challenge at once. It
seemed that he asked for nothing better than to bring to
naught these charges that were always urged against him
in secret. He might have pleaded that they could not
try him for heresy in the province of Rheims, but——
But he never tries to evade any questions; his hardihood
none can doubt, Héloïse cried. I can see him going far
as a conquerer, certain of his own power. He needed all
his power, Josiane replied, on arriving at Soissons, for
the clergy have preached against him, and the people were
ready to slay him for having preached, saying there were
three Gods, or that Father, Son and Holy Ghost are only
modes or aspects of God; nobody seems to know what he
taught, except that it was heresy. But he escaped, Héloïse
cried. Tell me what befell him, Sister Josiane. What
next fell out may be guessed. Abélard went to Conan,
the Pope's legate, and laid before him his book, saying
that he bowed before his judgment if he should find anything in it that might be said truly to lead the reader

away from the Catholic faith, and that he was ready to correct any error that could be discovered and to do penance for it, calling the legate's attention to a passage in the book itself in which he said as much.   It appears that his frankness embarrassed the legate, who gave him back his book, asking him to take it to the Archbishop and to his advisers, now become his accusers; and these read and reread the book, weighing every word.

And whilst they were doing all this Abélard spoke to the people explaining his faith, making it intelligible to all, and he did this with so much skill that it began to be said in the towns: it is strange to hear one who is accused defend himself so well, and those who accuse obliged to hold their tongues, and it may hap that in the end the judges will be brought to see that the error is with them rather than with him.   So did the folk talk, it is said, in the streets of Soissons, and the anger of the ecclesias-- tics was fanned by it till one day, Albéric, surrounded by his friends, stopped Abélard in the street, and after a few polite words said to him: I notice in your book a passage which surprises me, for God having begotten God, it seems to me that you cannot do else than admit that God begot himself.   That is a point I can make plain to you at once, Abélard answered; it is in truth the very theme of my essay on the Trinity, and if you wish I will demonstrate it according to the strict rules of logic.   We set no store by logic, Albéric replied; we rely upon authority.   Turn the leaf then and you will find my authority, Abélard answered, and he took the book from Albéric, who happened to have it with him.   And it was the will of God that he should open it at the very page, his eyes falling on the passage, which Albéric had overlooked in his hurry to find something that would tell against Abélard

—a quotation from St. Augustine on the Trinity, Book One: He who believes it to be within the power of God to beget himself is mistaken as much in regard to God as he is in regard to every creature, spiritual or corporeal, for there is none that can beget himself. Albéric's followers were surprised and thrown into confusion, and to defend himself Albéric said it was necessary that the whole thing should be explained. But there is nothing new in it, Abélard answered; you said that you put human reason aside, relying upon authority. I give you the text. If, of course, you wish to understand it, I am ready to make plain to you that if you hold any other opinion except the one I have expressed, you fall into the heresy that the Father is his own Son. How quick he is, Héloïse replied. He sees the point at once. At these words Albéric raised his fist, but he did not dare to strike and went away talking in his beard, declaring that neither authorities nor reasons would help Abélard in this issue. Go on with your story, Sister Josiane, tell me how it was that he was defeated, for they brought about his defeat, so I have heard, forcing him to burn his book with his own hand, condemning him to perpetual imprisonment in a distant monastery. Well, said Sister Josiane, on the last day of the Council, the legate and the Archbishop deliberated privily, for they were not certain how to act; all the clergy were not with them, and Godfrey de Léves, the Bishop of Chartres, notable for his piety and for his learning, called on the council to remember that Abélard was a great philosopher, whose teaching was known, he might say, to all the world, and he warned them that if they were to condemn him without a public discussion many people would say he was condemned unjustly. But despite his earnestness the advice of Godfrey, Bishop of Chartres, was received with murmurs, and every now and

then the joke went round that if the Council wished
to show its wisdom to all and sundry, it could not do
better than to enter into disputation with the celebrated
wrangler.

Godfrey answered that Jesus was a more skilful dis-
putant, yet Nicodemus desired that he should be heard
out of respect for the law. And then, seeking for a way
out of the dilemma, he asked for an adjournment of the
debate, pleading that Abélard should be conducted back
to his monastery by his abbot, who was present, and that
another Council of the most learned should be called who
would look into the matter attentively and decide what
was to be done. In difficult and thorny questions an
adjournment of the debate is always welcomed. Conan
rose and left the Privy Council to say Mass, and it was
while on his way to the Cathedral that he sent Abélard
word that he would be acquitted. Indeed, it seemed as
if he were certain of an acquittal, but his enemies were
powerful enough to persuade the Archbishop Raoul that
for him to allow the Council at Soissons to adjourn without coming to a decision would be tantamount to an
admission that he and all his coadjutors were unable to
settle a theological point between them; and, they added,
Abélard will escape us if the matter be not settled by us;
for elsewhere we shall have no chance of getting a verdict
condemning him, which we have a right to do, for why
should he, who is not even a simple priest, publish these
books without the consent of his own bishop or the Pope!
The Archbishop yielded to persuasion, and rising from
his chair he made as good a case as he could against
Abélard, saying that the Father was all-powerful, the
Son was all-powerful, the Holy Ghost was all-powerful,
and that anybody that held a contrary opinion should
not be listened to. Whereupon Terric, a professor of

theology, answered with a quotation from St. Ambrose: yet there are not three Almighties, but only one Almighty, bringing upon himself a rebuke from the Archbishop. But Terric refused to give way, and cried out the words of Daniel: it is those senseless sons of Israel that, without seeking verification of the truth, would compel a son of Israel. On this the Archbishop rose again and repeated his words, changing them a little to suit the need of the moment. It is without doubt the Father is all-powerful, the Son is all-powerful, and the Holy Ghost is all-powerful, and whosoever calls this dogma into question does not deserve to be heard. All the same, it might be well that our brother should make a public confession of his faith, and Abélard was about to rise to confess and exhibit his faith, with the intention of developing it according to his wont, when his enemies interposed, saying that they did not wish for any words, for all that was needed was that he should recite the Athanasian Creed; and lest he should pretend ignorance of the text they put the book into his hand, telling him to read, which he did amid tears and sobs. And then, as one who had pleaded guilty, he was given into the charge of the Abbot of Saint-Médard, a sentence of confinement in that monastery being pronounced against him. But, cried Héloïse, what is hard to understand is why he did not persist in defending himself after obtaining the promise of the Archbishop that he would be given a hearing. He was advised, it is said, by the Bishop of Chartres not to insist, for any argument that he might use would anger the Council against him still further. He was persuaded by the Bishop to submit, and he did well, Sister Josiane said. To agree to a sentence, cried Héloïse, of imprisonment in the Abbey of Saint-Médard? A sentence only in name, Sister Josiane replied, for though the words were: perpetual seclusion

in a monastery, it is certain the Pope's legate will remit
the sentence and that he will be at liberty, if not in a
few weeks at least no later than a few months. So that
is the whole story, Héloïse said. The whole story, Héloïse,
as told to us by Stephen, our chaplain, and we shall hear
no more till the news comes of his release. Shall we go
out? Sister Josiane asked, breaking the pause suddenly;
the evening is fine.

Héloïse rose to her feet and the nuns walked out of
the convent and stood looking at the river and the mists
that were now rising in the valley, sweeping away shadows
of distant hills and trees. Only half of the tall poplars
could be seen above the white shroud and very little
of the naked branches of the willows. Long herds of
cattle came up from the water-meadows, the convent cows
in a long file, lowing to be relieved of their milk. The
day is moving into night, nothing is ever still, said Héloïse;
a tide is bearing us on, trees, river and animals alike.
Hark to the cry of that bird. Only an owl, said Sister
Josiane, and Héloïse was astonished that she should have
recognised the cry as the owl's, for Sister Josiane saw
and heard little. Her world was in her own mind, and
she was thinking now not of the river nor of the fading
of the fields from sight, but of some thought that John
Scotus Erigena had set forth with startling originality.
And she continued thinking, turning it in her mind, until
Héloïse's sobs called her to her friend's aid. The story I
have told you, she said, is a sad one, but there is this
of hope in it that the Pope's legate will release him from
the monastery.

But it is not for his term of imprisonment that I am
weeping, Héloïse answered, but for the sadness of all
things. In this dim hour we feel that all things are
hopeless and that we know nothing and can do little

except to suffer pain.   Open your eyes, Sister Josiane;
forget the inner world you live in for a moment, for
mists are rising; and the whisper of the river breaks my
heart.   But why should I ask you to see and to hear
what breaks my heart?   I am afraid, Sister Josiane, that
I hardly know what I am saying at this moment.   His
book has been burnt and himself condemned to imprison
ment in a monastery.   What will be the next hap no mai,
knows.   Sister Josiane felt that Héloïse needed kind
words; but she was unable to speak the words that would
hearten her, that Abélard was as great a man as John
Scotus, and the nuns walked towards the convent drawing
their habits about them, for the night was col l though
they were in May.

CHAP. XXXIII.

THE theological chatter roused by the burning of Abélard's book at Soissons came to an end slowly in the
convent of Argenteuil during the summer of 1121, and
his name was not spoken once during the winter, not till
the spring of the next year, in April, when Stephen
returned from Paris one day with the news that everybody
was asking what had become of Abélard, some saying
that he had left France for England, to which Héloïse
answered coldly that nothing was more likely than that
he had gone to England to meditate on the Trinity, like
Roscelin.   Abélard considers the opinions of his enemies
impartially, she said, with the view of finding what truth
there may be in them rather than in the hope of discovering some crack in their arguments wherein to drive a
wedge.

So, Héloïse, thy belief is that Abélard has gone to
meditate on the mystery of the Trinity, like Roscelin,

said the Prioress; and Roscelin's exile in England started her out on long flights of grey narratives, with which she hoped (perhaps) to entertain Héloïse, who sat opposite her, hearing but little, her thoughts far away among troubadours and gleemen, for she had begun to think that the sentence pronounced against Abélard at Soissons might have turned him from philosophy, and that in despair at the hatred of truth among men he might have travelled southward; and, under the name of Lucien de Marolle, found a place as gleeman in the court of some rich nobleman. But it could not be that he had forgotten his pledged faith and troth, and she began a letter:

The news that our chaplain, Stephen, has brought back from Paris is that all are asking: where is Abélard? some saying that, following the example of Roscelin, thou hast gone to England. But this I will not believe, for it is to me, who know thee better than another, more likely that the shameful sentence pronounced against thee at Soissons might have turned thee from philosophy to the composing and singing of songs as of yore. Were it not that I am here this would be easy to believe. But thou canst not have left me to the fate of a black Benedictine robe, not willingly, but the heart of man is dark to himself and to others, and who can say, even thyself, why thou hast left me without a letter for so long? It is not much to ask for, a few lines, an hour of thy time, that is all, and this thou wouldst have given long ago if reasons of which I know nothing did not prevent thee from writing. Then why do I allow evil thoughts of thee to come into my mind? For thou art not recognisable in a cruel treachery towards one who has never sought anything but to please thee rather than God. Thou hast not forgotten that it was thy wish rather than the love of God that made me take the veil? Abélard, write and

soothe an aching heart. Soothe, the word brings back
remembrances, and I would that thou wert by me to
soothe the desires of my soul. Think not well of me,
Abélard; do not believe in my courage but in my feeble-
ness.

Her hand stopped suddenly, and, her eyes fixed on a
far corner of the library, she said: He keeps silent for
some good purpose. It cannot be that years will go by
without some news drifting into the convent. So she
tore up her letter, and, when, some months later, a story
reached Argenteuil that Abélard was living as a hermit
in a mud cabin by the river, she thanked God that she
had not sent it. How lacking I should have seemed in
his eyes had I sent that letter. And then, forgetful of
herself, she began to consider the injustice of men as
typified in the story of Abélard, the great philosopher,
living in wet and wretchedness, without books, without
raiment, without mental or physical comforts, in a mud
cabin by the river. But he was not false to me, and
immediately she was in the midst of a great joy, saying
to herself: It were better to hear of him in a mud cabin
with one disciple than lute-playing amid green swards
under trees. Her great pain had stopped suddenly, for
now she knew that he had not abandoned her, and full of
the thought of the love that he still retained for her, she
began to dream of seeking him in his hermitage. The
Prioress may be persuaded, she said. But no; for me
to seek him in his hermitage might imperil all. But is
there anything, she asked dolefully, her joy changing
swiftly to grief—is there anything left to imperil? There
may be something of the woman he loved still left in me,
but if he delays much longer in the desert he will find
but a shadow of me, and I shall be ashamed. The door of
the library opened. A lay sister, she thought, going

round the convent in search of a nun who is wanted in
the parlour. Sister Héloïse, may I speak to you?   Of
course you may, Sister Paula, and laying her thoughts
aside she welcomed the nun whose baby had scandalised
the convent some years ago.   Paula's eyes are like a
balm, and her mouth, natural as a rose, soothes me,
Héloïse said to herself; and she is not a day older than
she was on the day when the Mothers met to consider
her expulsion.

As she was thinking what the sister's errand might be,
Paula came across the room, her round, childish eyes
amazed; Sister Paula always entered the library amazed
at the sight of so much learning. Have you read all
these books, Sister? Well, not all, Héloïse answered, with
a smile. But you are always in the library, and when
you go out to walk in the orchard you often have a book
in your hand; and I have seen you sitting on the bench
at the end of the broad walk reading instead of watching
the coming and going of the ships. I have often wished
to speak to you, for you were here, Sister, a monitress in
the convent when—— You haven't forgotten the scandal
when my baby was born? You didn't come to see my
baby. But some of the nuns did. Your baby, Sister
Paula, was out at nurse at Argenteuil, and I was not a
sister but a monitress, Héloïse replied. Was that the
reason that you kept away—because you were a monitress?
It was one of the reasons, Héloïse answered, but if I
remember myself rightly, I was at that time a somewhat
learned girl, who thought that books were the whole of
human life. You haven't changed much, Sister Héloïse.
I haven't ceased to value books, Héloïse answered, but I
understand their place in life better than I did.

Of course you were always very learned, Paula continued, and we were all a little afraid of you; but we

liked you and were glad to have you back with us. But
we never thought that you'd come back, and we thought
still less that you would marry, and if anybody had
spoken of our monitress having a baby, we should have
thought—— Well, I don't know what we wouldn't have
thought; we would have looked upon whoever had spoken
as one out of her mind. You were always a puzzle to
us, for religion didn't seem to have the hold upon you
that it had on the others—my sister Catherine came into
the convent for the love of God. You were more like me;
religion is but a part of my life, and that is why the
Prioress and the Mothers seemed to me to blame the birth
of my baby without enough reason. What do you think,
Sister Héloïse? In the end we all come to think as you
do, Sister Paula, that life cannot be halved or quartered;
we must look upon life as a whole. Now I am beginning
to see, Sister Héloïse, that you have changed, and for the
better. A baby brings a great change into a woman's life;
I think every woman is better for having a baby, even
a nun, but you mustn't say that I said it, for I am still
under a cloud, you know. But you are a married woman,
Sister—— I wasn't married when my baby was born,
Héloïse interrupted. Whoever would have thought it!
said Sister Paula, and the little nun sat, her round blue
eyes fixed in astonished gaze. So the learned Héloïse
cannot mind herself any more than a poor little mite
like me. But he married you, which makes it all the
harder to understand why you should have come here,
leaving your husband, the great Pierre Abélard, who, it
is said, puts to shame Plato and Aristotle. And you
aren't a woman that a man would leave in a hurry.

A sad little smile gathered in Héloïse's eyes, and she
answered: It seems to me that the call to leave the world
for the religious life was a mutual one. The world needs

Pierre Abélard, and the work God chose him to do can be better done by a celibate. I don't think, said Paula, that I could have put aside my husband, if I had had one, for the sake of the world. Why not, Sister Paula? Do we not all owe something to the world and to God? Well, I don't think, Paula answered, breaking a little pause, that I should have had the hardihood to throw my luck into the water to swim ashore as best it could, to drown if it couldn't, like the poor dog that the sailors threw out of one of the boats going up and down the Seine last week; we saw him whirled and whirled about in the current and sucked down. But you know best, Sister Héloïse, only I couldn't have done it. We do not know what we could have done, Héloïse said, until the task is set before us. Jesus Christ was deeply troubled in the garden of Gethsemane; he asked that the chalice should pass from him. But, Sister Héloïse, you are not Jesus Christ. The simplicity of Paula's reply took Héloïse aback, and it was some little while before she could collect herself sufficiently to murmur: We must try to follow in his footsteps, however slowly. Now you are talking like Catherine, Paula said. And you do not like me when I talk like Sister Catherine? Not as well as when you talk like yourself, Paula replied. Your sister's mind counted for a good deal in your life, no doubt, Héloïse replied, but Paula's thoughts were far away; and then, speaking suddenly, she said: neither of us knew anything of the world, Catherine even less than I did; we just crossed over from the village to the convent and back from the convent to the village. But you don't know the village, do you, Sister Héloïse? Well, there isn't much to see in Argenteuil. You've been to Paris, you've been up the Loire and away in Nantes; you've been married; you've read all these books; your lot was all that can befall a woman. But I have had nothing, or so very little! to follow my sister into a convent and to have a baby. If father were to hear of my baby! But how could he have failed to hear of your baby? Is he not of the village?

Our house was at the farther end of the village, standing a little apart, and a very pretty house it was. All kinds and sorts of noble folk were often before our door. My father was a lutanist, as you know; but perhaps you don't know that some of the best lutes in France were made in our workshop: viols, vielles, gitterns, citherns—all the stringed instruments. We often had orders from some of the Paris houses for lutes. Our customers were many great counts and viscounts, barons and marquises. The Comte de Rodebœf had many a lute from my father, and I have seen Jean Guiscard in our workshop talking with father. All the lutes and citherns in the convent were made by father, and that is why, perhaps, I never had any taste for reading, and am never happy unless I am singing to a lute or playing the viol or gittern. I often envied you your music, Sister Paula, for music releases us from sad memories better than books. But it was your choice to come here, Paula answered. Was it not yours, Sister Paula? We came here for learning just as you did, Paula replied, and when I was sixteen and Catherine eighteen we left the convent, for father and mother did not wish us to be separated. It was pleasant at first to get away from the ringing of the bell announcing the different lessons, calling us to chapel and to the refectory. We liked the garden, planting vegetables in the spring and gathering fruits in the summer and autumn; we liked to creep into the workshop and to meet father in his leathern apron examining a lute that had come to be mended, to hang round our workman again, to talk about strings and stops, and of all to watch the barons and the counts and the marquises ride up to our gate asking to see father. But after a year or two we began to feel that we had no part in the spectacle. The barons and the counts took no notice of us: they might have if it hadn't been for mother, who shut us away, leaving us to peep through the top windows. An armourer and his wife were the only ones that came to see us, for in the country around there were but hovels and castles. Every morning a bell rang calling the lord's serfs to work, and the lutanist and the armourer were like stranded ships, high and dry; the nobility above us and the tradespeople of Argenteuil below us. So it may have been our loneliness that decided Catherine to return to the convent, or it may have been—— She stopped suddenly and Héloïse sat watching the nun's blank face, guessing her thoughts to be far away, reliving an incident. Of what are you thinking, Sister? she said at last. Paula started out of her dream. Of what am I thinking, Sister? she asked. Of what good to tell a sad story? Sometimes it relieves the mind, Héloïse answered, and then, forgetful of Héloïse, almost as if she were talking to herself, Paula said: It often seems to me that a disappointment in love was a partial motive in determining Catherine's vocation. But I am not sure; Catherine could not tell herself; not now.

All the same a young man given over altogether to the art of lute-playing and singing, at whose castle many festivals were held and who was reputed to be in love with a lady of his own rank, came to our house with a lute to be mended, and while talking to father he stopped suddenly, saying: I hear singing in the room above us. My daughters are singing, father answered, and the Baron, for he was one, and a great power in the country,

said: I can hear but indistinctly, missing many notes.
Whereupon my father called to us to come down; he
bade us sing to the stranger, who pronounced himself
pleased with our singing, and said he would send for
the lute; but instead of sending he came himself to fetch
it.   May I not sing a song or two with your daughters?
he asked, and my father, being much flattered, begged
him to come through the shop into that part of the house
in which we lived.   My thoughts always go back to that
first evening. The evenings that followed it are not so
clear to me; but all that summer-time was pleasant, trying to please the Baron and he trying to please us. Almost
every evening, two or three times a week, he rode over
from his castle.   Mother shook her head, saying, in
answer to father, that though it might be that my sister
and I were no more to him than two voices, it was by no
means sure that a preference would not begin to appear.
Moreover, there are the girls themselves to consider. We
began to hate mother.   It was in the summer-time, and
the evenings went by in our orchard singing, our visitor
walking between us, accompanying us, the moon looking
down through the branches.   Mother often sent father to
bid us to the house, the pretext being cake and wine.
I hated her for it, but Catherine—— I don't know what
she thought, she kept her thoughts to herself; we feared
confidences, for we were both thinking of him; and if
we spake of him it was in the presence of our father and
mother rather than when we were alone, each keeping
her secret, neither trusting the other.   A week rarely
passed without our seeing him; it was in November that
he did not call or send a message and we were all agog.
At last the news came that he had married a lady for her
money, one of his own rank, and we knew we should see
no more of him.   It was then that Catherine spoke of

entering the religious life, and it was with her going
that trouble and loneliness came into my life, for I don't
know that I was in love with the Baron, and Catherine
kept writing that she was offering up prayers that I might
join her in her happiness, the only true happiness, and I
began to think that now the Baron was gone there was
nothing else for me to do but to follow her example. So
I often fell down upon my knees before my bed and
prayed that somebody else might come, for I dreaded the
convent.   But nobody came, only the winter, which is
always hard to bear; and the winter that followed the
Baron's departure was lonelier than the winter that pre-
ceded his coming: cold and wet, with storms of wind,
and afterwards the snowfall, and there seemed to be
nothing but silence, with great falls of snow.   Father
and mother were always talking of the sunset of their
lives, saying that not many more years of life lay in front
of them, and that they would die happy if they knew
what would become of me when they were gone.   At last
I summoned all my courage and said: but father, mother,
if I were to follow Catherine's example and enter the
convent, what would become of you?   You would be
alone.   No answer came from them, but I could see that
there was something in their minds; and at last, in reply
to repeated questions, they confessed the truth to me,
that if I made up my mind to enter the convent, they
too would separate, one going to a monastery, the other
to a convent.   And we all three sat looking at each other,
unable to speak.

Mother died with the melting of the snow and I was
alone with father, who, I could see, couldn't forget his
soul for five minutes together.   His lips would begin to
move and he'd lay the half-finished lute aside, and he
as good as told me that if I entered the convent he would

leave his money to Argenteuil and Saint-Denis, getting
many Masses for the repose of his soul. It was lonelier
than being in the house by oneself, for he walked about
like one in a dream, and when we met he started as if
at the sight of a stranger, as if he had forgotten me, and
I'd answer: Wake up, father, hast forgotten me? And
then he would smile and become himself again; but only
for a little while, and the estrangement continued, getting
worse day by day, till we were apart, even when we were
together, for he was thinking all the time of the prayers
that awaited him in the room overhead. Everything else
was forgotten, and of all the workshop; those who gave
him lutes to repair went away with their broken instruments to be mended in Paris. He has come to hate the
house, I said, for it is part of the life of the world, and
so am I, and if I stay here much longer he will begin
to look upon me as the barrier between himself and his
monastery. So in despair I fell once more to praying
that another baron might come and marry me. Every
night I prayed, but none came; and one night father and
I were alone in the house together, father in the room
above, I in the room below, and I could hear him singing
psalms, praying and striking his breast. It was then
that I gave way. I had borne all I could, and knowing
that I couldn't resist father any longer, and that the
convent waited half-a-mile down the road, the river came
into my mind, and I bethought myself that I might run
thither, not to drown myself but to buy or beg a passage
in one of the ships plying between Paris and Havre. You
know they anchor at night by the shore, and my idea was
to stand on the bank screaming till somebody on board
awoke; maybe the captain, I said, who will take a bribe,
or a sailor; and with no other thought in my mind but
to escape from everything I had ever seen or heard, I

ran on till I reached Stephen's house, and there I was stopped by the sight of the priest reading by the window, the lamp at his elbow. Father, I said to myself, will not miss me for a long while, but he will miss me sooner or later and it is wicked to go away without leaving a message; and with whom can I leave it if not with our priest? Something laid hold of me. It is said that a guardian angel is always on one side of us and an evil angel on the other, the good angel trying to overpower the bad, the bad trying to overpower the good. It must have been like that with me then, or something like that, for I couldn't pass the house. My good angel must have got the better of the bad angel at that moment, giving him a fall, and before the bad angel could rise again I knocked at the priest's door, which was opened to me by an old woman, his housekeeper, who said: It is late to see his reverence; his reverence is tired. But I wouldn't go without leaving my message, and after a while she said: I'll ask his reverence if he will see you. Come this way, he said, and took me into his room, and I told him what my life was, and that I hoped in a few hours to be far away. I remember all I said and the stillness of the room, with the priest listening and speaking not a word. Now I must go, I said. It is my duty to warn you, he answered, that when your father hears that you have gone away for ever to live with sailors—— That it will kill him, I cried; well then, there is no escape for me, I must enter the convent. But you do not know, my dear child, he answered me, what the life on board those ships is, and the violence that the sailors offer to women. Life in which there is nothing is worse, I said. You must return home, my dear child, to-night. And then, feeling that my project had come to naught, I fell to weeping, my head thrown across the priest's table. How I wept! My

sobs were so loud that he must have thought my heart
would break, for he called in his old housekeeper, who
took me in her arms, but I shook her off. Stephen begged
of me to be calm, but I cried: Leave me, leave me. Tears
there were everywhere, on the priest's books, on his table,
on the floor. I must have wept a great deal, and there
was reason for my weeping, for never was anybody
unhappier than I was in the half-hour I spent in the
priest's house. In the garden was a syringa, and whenever the night sighed the thick, sickly perfume came into
the room, and I think it was because I could not bear the
cloying scent any longer that I escaped from him. But
Stephen followed me, and when we were in the road, he
said: You have come to me to-night and it is my duty to
protect you from yourself. I will not warn your father
of your project, but to-night you must return home, for
you are acting on impulse; if to-morrow night you wish
to leave everything you can do so, but not to-night; to-
night I am responsible for you. My strength was gone
and I could not dash away from him.

Father was still praying when I entered the house, but
it didn't matter; I was exhausted. But the next night?
Héloïse asked. Next night Stephen came to see us; he
came the night after and every night till he persuaded
me to become a nun, and here I am, a Benedictine nun
with a baby. But the father of your baby, Héloïse asked,
do you see him? Do not ask me to tell you my secret:
it is the only thing that remains to me, the only thing
really my own—that and baby. And then, misinterpret-
ing the change that came into Héloïse's face, she said:
But you're not angry? You'll allow me to keep my secret?
Did you come to the library to tell me your story?
Héloïse asked. I hadn't thought of telling my story to
anybody, Paula answered; I came to talk about my baby,

but it seems to me that I have talked only of myself. If you care to see my little girl, the Prioress will give you leave to come with me to Argenteuil. Yes; there was something else I had to say to you. Why don't you send for your baby? Ask the Prioress's leave. The convent would be less dreary with a little fellow running about. Mine is but a nun's sin, and she can't come hither, though I begged and prayed the Prioress, if it was only once a week or once a month. But she wouldn't hear of it, my baby is a scandal, so it would seem. But why? for a baby is such a natural thing. We have talked of all this already, and I have kept you from your book. Now I must hasten away.

The door closed softly, and Héloïse sat thinking of Paula, who seemed to her like a flower long shut in a book which still retains some of its colour and perfume; and then her thoughts turned to Astrolabe, a child of three, for whom she would have to wait three or four years, for so young a child could not bear the long journey. Not till he was six would it be safe to send for him. For three long years she would have to wait, and all that time perhaps without news of Abélard. For none came to the convent, and the rare letters that reached her contained no mention of him, and she asked herself wildly if Denise thought that because she was a nun she ceased to be a wife and a mother. Six months passed without a letter and then a letter came, bringing news of Astrolabe, she said, and on turning the page her eyes caught sight of her child's name, brightening her face, but only for a moment for the news that the letter brought her was that the child was ailing and that they had sent him to the sea with Madelon, to her own country. Where French is not spoken, Héloïse said; so the child that Madelon will bring me sooner or later will come to me without French or Latin. On reading a little further she learnt that the child had recovered his health, which was good news; and she took heart, for a child forgets a language as easily as he learns it, and nearly persuaded herself that she did not care to have him back till he had learnt French, for a child with only Breton on his lips would not be her child; nor would he be Abélard's, who knew no word of that language. It would be hard to be without him for three years, and harder still to be without news of Abélard. It seemed to her that she could bear with the absence of one but not of both, and she often asked herself if she were given her choice which she would choose. Abélard, her heart cried, comes first, but she loved her baby boy, who was not only hers but Abélard's; and when he returned to her she would begin to teach him French and Latin. But out of what book would she teach him French? Out of his father's songs? But there is very little of the language in a song, and Astrolabe would ask her to tell him stories, saying: Madelon used to tell me beautiful stories of giants and wizards, and of Peronnik, the village fool, who was not such a fool as he seemed to be, for he overcame the enchantress in her castle and released all the prisoners she kept under lock and key in the castle dungeons. The story had almost passed out of her mind, but she might recall it. . . . Already it was coming back to her, and the task of writing it would be a pleasant one if she could only remember how Peronnik met the enchantress. But all she could think of was that she used to ride by on a black horse followed by a foal, and not being able to fashion a story out of this material, she bethought herself of a white knight riding through a village perishing for want of rain from a drought brought about by the golden bowl and diamond spear having fallen into the power of the

enchantress.   The enchantress might send one of the
knights she had enslaved to waylay the knight in quest
of the Grail—a cripple, Héloïse said to herself, and her
arm was stretched across the table for a pen.   With
rhymes and notes to help it the common language was
delightful but without them French seemed so strange,
so incongruous in prose, that she would not have dared
to continue the story in it if it had not been that she
must have something in French out of which Astrolabe
could learn his native language.   As Astrolabe did not
speak French he might as well begin his lessons in French
as in Latin.   But it is not easy to write in a language
that one has never seen written.   And there were other
difficulties; the Latin construction was always getting
in her way, and very often she lacked courage to write a
sentence as she would speak it.   Living speech seemed
to her so barbarous that perforce she must juggle with it;
it was not amenable to grammatical forms.   But it is
meant only for a child, she said.

After writing a few pages she began to enjoy the
prattle, for it is no more, she said, excusing herself to
herself.   My boy shall read of Æneas in Latin, and
of Peronnik the Fool in French, in the language that
the Breton had learnt in the French village, for
Peronnik was a Breton.   Or was it that Peronnik was
a backward child who learnt no language from his mother,
of whom he remembered nothing, and knew not whence
he came?

CHAP. XXXIV.

THE wet summer of 1127 was followed by an autumn of
sunny airiness, blue skies, with white clouds unfolding,
the afternoons passing into glowing evenings and the

evenings into soft, still nights, the like of which Cherriez,
the convent gardener, couldn't discover in his memories.
And the decline of the year was as lovely on earth as in
the skies, the slender leaves of the willows falling unob-
trusively through the branches into the current, the crum-
pled leaves of the crisped orchard, reft of its fruit a
month ago, falling now and then with a little crinkly
sound, the robin singing the dirge of the year from the
hedge's highest spray all the long day through, till the
rooks came wheeling home to the dishevelled elms showing last year's nests. And while watching the starlings
in the fields over which the swallows had circled during
the wet days gone by, Héloïse told the sisters who walked
beside her of the bird she had freed from lice in the rue
des Chantres, at which they all wondered, till the starlings
went away with a whirr of wings, unable to bear any
longer the gaze of human eyes. The nuns resumed their
walk in thoughts of the mysterious summer-time, come,
it seemed to them, from beyond the skies, a miracle vouchsafed by God, since Cherriez could not explain it. Even
the chill that a few evenings later caused them to draw
their habits about them as they came up from the river
did not shrink their belief that they might escape the
winter, nor did the cold night and the colder morning,
that brought the nuns forth from their cells shivering
in the dark to pray, for the Angelus bell was ringing.
After the prayer, Sister Agatha said: fog and frost, what
a change from yesterday; and when the nuns looked out
of their doorways the ghostly landscape turned their
thoughts eastward, and it was in every mind that Jerusalem had fallen into the hands of the Saracen. Somebody avouched it. But a few hours later their belief in
the Infidel's triumph was dispelled by the top branches
of the elms showing above the mist, glowing in the light

of a pallid, rose-coloured sun, full of promise of a fine
day. And certain, then, that the Sepulchre was still
safe in Christian hands, the nuns set themselves to the
enjoyment of the sunshine, which lasted for many days
more, for nearly two weeks, till a storm began at midnight, clattering so loudly among the roofs that the nuns
quaked in their beds thinking perhaps that God was
preparing the world's end. The leaves rustling on the
panes seemed to them angels bidding them awake for
judgment, and when Agatha opened the door she bade
the sisters behold a heap of dried leaves in the porch.
Leaves must fall, said Sister Tetta, but the storm cannot
have failed to bring down some trees. Even if we do
lose a tree or two, Sister Angela answered, we shall have
more firewood, for after so much fine weather the winter
is sure to be severe. Do not say that, cried Sister Tetta,
lest you bring to pass what you fear; none suffers from
colds as I do. Cherriez will be able to tell us, Sister
Angela answered, if a fine autumn precedes a cold winter.
The bell for Mass began to ring, and Sext and None
seemed longer that morning than they had ever seemed
before. But all things end, the nuns said, as they escaped
from the chapel and ran for their cloaks, eager to enquire
out the havoc the storm had wrought.

Only two trees had crashed, and some branches, and
among these Cherriez was busy with adze and saw. At
that moment a great gust fell upon the nuns, whirling
their habits round their legs, and carrying the feathery
seeds of the traveller's joy from the wall up into the air
like pale smoke. The gust gone by is naught to the
ones that are coming, said Cherriez, and when they have
blown themselves out it will be the while of the frost.
We shall be walking on the river before Christmas. No,
ladies, it isn't the black side that I see, but the white,

the old man cried after the affrighted nuns. If Cherriez speaks the truth let us pray that God may send us another storm, said Angela. And next year, when there are no more trees? asked Tetta. None answered her, for it was in everybody's mind that next year must look after itself; and with the news that two trees were down and many great branches, the nuns turned to the convent in the hope that Mother Ysabeau, in view of the wood the storm had provided, would allow them a fire in the community-room. But we are still in November, she answered, and our provision of firewood is scantier this year than last. No fire till December! cried Sister Angela. Nowhere but in the kitchen and in the Prioress's room, Mother Ysabeau replied, and all checked the words on the ends of their tongues: the Prioress conceals a box of live charcoal in her muff.

I'd like to hear what you thought of the cold in Brittany; it's twice as cold by the sea as it is here! cried Astrolabe. But you nuns roll yourselves up in your warm habits like little hedgehogs. Cherriez found one in a ditch and he wouldn't unroll till we put him in a tub of water; and then he began to swim, and we saw his little black snout. But wasn't it very cruel, unkind, said Sister Tetta, to put the hedgehog into cold water? We wanted to see his little black snout, Astrolabe replied, and he didn't mind the cold water. I am never cold; I could run down to the river naked, and could come back hopping and leaping—— Like a little hedgehog, interjected Sister Tetta. Hedgehogs can't hop and leap, Astrolabe answered, but fleas can, and I'd come back like a little flea. Dost know what I'd do? I'd run up and down thy back, biting little pieces out of thee. Astrolabe, I forbid thee to undress thyself, and a little more strictness in thy speech would become thee. But, mother, all the sisters wear heavier stuff than I. Thy clothes, mother, are thicker, warmer than mine: feel. Hush, hush, Héloïse replied, for thy bad French wounds our ears. But, mother, three months ago I had but Breton and thou couldst not understand me, and now we are talking together easily—— Hush, hush, said Héloïse, and all the nuns laughed and were pleased to see Héloïse's pretty, small-featured son, eager and blithe as a blackbird, lean across the table, minded to question his mother or anybody who would listen to him, his eagerness, however, checked by a slight stutter. They vied with each other as to who should spoil him the most, and every nun, old and young, liked to kiss his sunny face. But he liked kisses so little that, after his promise to kiss Sister Angela if she ran a race with him round the cloister, he only offered his cheek, and when she kissed him according to her taste, he cried: Sister Angela, I do not like wet kisses, nor kisses at all, but the wet ones least. Astrolabe, thou'rt rude, uncouth, Héloïse said, for all the nuns have been kind to thee, Sister Angela more than any other. Yes, mother, but my promise was not for a wet kiss—— We have heard enough, his mother answered, and the thought came to her that Astrolabe must beg Sister Angela's pardon; but on second thoughts it seemed to her that if she said nothing the child's aversion for Angela's kisses would be forgotten more easily.

It was some six weeks after this quarrel with Sister Angela, at the end of a snowy afternoon, that Astrolabe began to beg the nuns to chase him round the convent, saying that if they caught him they might eat him as hounds eat a fox. But you won't eat me, for I am as cunning as the fox and will lead you a scamper till you're worn out. Astrolabe, Astrolabe, Héloïse cried, and then, turning to the trembling sisters, she said: If there **was**

a fire on the hearth I would read you the story that I
wrote for my son to learn French out of. Oh, mother,
let us have a fire. It isn't for thee to ask for a fire, Astrolabe, for thou'rt never cold. He says he is never cold,
but I know better than that, said Madelon, and she began
to relate her journey from Brittany, but was cut short
by Sister Angela. We'll hear that journey another time;
we are now thinking of a fire, or praying to Mother
Ysabeau for one. Wood is very scarce, said Mother Ysabeau. But we are now in January, cried many voices;
snow is falling and we are so cold that we couldn't listen
to the story that Sister Héloïse has written without some
logs. Well, well, said Mother Ysabeau, and without waiting for more the nuns, with Astrolabe at their head, ran
for light wood; and before the logs were burnt through
many were asking Héloïse to read, but she said: As soon
as the fire has begun to warm the room; it is still as cold
as before, and you'd be thinking of your toes all the time.

More and more logs were required, and when Héloïse
had finished reading the story out of which every morning
Astrolabe learnt his lesson, Mother Hilda said: Speak to
us, Astrolabe, of thy mother's story, so that we may see
if it be plain to thee. It is all plain enough, he answered,
but it isn't the story they tell in Brittany, not altogether;
some things are the same, but not all. And which
story dost thou like the better, thy mother's or Madelon's? Mother Hilda asked him. But he kept silence,
and something like a scowl came into his face, and remained in it till his mother began to chide him for not
answering Mother Hilda. Which story is to thy liking,
darling? I like both, so I'd have mother put the two
together. And when Mother Hilda asked him what there
was in his mother's story that he'd have put into Madelon's, he answered: An old withered tree with no leaves

and but one branch left for the black ravens to sit upon and talk to each other. That is what Madelon told me, and she says that Peronnik thought the ravens in the old tree were tame, for his was tame and fed out of his hand. So what do you think he did? He climbed high enough to hear the birds talking, and what he heard was: Look here, look there, look everywhere. Peronnik thought that they were talking to him, so he peeped down the hole in the tree, and what do you think he saw?

Astrolabe would not continue his story till all the nuns had tried to guess what he saw, some saying gold, some saying great treasure, some bethinking themselves of the golden bowl and the diamond spear; but Astrolabe shook his head at all the answers. At last a sister said: A sword, to which Astrolabe replied: Yes, he found a sword in the tree, but something else; guess again. The nuns could think of naught likely, and to soothe the child they said books and candlesticks and crowns and sceptres. No, no, no; Peronnik saw a knight's helmet, and Madelon says that where there is a helmet there may be a head, and perhaps a man's body, too. So Peronnik was afraid that there might be a little secret door out of which the man would come and kill him; and he was so afraid that he would not go near the tree for a very long time. He tried very hard not to think of the knight, but he could not help it, mother, and at last he went to the tree to have another little peep. The knight was still there, and Peronnik climbed down the tree in a great hurry and was going to run away, when the ravens flew round him crying: Look here, look there, look everywhere. Peronnik was frightened, for he knew ravens were sometimes very wicked birds, but he hadn't gone very far when he began to say to himself: Perhaps the knight isn't alive and cannot hurt me. So one day he came with an adze

and chopped a big hole in the bark, and what do you
think he found? A big suit of armour with nothing in
it but the knight's bones.

O, what a dreadful tale thou'rt telling us, cried the
nuns. We shall not sleep to-night. All the same, said
Sister Tetta, tell us what the armour was made of, if it
was the work of a wizard. It was all made of silver,
Astrolabe answered, and mother says it was not a wizard
but a wizardess, who kept many knights in the dungeons
of the Grey Castle. Every one wanted to kill her, but
she was very clever and promised to wed the one who
could ride round the castle ramparts. Did Peronnik do
this? Héloïse asked. He did, the child answered; and
when he came back leading his horse by the bridle, the
wizardess, I think, was afraid of Peronnik. And what
befell him on the battlements? Mother Hilda asked. O,
I forgot to tell about his jumping from battlement to
battlement, and the wizardess, who wished to watch him,
told one of her knights, who was a poor cripple, to hold
up a silver shield so that she could see Peronnik. He
jumped and jumped his horse, and then rode down a
long flight of steps and ran up to her. She was so frightened that she gave one big cry and turned into smoke.
She left her keys behind for Peronnik to unlock the
dungeon door, where she had shut up the poor knights.
When they came out and saw that they were free they
all sang a hymn. And then they went away with Peronnik—— Here Astrolabe hesitated. Yes, darling? said
his mother. Then they marched away to win the Holy
Sepulchre from the Saracen. Bravo, little man, said
Mother Hilda, thou hast told the story as well as thy
mother did. But might not the two stories be put into
one? Astrolabe asked. I like Madelon's story, for in it
are the blasted tree, the ravens, and the suit of armour,

and a wizard; I do not care for mother's wizardess, for I don't think a woman would have a castle and keep knights in vaults. The knights wouldn't listen to her; knights are not such fools. In Madelon's story the wizardess is a wizard, a man with a black beard; his name was Rogéar. And a man with a beard is more to thy taste, said Mother Hilda, than a wizardess? A man should have a beard always, for without one he would be the same as a woman, wouldn't he? Before Mother Hilda could answer, the door was opened and the portress ran through it crying: There's an old man begging at our gate for shelter, Mother Prioress. He is numb with cold and weary almost to death in his limbs, for the wolves are after him; such is his story and 'tis easy to believe him, for I have heard the devils howling down by Cherriez's hovel. What say you, Sisters? Many voices spoke of the Prioress. But, said the lay sister, the wolves are after him, and in a few minutes will take him by our gate if it be not opened to him. Then open to him and we'll seek the Prioress, cried the many voices, and the talk fell on the age of the man and the peril he stood in by their gate and how he could be saved by their mercy. May I go to see the wolves through the grating, mother? If it pleases thee, Héloïse replied. But Sister Agatha, away with thee, for while we talk the wolves may be quarrelling over bones. Away they all went at a scamper, and a few minutes afterwards an old stooped and grizzled man, with a musical instrument tied on his back, tottered into the room, the nuns making room for him by the fire. Thou'rt so cold, gleeman, that thou canst barely move thy fingers, said the Prioress, and the old man lifted his eyes to her and mumbled: Yes, indeed, so frozen am I that I can hardly move my fingers. But you shall have some music when my fingers are loosened.

Some more logs were thrown on to the hearth and a great blaze was soon flaring, for which the gleeman thanked the sisters, saying: it will be some time yet——— But we're not thinking of thy music, good man; warm thyself, Héloïse answered, and the sisters drew together, for the smell of the thawing man was not sweet, saying: We cannot turn him out to the wolves when he is warm; he must sleep somewhere. He must indeed, but not by the fire in the community-room, said one. He will be cold in the woodshed, said another. Not so cold, Mother Hilda interrupted, if we can give him some rugs, and meanwhile some warm milk will help him to recover himself. You're in luck, ladies, to have cows giving milk, and I hope that the door of the byre is a stout one, for the wolves are in plenty in these parts and will be scratching and gnawing at the planks every night; and should they find a loose one they will have it out, and if there isn't a loose one they will be striving to dig a hole under the planks. But the ground is too hard for digging, so there's no fear that way. But see to your planks every morning, or when you come with your pails only some scattered hoofs and horns you'll find. Drink, gleeman, said Héloïse, handing him the cup. And may a high place in heaven reward you, lady, the vagrant answered, as he handed back the empty cup to her and stretched his legs anew to the fire.

The icicles with which he was covered began to drip; they were in his hair and beard, in the tattered hose that covered his legs, and the eyes of the nuns followed the rents and the patches in the old green cloak, green-worn with age and weather that he wore from his chin to his knees, his only garment, maybe, else he would have thrown it away so that he might run faster across the fields from the wolves. And as if guessing the thoughts that the nuns were thinking, he said: If it hadn't been for Cherriez's ass, that had wandered from his stable, foolish fellow, I should be picked clean by now. Thou hast in mind a clean-picked ass, said Sister Angela. That was in my mind, indeed, the vagrant answered, for the wolves were at my heels and the ass crossed my slot; but one ass among twenty hungry wolves would be but a mouthful apiece. The tearing and the quarrelling over him gave me time to run across the fields, and lest, ladies, you think that I am lying to you, come with me and you'll find that my scent has brought the wolves to your gate, still licking their lips in memory of the ass. May I not put my eyes to the grating to see the wolves licking their chops, mother? cried Astrolabe. But what wouldst thou see in a wolf, my son? Héloïse asked. Why, a wolf, mother, what else? Whereat the nuns laughed, and the Prioress said: Let him not be disappointed. Since then, Astrolabe, the Prioress wishes thee to see a wolf, go fetch thy cloak and wrap thyself in it well, and I will take thee to the gate and lift thee up to the grating to see whatever there may be to be seen of the wolves.

And many of the nuns being as curious as the boy to see the pests, the Prioress cried after them: Let the grating suffice; do not open the door to peep if the wolves that are in front of the grating be round the corner, for such would be playing with the danger which our visitor here will tell is a danger indeed to all who have not a high wall between them and the fields this night. Shall we see the wolves, mother, licking their chops? Before Héloïse could answer, a sniffing under the door told them that the wolves had not lost the scent of the gleeman, though a powder of snow had fallen since the ass was eaten. Lift me up, mother. Yes, there they are; one, two, three, four, five, and two sniffing under the door;

great hairy things with long tails and mouths filled with great white teeth. Could we not throw something at them, mother? Could we not do them some harm for having eaten Cherriez's ass? cried Astrolabe. But they were hungry, Héloïse said. But should one animal eat another animal if it be hungry? The laws of wolves and the laws of men are not the same, my dear child, Sister Angela remarked sententiously. But aren't they? cried Astrolabe. Should we not eat all we could get if we were hungry? No, I do not think we should, Héloïse answered, and as Astrolabe still seemed doubtful, she said: Thou wouldst not eat the old man who is warming himself by the fire inside? But the wolves would. Art sure, mother? queried Astrolabe. Well, the old man thinks they would, and he doesn't feel called to put the wolves' appetite to the test. So come, let us go back to our fire, for it is cold here.

Our gleeman's fingers are thawed, said Astrolabe, for he is playing his instrument, whatever it may be, to please Mother Prioress. Let us hurry to see him, and suiting the action to the word, Sister Angela and Astrolabe ran a race up the corridor. Well, did you see many wolves? the Prioress asked. Yes, there were seven, Mother Prioress, cried Astrolabe, waiting to chew the old man up. Be not so precise, Astrolabe, Héloïse said, waiting for the man here is enough. Mother Prioress, I wanted to drop a blazing torch or pour some boiling water on them for having eaten the ass that Cherriez said I should ride. You'll never ride that ass, gentle sir. He was gobbled long ago, and if I had not had legs enough to run across the field in front of them and to make one of you ladies hear my knocks when I did, you'd have found my bones on the threshold, with my organistrum beside me, a gift from the beautiful Comtesse D'Urgel. Denis raised his eyes, and looking through the half-closed lids he forebore, not certain yet if the story which was part of his wont to tell, for it raised himself in the consideration of donors, would be well received in the company in which he found himself. But as the hour wore by he was encouraged to speak of the giver of his organistrum, and he told that his mother was a bakeress at the Comtesse D'Urgel's castle, and that when she drew the bread from the oven she threw the loaves into a basket, which it was his business to carry round the castle, distributing them as he went. Going up one stair and down another, the old man said, I sang my songs; and on coming near to the Comtesse's apartments I always remembered to sing my best songs, so it came to pass that she delayed me on my rounds, asking me to sing my songs over and over again to her; and there being many instruments of music in her rooms, she would give me them one after the other. My mother was but a bakeress, but the Comtesse said that my mother mattered naught to her so beautifully did I follow her voice on the lute. Again Denis raised his lids a little, and judging the company to be favourable to his story, he continued to tempt them with it, saying: Good ladies here, I durst not tell how I came to hope that a great lady like the Comtesse D'Urgel could love a bakeress's son, though he sang as the angels sing in heaven. My love for the Comtesse was far from mortal sin, far from that which is venial, yet not to divine love would I compare it, though all love that is not sinful is akin to divine love. . . . Who shall say? Not the same, of course, ladies, only a shadow of the love we hope to come into hereafter. Now lest I am not plain to you all I will go further and tell that though my mother baked the castle's bread and I was but the carrier thereof up and down turret stairs, the thought laid hold of me that I might send my songs to the Lady D'Urgel, which I did, till she said to me one day: Some great trouvère loves me from afar, for songs in praise of my beauty reach me. And why, Lady D'Urgel, must it be some great trouvère? Who else would dare, and who else could fashion such melody? As she was about to sing to me my heart took fright, and I could not do else than to beg the Lady D'Urgel's permission to finish my round, for with so many waiting for the daily bread, I said, I shall not be able to give my thought to the song. Deliver thy bread, boy, she said, and return to me with thine empty basket. At which my heart was so uplifted that I began to sing one of the songs I had sent the Comtesse, as I crossed the courtyard, stopping singing suddenly with a great fear in my heart lest I had betrayed myself. But the mischief was done; the Comtesse's window was open; she had heard me.

He was about to continue his story, but before doing so his watchful eyes, accustomed to spy peril everywhere, went round the company, resting longer on the Prioress's face than on any other, and meeting nowhere a frown but only eagerness to hear him, he said: Ladies, I will tell you that my rival in this, my first and last love, was the great Comte de Montfort, and when he returned with his gleeman to the castle, Catherine, Comtesse D'Urgel, thinking no harm, showed him one of the songs she had received from the bakeress's son, a minstrel by the grace of God discovered to her by his singing of this very song as he crossed the yard. She would have had the Comte make me one of his retinue, but the Comte could not believe in the purity of his lady, and I was driven out, and being but a boy did not know how to seek services as gleeman, and so enlisted myself in the holy army for Palestine, where I fought the Infidel for three years.

I was at the siege of Antioch, ladies, and afterwards at that of Jerusalem, but found no recompense for bravery when I returned to France for the Infidels I had slain. But perhaps you ladies are weary of my story, for this is no story such as you should listen to. I have heard nothing unworthy in thy story, Denis, said the Prioress, but much to thy credit, and we pray thee to proceed into it.

And the gleeman, thus encouraged, continued a little while longer, telling that he met in his wanderings another lady whose praises he sang for a year or more. But at the end of the year a whispering came into his heart: Denis, thou'rt losing the love of thy immortal soul for the love of a mortal woman; better that thou shouldst return to the Holy Land, was what the voice said to me. I am not learned, ladies, in words, but in songs, and now I have told you all or nearly all. But didst return to the Holy Land a second time? the Prioress asked. I did, troth and faith, and when I returned from the Holy Land, weary and ill from wounds and feeble, I again found no recompense, and so I have wandered on, singing by waysides and in castle yards till I reached your door. But, said Héloïse, the instrument that thou playest so beautifully was given to thee by her? By the Comtesse D'Urgel. Look at it, I pray you, ladies. Did it accompany thee to the Holy Land? Héloïse asked. No, he answered; I had to separate myself from my beautiful organistrum, and that was the heartbreak of it all. I left it in trust with a friend, who sold it in my absence, and by some strange chance it found its way back into the hands of the Comtesse D'Urgel, to whom I went on my return, and she said that I had been accused of selling the instrument, and that she had kept it, for she knew that I could not sell that which came to me from her own hands. It was given to me again with these words: Denis, what I have given I have given, and would keep thee here for my gleeman, for I shall always remember the songs that I received from thee. But I may not. Her very words, ladies. So with some pieces of money I was sent away again, and have since roamed with varying fortune, mostly ill fortune, for no fault of my own, ladies here, I beg you to believe. And full sure that the ladies were beguiled by him, he ran his fingers over the strings, saying: I could have arrived at your gate a few minutes sooner if I had dropped my organistrum in the field, but of what good would my life be to me if I were to lose what a gracious lady had given me in my boyhood—a memory and a consolation to me in all my misfortunes?

I am safe in this convent for a week, he said to himself, and out of the joyousness of his heart he began to sing one of the songs that he may or may not have written for the Comtesse D'Urgel. I would like to learn that song, Astrolabe said; wilt thou teach it to me? And may I look to see how the instrument is played? Why not, indeed? and he put forward into the child's hands an instrument more than twice the size of the ordinary lute, with keys. You will heed that the keys are placed on the neck, Denis said, and are raised a little to touch the strings by means of handles at the side of the neck. The strings go over this bridge just as in a common lute. But the other bridge is a wheel, which is turned by a handle at the end of the instrument, making the strings vibrate. One of us turns the wheel, the other manages the keys. How wilt thou play to us if I do not turn the wheel for thee? Astrolabe asked. I can turn the wheel and manage the keys myself, the gleeman answered, and I will show you how the wheel is to be turned, which he did, the nuns marvelling at the interest that the child showed. All else but what he was learning at the moment was forgotten, and when the wheel was understood by him the gleeman began to make plain to him the secret of the keys, and the first lesson in the playing of the organistrum was not over when Astrolabe said: May I have it on my knees, for I think I would like to see if I can play it? But what wilt thou play, darling? Héloïse asked. The song that I learnt from thee yester morning, mother; father's song. May I not play it, mother? Yes, if Denis will let thee have his instrument. And the nuns crowded round, some saying: Thou wilt never be able to play an instrument with those keys and wheels and handles, Astrolabe. Let him try, said the old gleeman; I will hold it upon his knee, for it is heavy and he might drop it.

Yes, indeed, the lad is a musician, the old gleeman said, for he was mazed at the boy's quickness, and if the lady of the house will let me bide here till the snow be off the ground and the bears and wolves have returned to their lairs and I am out of peril from them, I will teach him many a song; before I pass this way again he'll be delighting you all with his talent, which has come to him from his father, for didn't I hear the lady say the song he played so well was his father's? Lady of the house, you'll not turn me out to-morrow to the bears and the wolves, will you? the old man said. We will not turn thee out, the Prioress answered, till the country be safe for travelling, and Cherriez, our peasant, will be able to give thee a bed in his barn. I'd like better the woodshed, for those beasties are still a-dallying round Cherriez's hut. Well, we'll see what can be done to-morrow, the Prioress replied; and the gleeman felt that it would be unwise to press his requests any further. And now belike you would hear the organistrum before bed-time; and all consenting he played to them for a little while, stopping suddenly to ask them to sing so that he might learn how their voices pitched. Ye have all pleasing voices here; pleasanter I have never heard, and some eight or nine might be picked for a short choir. The altos and the trebles are about equal, and if you ladies are not going to your rest we might practise a while together. The Prioress gave no answer, and her silence being taken to mean her permission, the gleeman began his teaching.

Now, said he, a very pleasant musical game can be played this way. We take a tune, and the altos begin it on the A, and the trebles continue it a fifth higher, and so on; the altos again come in a fifth higher and then the trebles, and so on, turn and turn about, until you have come to the end of the tune. You all know *Vexilla Regis?* The nuns replied that they sang it in chapel. Then let us see if you can sing it in fifths, said Denis. We should have an instrument to give us the note; now, my young sir, will you be good enough to give us the A? Astrolabe turned red and was embarrassed, for he did not know the notes, and Denis had to come over and show him how to get it. We should all be in our beds, the Prioress said, but Christmas is a time for thanksgiving, and it does not seem to me that any harm is being done. But, mother, cried Astrolabe suddenly, may I not stay up a little longer, for there are many things I would like to ask Denis about the notes. My child, thou hast been out of thy bed since early morning and thine eyes are closing, Héloïse answered. Never mind, my little sir, Denis whispered, I will teach you all the notes to-morrow. My kind ladies, before you go may I ask for a rug to wrap myself in, my cloak being thin? Two rugs thou shalt have, for the woodshed is a cold bed-chamber. He may miss it, Mother Prioress; may I not show it to him? Astrolabe cried, and leave being given to him he ran after Denis, whispering to him: thou'lt teach me to play tomorrow? I will be down early; I will speak to the cook myself, and mother will.

Other promises were exchanged between them, all of which were fulfilled next day, and in return Astrolabe spent an hour with Denis over the keys and the wheel. But, said Denis, you must learn how to read music. To read, said Astrolabe; can it be read? And they were deep in the mystery of the written notes when Héloïse interrupted them. Mother, look what Denis is teaching me. But it will take weeks and months to learn all that Denis knows, mother. May he not be given leave to sleep in the woodshed every night till the snow melts, for the wolves are about all day? Do, mother, speak to the Prioress. I will speak to the Prioress, Héloïse answered. From whom, lady, did he get his musical ear? Denis asked tactfully. From his father, Héloïse replied, and moved by the thought of Abélard's delight at finding his son proficient in music, she sought the Prioress, leaving Astrolabe to discover Denis's accomplishment, a thing he was quick to do, finding before his mother returned that Denis played many other instruments besides the organistrum, the lute, the violin, the pipe, the bagpipe, the syrinx, the harp, the gigue and the lively little gittern, the symphony, the psaltery, the regals and the tabor. But there is much else for a man to learn who would be a gleeman, said Denis, as soon as they were alone again. He must sing a song well and make tales and fables, throw knives into the air and catch them without cutting his fingers; he must balance chairs and walk on his hands. But, Denis, canst thou walk on thy hands? I could walk upon my hands, the old gleeman cried, when I was your age and

long after it, but stiffness has come into the joints and
I cannot pitch legs over head any more. Astrolabe asked
him if he could teach him all the gleeman's craft, to
walk on my hands, he said, and throw knives into the
air and catch them? May I get thee some knives? Bring
me the knives and I will catch them. I can catch apples
on the points of knives, he said. May I fetch some? cried
Astrolabe, and returning with six, the old juggler was
throwing knives and catching them and the apples that
the child threw to him when Héloïse returned to the
room, saying that she would not have knives thrown into
the air and Astrolabe standing by. For if one were to
fall into thine eye, what answer should I make? Denis,
missed a knife yet in my life. But Héloïse was not to be
gainsaid. If thy father were to come here and find thee
with a great scar upon thy cheek, or if a knife should
fall into thine eye, what answer should I make? Denis,
thou must promise me not to play any perilous tricks
except at a safe distance. But, mother, may I not go
for walks with Denis? He knows how to set springs for
birds. What birds would he snare? Héloïse asked, but
instead of getting an answer to her question another
request was put to her. May we go to the river, mother?
But why to the river, Astrolabe? it is frozen. But that
is just why, mother, for we cannot drown in a frozen
river. The river is only frozen in parts, Astrolabe, and
I should have no peace all day long thinking of thee upon
the ice. But I promise thee not to walk far from the
shore. Well, to the river thou mayest go, darling, but
promise me not to put thy foot on the ice, not one step,
and not to go nearer the river's edge than one yard. If
I have thy promise and Denis's promise that he will see
that thou dost not forget thyself, well then thou mayest
go and set snares with Denis.

I shall be glad when I am a little older, Astrolabe said, taking Denis's hand. And what will you do, little sir, when you are older? I cannot tell thee, Denis. There are no boys here, only women. Thou'rt the first man, or very nearly the first, anyway the first I have ever had any real talk with. But aren't we going to the river, Denis? Well, sir, I was thinking that we might spend our day in building a great snare for the wild ducks that come up the river every evening. I saw a great flight of them settle down last night, and began to build the snare yesterday in the woodshed; and going thither Astrolabe was shown the beginning of a long wicker basket, wide at one end, narrowing, and ending in a net. It is so wide at this end that the ducks are without thought of danger and swim into it, thinking to rejoin the ducks they hear at the other end; it will be my voice imitating the talk of ducks they'll hear. Canst imitate a duck as well as that, Denis? asked Astrolabe. And many other birds too, Denis answered, for in our wanderings we often have to live upon what we catch in the woods; and forthright he began a gabble that no duck would have known was not his native language. But I must learn to quack like that, and while the snare was being woven Astrolabe practised quacking, becoming quickly so skilful that his quacking deceived the nuns, setting them talking and asking each other how the duck or ducks could have got into the convent.

The boy was tiresome withal, for once his thoughts were set on a subject he could think of nothing else, and the nuns wearied a little of his constant running in and out to ask them to come to the woodshed to see the wonderful snare that Denis was making. But when the night came for the setting of the snare he besought them to remain indoors, which they promised to do, a little weary

of his antics, saying that they would be glad when there
was no more question of catching ducks. The ducks came
and many were caught, but the birds were so thin they
were not worth killing, and several had their wings cut
and joined the tame birds in the poultry yard, feeding
with them, and, like them, fattening themselves for the
table.

CHAP. XXXV.

EACH day was a margin of dusk that soon darkened into
night, and there was no change in the thick grey sky save
when it turned to sulphur over the horizon. It was often
said: We shall have more snow, and one morning Astrolabe came running up from the river with the news that
men were crossing it on the ice. Might he do likewise?
Thou hast not ceased, his mother replied, for all this
week and as far back as I remember, to ask me if thou
mayest do this thing and that. Alack, it seems to me that
I spend all my time saying no. Unabashed, the boy
strayed aside, telling of strange birds that came up the
river so weak that they could hardly fly, and so thin are
they, he said, that cook won't pluck them; and, mother,
the village is full of wanderers from all parts unworthy
to be called gleemen; gangrel rogues Denis calls them,
and the words brought the thought to Héloïse that Denis
must be bidden away—Cherriez must harbour him. She
laid the matter before the Prioress, but her stratagem
availed her little, for Denis came up every day from the
village to teach Astrolabe music.

The nuns, too, were anxious for instruction in music,
and part singing wore away the snow's monotony till the
rain came, at the end of February. But it could not melt
the snow, so thickly did it lie, and up and down the Seine

valley the winds ranged, shaking the poor poplars till the eye pitied them, so tortured did they seem in the blasts. Never shall we see the springtide again, everybody was saying, till one evening the dusk seemed less cold.

Next morning the sun was shining, the birds were singing, and Cherriez's wife thought that the day had come to rid herself of the vagrant that the convent had imposed upon her for nearly three weeks. Thereat Astrolabe was in tears. But, dear boy, he will return, said Héloïse, taking him in her arms, but detaching himself ruthlessly he cried: Ah, here he is, coming to say good-bye, mother; and Astrolabe ran to meet Denis in the cloister, and taking him into the community-room Denis took his farewell of the nuns, who, he said, had been very good to him, and he would remember them always. But when may we see thee again, Denis? Astrolabe asked, little concerned whether Denis remembered the nuns or forgot them. Before the summer is over. Bring a gittern with thee, the boy cried, for I would play the gittern and the rebeck and the flute. Now that I know how to write down the tunes, I shall write down every one that comes into my head. We'll sing them together in the summer, won't we, Denis? If I am alive I will return, little sir, Denis said. But I've been about a great deal and am worn out, as a man is who has travelled France, singing it all over, bringing the news from the north to the south, from the south to the north, for—ah, how many years! As well as I know I am nearly fifty, so set not your hearts on seeing me again, and if it should hap that I die by the roadside, I shall be praying for you in heaven. Not that ye need my prayers, ladies, I know, not as I need yours, and maybe my while in purgatory will be a long one, for no man on this earth can say that he is altogether a good man. But if God spare thee, Denis, and thou shouldst return to us, bring us back news of Jerusalem, said the Prioress. Many are going forth and many are on their way back; hear them all, and we shall welcome thee for the tidings thou bringest. But why, cried Mother Hilda, dost thou speak so dolefully, Denis, as if death were a welcome thing? Well, ma'am, it is welcome to the vagrant, for the vagrant drops into old age soon after forty, and an old monkey, as the saying has it, pleases nobody. None but yourselves, ladies, would have thought it worth the trouble to open a door to save him from the wolves. I take my leave of you all, hoping to see you again. Now, Astrolabe, leave go of my habit and return to thy dinner. Mother, ask him if he will leave his organistrum. But it is with that he gets his living, my boy. Do go back to thy dinner; hast forgotten that there is pudding? So there is, mother; yes, there is pudding to-day, he replied, and ran away. But the pudding was barely eaten when he was asking for a lute or a rebeck, and on being offered a pair of regals he turned aside affronted and walked about disconsolate, confiding his sorrow to nobody, which was strange, for reticence was not in his humour. A few days later he had recovered his humour enough to ask his mother for a gittern. I have not money enough, she answered him. When father returns will he have enough? Does father play the organistrum as well as Denis? he asked, and in his eagerness for a musical instrument he would have put many more questions to her if Cherriez had not come in with the news that Denis had been found dead by the roadside, having tumbled, he said, into a snowdrift. We all thought, said the Prioress, that thou wert weatherwise and knew as well as the birds when the spring was coming in. That is so, madam, but the birds themselves come too soon or go too late. But Denis is

not dead? He is not like the birds that we caught together by the river? cried Astrolabe. Not really so dead
that we shall never see him again? He wasn't dead, young
sir, when we found him; he spoke a word or two about
his organistrum, and we understood him that it should be
given to the lad who can play it best, and who can play it
as well as his pupil? So now, sir—— Astrolabe turned
aside and began to cry hard. But, young sir, since it was
his wish for you to have it—— You all hated him, the
child replied passionately; you wouldn't let him sleep
in the woodshed, but sent him down to the village and
you, Cherriez, turned him out into the snow. I couldn't
keep him any longer in my hut, Cherriez said, speaking to
Héloïse; and you ladies couldn't keep him here, he added.
But this I'll say for him, he was the honestest gleeman
that ever came through our door—a wicked, lying, black-
guardly lot them gleemen; thieving fowls, ravishing girls,
telling lies and singing songs, are all they are good for,
and their songs are not always good for children to hear.
If he had only waited a few days longer, said the Prioress. The spring day tempted him, Cherriez answered.
Well, he's gone now, and I wouldn't have the boy take it
so to heart. My young sir, he sent you his organistrum.
You wouldn't let him sleep in the woodshed, you all hated
him, Astrolabe howled. But do not put aside his organistrum, my darling, Héloïse said, since he wished thee to
have it, and while playing it he will come back to thee as
plainly as if he were here. Play one of thy pieces for us
and for him. Mother, I can't, but I will to-morrow.
Cherriez waited for some recompense for his honesty in
refraining from the theft of the musical instrument, and
to lead the Prioress's thoughts to her duty towards him,
he began to speak of the fall of snow, which none could
have foreseen, not even he, though he was weatherwise

beyond any man, if the Seine were followed to the sea in search of one. It was as if God had wished Denis's death for his own good reasons; God must have desired to take Denis to himself, he said. It may be as thou sayest, the Prioress answered, and this seeming to be the moment to reward him, she sought for some coins in the satchel that hung from her girdle and gave them to him. And the nuns and their gardener went forth to watch the spring-tide, the thought in them all being that it seemed certainly as if God had wished to encompass Denis's death. For had he waited a few days more the sweet south wind that was blowing, calling the early flowers into being and the bushes in the garden into buds, would have melted the snow. Denis would have found a lodging and followed some troupe of gleemen during the summer, coming back in the early autumn or winter. The underwoods were lighting up, and along the river's banks kingcups had begun; and Héloïse once again looked back and considered her life, the joy and the wonder of its springtime, now nearly eleven years ago, for she had waited for Abélard in this convent for eight years. Where was he? and why had he not come to release her? Alas, she did not know anything, and lived like the weed in the field. True to him, she was. But of what use is fealty if there be no reward for it? If he has forgotten me, why should I be true? Has he been true to me? Man is never true. And then her thoughts suddenly breaking away from him and from herself, she said: Every nun, except the old ones in whom life is almost dead, burns in this springtime as I do; and a talk she had had with Angela years back returned to her. Sister Angela had told her that some gleeman or trouvère had won Sister Agnes away, and on asking how it was that a woman could love another so deeply as she seemed to have done, Sister Angela answered: Nature will have her way with us despite vows, in dreams if we resist one another too long. And when Héloïse pleaded a more natural affection, Angela answered: sex does not seem to matter, what is important is to love. She had not forgotten Angela's words, and though they were strange to her they found an echo in her, whose nature was to love one man only. Angela, she said to herself, is now thinking of Sister Agnes with the same passion and the same folly as I am thinking of Abélard. Mother Hilda is dreaming of her husband, saying to herself: The dead live in our memories, and they are not dead until we cease to think of them. The dying Prioress sits in her chair dreaming of her husband as a restless spirit demanding further search for his body on the field of battle and its burial in the Church of the Holy Sepulchre, thinking, no doubt, when she does think, of a grave for them both far away in the Holy Land. We are always remembering what has been, Héloïse added; how else should we live, we who have left life behind? And these springtimes are bitter to us. The return of the sun to the earth, the return of the birds to their songs, the return of the flowers to the air remind us that for us there is no return, life will never summon us again. Only the very young, who have no past to embitter the present, nor any thoughts of any future, like my boy, are happy in the springtime, and only for a short time, for in a few years love will fall upon him, and he will become restless and unhappy, as I am. At what age will he begin to form projects, projects that are never realised?

The sound of the organistrum woke her from her reverie, and she saw Astrolabe going towards the low wall over against the river to play his instruments, his audience the boatmen that passed up and down the current in the great barges. He will weary of this convent, she said, he will weary of me; and the pang that came into her heart hurt like the stroke of a knife. One day he will leave us, mayhap with these gleemen, who will make a singing boy of him, and in her own restless imagination she heard his words: I want to live among men, and once more she began to think that the boy was but an image of his father mentally as well as physically, the same high darling rounded brow overhanging the strangely eager eyes. I am hardly represented in him at all, a look now and again; he is all his father. And Héloïse was jealous of Abélard, and asked why he should have possessed himself so completely of his offspring. And seeing Astrolabe sitting on the convent wall singing to his organistrum, his eyes fixed on the great brown sails of the loaded barges that the wind was bringing up the river quickly, she began to wonder when Abélard would step ashore, saying to herself: Men return if they be not dead, and of all in the springtide; why not Abélard? The grass is green along the river bank, the reeds and flags are in flower, the poplars well past their russet hue. But we are not as they. My life, is it over and done? Can it be so? Affrighted, she passed into the convent, and at the same moment a ship steered towards the bank. What ho! a boy, cried one of the motley crew on board. Thou playest an organistrum well; wouldst come with us and play it? To which Astrolabe answered: My mother lives here, and though I would like well to sail on the river I cannot do so, having promised her not to leave the shore. Whereupon there was whispering among the gleemen in the barge, of which Astrolabe took no account, his attention being fixed on a hat trimmed with tall feathers bending in the breeze. He admired, too, a jacket trimmed with streaming ribbons and decorated with many coloured rosettes. Shall I wear a pea-green jacket, he cried out, if mother lets me come with you? Wilt give me a pea-green or a peach-coloured jacket? Any colour that is to thy taste thou shalt have and hose of red and blue, cried the gleemen. The wallet that thou wearest would be too big for me, said Astrolabe. Hast no smaller one? To which the gleemen said there was one that he could wear comfortably. And what shall I put into it? he enquired. All manner of fruit and bread and onions, and maybe a chicken or rabbit from the hedgerows. Astrolabe had seen them cooking on the barges as they went up and down the river, and answered: May I cook my rabbit or my chicken as we sail? At which all the gleemen laughed till Astrolabe felt a little ashamed, thinking he had said something foolish. But he was reconciled to himself, when the man with the peacocks' feathers in his hat said: Thy rabbit and thy chicken will go into the common pot and thou'lt eat with us. If I'm to eat with you I'll run to mother, for indeed I cannot go without telling her. Be not in such a hurry, little man, but tell us first who lives with thee in yon building. Yon building is a convent, said Astrolabe, and the rule is St. Benedict. A convent, cried the tall man, as he jumped ashore. And where did thy organistrum come from, and who taught thee to play it? A gleeman who was with us all the winter sleeping in the woodshed. But he was sent away by the Prioress to sleep with our gardener, Cherriez, who lives in the village in the fields on the other side of the Paris road. And why was he sent away from the woodshed, little man? He lighted ferns and nearly burnt us out one night, Astrolabe answered, and he began to tell how the convent had escaped, and how the old man, who left them a couple of months gone by, died on the roadside. Cherriez, our gardener, found him, and he brought me Denis's organistrum. Old Denis! one of the gleemen

cried. But the tall man who wore the peacocks' feathers
did not remember the dead gleeman until the others
stepped forward to recall the old man to his memory by
many facts. It may be, he said, that the reverend ladies
in the convent would like a little instruction in music now
that Denis has gone whither there is neither music nor
dancing. But I thought that heaven was all music, Astrolabe answered innocently, at which remark the gleemen
laughed, raising the thought into his mind that perhaps
they did not all hope, or perhaps even wish, to go to
heaven. If that were so, he hoped they wouldn't tell
the Prioress, who, if they did, wouldn't listen to their
music.

Can you tell stories of the Crusades? he asked. Troth
and faith we can, they cried. Have we not come from
Palestine? Then you'll be welcome here, for the Prioress's husband, the Comte Godfrey de Châtillon—— At
which name the gleemen became in their turn serious and
said: Show us the way to the front door of the convent
and we will ask admittance. Follow the river's bank
till you come to the lane-way, he replied; it will take you
to the highroad, and if you turn to the left, you'll be at
the convent door. Meanwhile I'll run up through the
orchard and tell them you're here. The Prioress is very
ill, he said, stopping suddenly and returning to the gleemen, but I'll ask mother if you cannot play your instruments in the quadrangle. But will you let me try the
flute when the entertainment is done before you leave?
Yes, thou shalt try all our instruments, cried the chief
gleeman. Said Astrolabe: Then thou mayest be sure
I'll cling on to the mothers: there are three, and my own
mother—the Prioress, Mother Hilda, and Mother Ysabeau, who looks after our food. And the drink, interrupted a gleeman; is there wine in the convent? There

is indeed, Astrolabe answered, and now—— Now stop a minute, cried the chief gleeman as the boy was going away. Give the Prioress this letter; and he wrote: The Comte Mathieu de Rodebœuf, just returned from Palestine after fighting the Saracens for the Holy Sepulchre, waits upon you. If you come, good sir, from the Holy Land, the Prioress will let us have the entertainment, you may be certain of that.

And he ran up the broad walk, arriving at the convent breathless, saying to one of the sisters: The gleeman gave me this for the Prioress, and do you give it to her, saying that he is on his way hither. The Prioress, the portress answered, is not strong enough to see anybody. But, cried Astrolabe, he has come from Jerusalem, the great Comte Mathieu de Rodebœuf, with his gleemen, so thou must go at once to the Prioress, for we should never be forgiven by her if the Comte were sent away without her knowledge. These words did not seem to admit of question, and Astrolabe said he would run on and find the other mothers, for the Prioress might leave them to conclude the matter, she being ill.

It seemed to Astrolabe that luck was on his side, for in the cloister he met his mother walking with Mother Hilda. On their way to church, he said to himself, for they waved him aside. But Astrolabe would not be silenced, and insisted that they should hear that the Comte de Rodebœuf was at their doors with all his gleemen. Héloïse shook her head, but when she heard that the Comte Mathieu de Rodebœuf had just arrived from the Holy Land she conferred with Mother Hilda, who promised to speak to Mother Ysabeau. They will play all their instruments, Astrolabe cried, clinging to his mother's rosary, and leading her by it; and when they entered the passage on to which the Prioress's door opened, Héloïse said:

Do not speak so loud, the Prioress may be asleep or resting. They were met by Mother Ysabeau, who stood barring their way; the Prioress is as strong to-day, she said, as she was yesterday. My son, Héloïse answered, has just brought the news that Comte Mathieu de Rodebœuf has returned from Jerusalem and would speak with the Prioress. The Comte Mathieu de Rodebœuf, from my country, from Arras, the Prioress answered quickly, he may bring news—— Mother Prioress, Astrolabe began, but Héloïse laid her hand upon his mouth and told the story herself, how the Comte Mathieu de Rodebœuf, at the head of a band of gleemen, stopped their boat to listen to Astrolabe, who was playing his organistrum at the end of the broad walk. And they would like, she continued, to give an entertainment in the quadrangle. An entertainment in the quadrangle, the Prioress repeated, and feeling that she was not equal to giving a decision in a matter so strange and unexpected that morning, she said: I should like to hear what Mothers Ysabeau and Hilda think.

You will enjoy it, Mother Prioress, Astrolabe cried. There are great gittern and rebeck players amongst them. Dost think I shall, dear boy? What I shall enjoy most are four boards, she rejoined, in an undertone, forgetful of the quickness of young ears, and the thought that we are all nailed between boards like Denis (Cherriez nailed something up the day that Denis died) came into his mind, chasing all the brightness out of his face, causing him to cling to his mother's habit, though he had but half understood. It was some time before he whispered to her: Dost think, mother, that she'll say yes? Mother Ysabeau's face told Héloïse that at least one mother would raise an objection; and the Prioress, too, feared that it would be difficult to win Mother Ysabeau's consent, a thing that she regretted, for if I refuse to allow the entertainment, she said to herself, the Comte Mathieu de Rodebœuf may go away in anger without seeing me. And then turning to Mother Ysabeau, she said: I knew the Comte Mathieu de Rodebœuf's father, and I knew the Comte himself when he was a child; and it seems hard to refuse to see men who went to the Holy Land willing to lay down their lives for the cross. I should not like to commit myself to such a refusal. But these crusaders are gleemen, and we have gained some knowledge of a gleeman this winter, Mother Ysabeau answered dryly. But, Mother Ysabeau, the Prioress replied, the Comte Mathieu de Rodebœuf is a trouvère, which is different from a gleeman, and, as I have told you, I knew his father, and I knew the Comte himself when he was a child; our estates were by each other, our castles visible from the ramparts over the tops of the trees. I can see you're in favour of allowing the entertainment, so I will say no more, Mother Ysabeau replied. But, Mother Ysabeau, I'm not willing to decide, but would wish that you and the other mothers should meet here in my room so that I may hear what you all have to say. Mother Prioress, I have no wish to withstand your will. You wish to speak with the Comte Mathieu de Rodebœuf, and if you refuse the entertainment the Comte would not be in the same humour to see you as he would if you received his company. If the other mothers are in agreement my prejudices may be set aside. But might it not be well to speak to our chaplain, Stephen, on the subject? On that point I am not in agreement with you, Mother Ysabeau, the Prioress answered; the direction of the convent is with us and not with our chaplain, who, although an excellent man, cannot understand many things that are plain to us. But, Mother Prioress, I would not have you overtax your strength. My strength is not worth considering, the Prioress returned, and if the mothers agree that the entertainment is to be allowed, I will come down to the cloister to hear the minstrels; my presence will be necessary, and of my health, I think I can speak with more certainty than another. I have some business, my dear Héloïse, with Mother Ysabeau, and shall be glad if thou'lt go in search of Mother Hilda. May we say, Mother Prioress, that you are for the music? cried Astrolabe. Tell Mother Hilda, the Prioress added, if thou canst find her, that I would speak with her.

I think we shall get our entertainment, Astrolabe said as soon as they had crossed the threshold and the door was shut behind them. For I've taught Mother Hilda to play my organistrum, and Sister Josiane likes music too. Mother Ysabeau is against us, but that won't matter if the other mothers are for us.

And dragging his mother after him he went in search of Mother Hilda, and discovering two sisters in the illuminating-room, whose influence it seemed to him important to have on his side, he appealed to them. The children, said Sister Cecilia, will be delighted to hear the minstrels, and Sister Josiane reminded her that the instruction they had received during the winter from Denis was of great use to them. This was enough for Astrolabe, who continued his quest, asking all and sundry for Mother Hilda, and finding Sister Tetta in the schoolroom sitting in a corner looking very wretched, her indigestion being worse than usual that morning, and averse from the encouragement of such vagrants, he went at her forthright, saying that the vagrants were the gleemen of the Comte Mathieu de Rodebœuf, winning her over by a plea for the schoolroom, which would be disappointed if the minstrels were not given a hearing.

His mother could not restrain him from telling the great tidings to some sisters coming out of church, and a wrangle began, the sisters ranging themselves on different sides, arguing among themselves, till Mother Hilda appeared. Her first words silenced the dissidents: We may not send away those who have fought for the Holy Sepulchre, so it seems to me. A few minutes after Mother Ysabeau came down saying that the entertainment was to take place at four, in the quadrangle. Whereat a great gabble began among the nuns, all telling the Prioress that the gleemen were gone to the village to seek beds for the night but this search would not detain them long, and an hour later a letter arrived from the Comte, saying that he would return to the convent before his men, for he wished to meet the Prioress before the entertainment began so that he might renew his acquaintance with her and tell the battles he had fought in the Holy Land, giving assurance that the city was still safe in the hands of the Christians.

I see that nothing I can say will dissuade you, dear Mother, from assisting at the entertainment, said Father Stephen. But you do not think, Father, that any harm can come of allowing these minstrels to sing to us in our quadrangle? She waited for him to answer her, and while he considered his answer she ran over in her mind the portly little cleric, the chaplain, liking less than usual his round head and round, rosy face, and of all his manner of chattering through his pursed-up lips. Of course, my dear Mother Prioress, if what you've been told is the truth, and that these men did really fight for the faith in the Holy Land, it would be wrong indeed to send them away from your doors without the usual welcome of bread and wine. But are you sure that these gleemen are speaking the truth and that they have come

from the Holy Land? I assert nothing; I merely put
it to you, are you sure? Stephen's lack of faith vexed
the Prioress, for though gleemen might not always tell
the truth, Stephen knew the message that had been sent
to her by the Comte Mathieu de Rodebœuf, and to impugn his veracity set her against her spiritual adviser;
and to convince him that he was wrong and that she was
right, she asked him if he believed that the man who
sent the letter that she had handed him to read was a
sham Comte Mathieu de Rodebœuf. For if he did not
cast doubt on the letter, why did he ask her if she
felt quite sure that the chief gleeman was the son of her
old friend and neighbour in the Arras country? I would
like to hear your objection, Father, to the entertainment
being given in our quadrangle. The songs of the trouvères
and gleemen, he answered, savour too much of the life
of the world for the ears of those who have embraced the
religious life. But you do not think, Father, that the
Comte Mathieu de Rodebœuf would allow songs to be
sung in my convent that were unsuitable to our ears and
to the ears of the school children, who are all clamouring
for the entertainment?

The argument was continued for some long time between the Prioress and the convent chaplain, till at last
a knock came to the door, and a lay sister opened it,
saying that the Comte Mathieu de Rodebœuf had arrived, and hoped to speak with the Prioress. You will
give me your arm, Father, the Prioress said; and the lay
sister and Stephen exchanged glances and their eyes
said plainly: our Prioress is wasting her last strength
and we shall not be able to keep her long after the excitement of this day. Will you place my chair, the
Prioress said, just here in the middle of the cloister, and
throw the door open, for I would see the Comte Mathieu

de Rodebœuf as he comes down the passage from the front door into the quadrangle; and you can put that cushion behind my head. I shall be well enough like that, for indeed my illness is one of your fallacies—a conventional fallacy. The old woman chuckled, for it annoyed her to see that her nurse and her chaplain were averse that she should leave her room to take part in the shows and diversions of the minstrels; and she could see, too, that they did not believe in the nobility of the trouvère or gleeman whom she was waiting for.

She was out of her humour, therefore, when the Comte de Rodebœuf walked across the quadrangle, and so strange was his apparel, so unlike that of a great nobleman, that she could not behold in him the Comte de Rodebœuf whose castle she had often seen from her window through her father's trees and his trees, and it needed all her strength to dissemble and keep her disappointment from Stephen and address Comte Mathieu de Rodebœuf with becoming smiles. I am in failing health, she said; pray be seated, Comte, and without remarking his strange clothes, she began to speak of his father. It is in keeping, the Comte said, with the noble courtesy that we cultivate in our country of Arras that you hide surprise, Prioress, at the strange motley you find me flaunting. And forthwith he began to tell her that although he was still the Comte Mathieu de Rodebœuf, his castle and lands were no longer his. In Palestine, he said, I am a soldier of the Cross, but when I return to France, the trouvère of other days can find no service, and is obliged to travel at a venture, his voice being sometimes with him and absent as often. And thy friend of other days is no longer a lutanist, for in leaping from a balcony his wrist and some fingers were broken. A strange story is yours, truly, sir. Tell it to me, the old woman said, speaking with gentleness and sympathy, for even in his motley Comte Mathieu de Rodebœuf was a knight, and his lithe figure, broad shoulders, and shapely face, lighted with sad blue eyes, pleased her. And the Comte, feeling that what he had to do was to pitch his story in a key suited to her ear, summarised his love adventures, representing them as one great passion which had absorbed his life till God's grace came and called him to the Holy Land. Such is my story, Mother Prioress, said Rodebœuf, since we lived together in the Arras country. Stephen, who stood by them, would have liked the Prioress to put some more searching questions to the Comte, and it was upon his lips to remind her that all gleemen tell the same story—all have been to the Crusades—but he was able to restrain his tongue, and when the old woman began to ask the Comte if he had met her husband in Palestine, and if her husband's grave were known to him, Stephen turned away, it seeming to him almost an immodesty to overhear the old woman's sweet folly.

And leaving the Prioress under the spell of remembrances that were her life much more than her daily duties, Stephen walked into the quadrangle, whither the lay sisters were bringing benches and seats, seats for the lay sisters and benches for the children, who were just arriving in charge of the schoolmistress, Sister Mechtilde, an almost young German nun, tall and slight, about whom the children grouped themselves, a little group of a dozen, every one anxious to hear what she was saying, to get near her, but every one orderly, none trying to push forward, for Sister Mechtilde was a strict disciplinarian inasmuch as she was always alert, watchful, when she was with the children, gaining their hearts by gentle firmness. Her life was lived with her children, and in their long, straight frocks and veils they made a pretty

group on the grass circlewise round her, asking questions,
some of which she answered hastily, bidding them to hold
their tongues, saying that they must have patience, and
leave things to explain themselves.

The choir sisters and the mothers were choosing their
places, and the Prioress was still talking to the Comte
Mathieu de Rodebœuf, forgetful of the minstrels who
were coming, and who arrived a little later, dissipating
some very sentimental memories by their parti-coloured
garments and their strange instruments. Sister Mechtilde, cried Clothilde, look at that great horn; will they
play it, and what sound will it give? Hush, Clothilde,
thou'lt hear the horn presently and be able to judge for
thyself. Sister Mechtilde, cried another child, look at
that round thing the third man this side is carrying;
what is it? That's a drum, dear; they will begin to
beat it presently. To beat it! Why should they beat it?
And there's another organistrum just the same as Astrolabe's, Sister; is it not the same? There's too much talking, you must have a little patience, and it will all be
made plain to you presently. Are they beginning to
play now? another child asked. No, dear, they are not;
they're merely tuning their instruments. Thine ear, Catherine, must be even worse than I thought it was. The
other children laughed, taking pleasure in the discom-
fiture of Catherine, who turned red and was unhappy
during the first part of the performance, but forgot the
rebuke in the excitement of that memorable afternoon.

At last the lutes were tuned, and rising from his seat
the Comte said: My minstrels are now ready, and by
your leave, Prioress, they will begin, whereupon the
Prioress, rising to her feet, bowed an almost royal consent, and the Comte crossed the quadrangle and taking
a seat on the edge of the deep wall, one foot on the

ground, the other leg dangling jauntily from the parapet, he sang to an accompaniment played by his own lutanist. Stephen asked if the Comte never played the lute. He was the great lute-player of my country, the Prioress answered, but his fingers were broken many years ago in a fall from a balcony.

To concede something to the Prioress's noble lineage, the first song sung was by William VII., Count of Poitiers and Duke of Aquitaine, and the authorship was announced with a note of deference by the Comte de Rodebœuf. Songs for single and several voices were sung with accompaniments on lute and lyre, and before each song the Comte de Rodebœuf announced the authorship. The next songs were by Circlalmon, and these were followed by the songs of Jaufre Rudel, Berenguier de Palazol, and Bernard de Ventardorn; and it was not till the audience had just begun to feel that they would like a break in the entertainment that the Comte de Rodebœuf rose to his feet, and addressing the audience, said: you have now heard some of the most beautiful songs ever composed in this world, and it has come to me to think that perhaps you would like to hear something about the lives of the marvellous poet musicians; if so—— The Comte waited to be told that all desired to hear; the applause left no doubt that they did and he related the story of Jaufre Rudel, who loved a princess far away whom he had never seen, only heard of, which was enough to make other loves seem worthless. The story of how he had journeyed to her, seeing her for but a few moments before he died, was listened to with a pleasure so intense that the tears often rose to the eyelids, and acceding to the demand for another story, the Comte de Rodebœuf told that Bernard de Ventardorn was the son of a baker-ess. and carried the loaves in a basket round the castle,

singing as he went. Denis had told the same story, and
it did not seem likely that two poets, Denis and Bernard
de Ventardorn, should both have carried loaves of bread
round a castle, singing. Which were they to believe?
Before anybody had concluded which was telling the
truth, the Comte de Rodebœuf told how this great poet
lived and was true to his love. You shall hear him tell,
himself, he said (man is only himself when he loves),
in one of the most beautiful songs ever made; and the
Comte, stepping forward, sang:

quan vei la lauzeta mover:

   The song is truly beautiful, the Prioress said, and she
sent her appreciation forward by her chaplain, Stephen:
and, after bowing in answer to the applause with which
the song was received, the Comte de Rodebœuf related
the friendship that had never been broken between the
two great poet musicians, Bernard de Ventardorn and
Berenguier de Palazol. And while in his story the thought
coming to him that the celebrated tenso held between
the two poets, one taking the part of a Pagan and the
other a Christian, was suitable for convent recitation, he
began; and the argument was followed with interest till
the last stanza, in which the Pagan seemed to triumph
so completely that the nuns waited with bated breath
to hear the audacious Infidel reduced to naught by the
Christian. But no answer came from the Christian, and
so natural did this end of the tenso seem to the Comte
that it was not for some time that he perceived his dilemma; and then, realising what was expected of him, but
being unable to invent a suitable answer for the Christian,
he clapped his hand to his forehead, and after a moment
of meditation he began to apologise to the company for

having forgotten the last and most important stanza, in which the downfall of the unbeliever is related. And to pass from an awkward moment, he asked permission to sing a song that had been composed for him, a song, he added, which had much to do with sending him to Palestine to fight the Saracen for possession of the Holy Sepulchre. But who shall I ask to accompany me? he cried aloud, and his eyes wandered round his own minstrels, seeking among the lute and the lyre players. Before his choice fell Astrolabe struck a chord involuntarily, and it seemed to Rodebœuf that it would be a gracious thing to call upon the child to accompany him.

Wilt thou accompany me on thy organistrum? he said, and Astrolabe answered that he thought he would be able to find a suitable accompaniment on his strings if the Comte would sing the melody over to him. A little re-hearsal, the Comte answered, and they walked back and forth, the Comte's hand on the boy's shoulder, singing in his ear whilst the boy sought appropriate chords. We may begin now, sir, and Astrolabe followed the Comte's voice with so much sympathy that all the company marvelled, and Héloïse shared in her son's triumph. But her face took on a look of perplexity, for it began to seem to her that she was listening to one of her hus-band's songs, not one she had ever heard him sing, but a song so much in his style and manner that she could not think else than that it was his song. It is his song, she said, and the Comte will tell me; but how can I get near him and talk to him without attracting attention? She could not but obey the spell that was upon her (Abélard's spell), and rising to her feet, was about to go to him; but at that moment the Prioress beckoned the kitchen sister to come to her: Our visitors would like to partake of some cake and wine; is there enough

for all? Plenty, Mother Prioress; I have been busy all
the morning baking, the kitchen sister answered, and
hurried across the quadrangle, returning soon after with
several lay sisters carrying spiced cakes on wooden platters, cider and wine in earthenware jugs.

At a sign from the schoolmistress, Mechtilde, the
children sprang to their feet, delighted at the permission
given to them to hand round the cake and wine, which
they did, begging of each gleeman to help himself more
liberally. Astrolabe needed even less pressing than the
gleemen, for with one piece of cake in his hand, and
another in his pocket, the greedy boy begged to be allowed to carry a platter to the Comte Mathieu de Rodebœuf. The moment appeared to Héloïse as hers, for
she could go to the help of her son without attracting
attention and after instructing him regarding the distribu-
tion of the cake, she asked the Comte Mathieu de Rodebœuf if the song he had just sung was by Pierre Abélard,
the great teacher and philosopher. My husband, she said.
Your husband, Sister? cried he. Yes; for I am Héloïse,
the niece of Canon Fulbert, she answered, and put her
question again to Mathieu; and, his mazed eyes fixed upon
her, he told her the song was written for him by Pierre
Abélard. But how came you, Sister——? Ah, that is
too long a story for me to tell you, Comte. But when
did you get that song from him? Abélard, said Mathieu,
was my gleeman when I was a rich trouvère. He left
music and art for philosophy, and we did not see each
other for many years, not until we came upon each other
on the road to Blois. On the road, she said, from Tours
to Blois. He left me at Tours with his sister and her
husband, who were to take me to Brittany, whither I
went with them, for I was then carrying that boy who
accompanied you on his organistrum. Pierre Abélard

wrote this song for me, Mathieu repeated, within hearing of Astrolabe. But my father's name is Pierre Abélard, Astrolabe cried. Mother, why didst thou not tell me that my father wrote music before? He wrote the song that I sang, said Mathieu. That I accompanied, cried Astrolabe again. Yes, Mathieu answered, and with which I should have gained the prize. Then the song did not win the prize? Héloïse asked. It won the prize, but I didn't get the prize, the Comte replied. Tell us the story, Astrolabe cried. But how could the song get the prize and you not get it, too, since the song was written for you?

A moment later they were surrounded, and there was only time for Rodebœuf to pass the word to Héloïse that he was in France but a month, which was interpreted by her that no tidings of Abélard had yet reached him. But her eyes were so suppliant that he apprehended his duty to be an immediate search for Abélard, and Héloïse, reading a promise of help in his eyes, was moved to say: To-morrow at three in the orchard, Comte; do not fail me.

CHAP. XXXVI.

THE news that came down next morning from the Prioress's room not being favourable, Héloïse presented herself before Mother Ysabeau to ask her permission to absent herself from certain duties, saying that the Comte de Rodebœuf was coming in the afternoon to speak to her of the journey he was about to undertake to Brittany in search of Abélard. Mother Ysabeau's face darkened a little, but she dared not refuse Héloïse permission to meet the Comte de Rodebœuf, knowing well that if she did Héloïse would go to the Prioress and get it. So with as good grace as she could command at the moment, she answered: The Prioress would give permission; why, then, should I refuse it, even if I were so disposed, and I am not, for it is but right that you should t ke all means to enquire out the safety of your one-time husband, who is now your brother in our Lord Jesus Ch ist. Héloïse thanked her with something like detestation in her heart, for she had read Mother Ysabeau's thought in her face, and was about to ponder on it when it was swept away by a memory of the promise she seemed to have read in Mathieu's eyes. He will not fail me, she said; my life here is ending; every moment is bringing our meeting nearer. But how will it come about? How will it befall? In what shape shall I appear to him? for I am no longer a young girl. Will he love me less? As she leaned over the parapet watching the river going by, her thoughts began to wind out of her present life into her past, and so far away were they from the actual moment that Sister Agatha had to call twice before she awoke from her reverie.

I am glad you have come, she said, giving her hand to Rodebœuf, and when the portress left them he said: of what were you thinking?—of Abélard? I cannot tell of what I was dreaming, she said, perhaps of the sadness of things. Yesterday there was a moment of hope; but your last words were that you had no tidings of him. But I must not weary you with my regrets. We can talk about him at least. Abélard has told me often of your first meeting, which was before I knew him, when he was a young man faring forth from his home in Brittany to teach the world. Yes, it was like that, Rodebœuf answered. I was riding from my castle, attended by my gleemen, when a charging boar set my horse plunging. A sudden swerve threw me out of poise, and while seeking my horse we came upon Abélard in an oak wood

at midday. My horse had already found him. Abélard
held him by the bridle. The very story that he told me,
Héloïse answered. Faith, the Comte repeated, it was my
horse that found him and asleep. And you challenged
him, Mathieu, with the words: Young man, thou'st a
lute upon thy back, and Abélard said that a lutanist he
was, and you answered: My castle is close by. Yes, it
was as you say it, Héloïse. You engaged him, Héloïse
continued, to put your songs in order—— He being a
better musician than I, the Comte interjected. But did
he tell you of the prize song he wrote for me? No, he
couldn't have, for it was after leaving you at Tours with
his family that he met me on the road to Blois, a ragged
gleeman, whom he could barely believe to be the Comte
de Rodebœuf. We went on together, for I said to him:
A coach will be dragging wearily up yonder hill-side, and
if we are there before it we may be rewarded for our
singing by the travellers. But, said I, you'll have to play
for me, for all that is left of the Comte de Rodebœuf
is his voice. I showed him my broken fingers, telling
him that I had to leap from a balcony to escape the
sword of Raymond de Castel-Rousillon. As Héloïse's
face told him that the story of his last meetings with
Abélard would not be clear if he omitted any part of
the story of the evil bird that had betrayed his love of
Margherita, his neighbour's wife, he related the adventure, and how his next love story had led him into the
love of a woman whose one thought was tournaments and
feasting, and that to retain her love he had assembled
many times great companies of knights and tilted with
them all, glad to win her favour at the cost of all his
lands. All my possessions passed from me, he said, like
sand through the neck of a glass, and the trouvère is
now a gleeman.

You have been to the Holy Land? Héloïse asked, and
the Comte broke forth again into the story of his unfortunate life; and Héloïse heard that it was about nine
years since Abélard overtook him on the road to Blois.
Nine years ago! she repeated. I was with child then
and had journeyed with Abélard from Paris to Tours,
where he left me with his sister and brother-in-law. But
go on with your story, Comte; you met Abélard on the
road to Blois. A Court of Love was in session, the
Comte continued, and I said: Many heavy purses are
being awarded for poems; if I could win one I should
not have to go to the Holy Land to win the Holy Sepulchre
from the Saracen. But, said Abélard, no evil bird has
cast a spell upon me, so I will write for thee a song
that may win the purse thou needest. Now is there a
tavern nearby where we might write it? There is one
by the castle of Chatelleraud, said I. We went thither,
and all night long, whilst the gleemen were drinking and
singing and chasing gleemaidens in the garden, Abélard
and I were set on the composition of our prize song.
You heard me sing it yesterday; a beautiful song it is; it
gained the purse of gold, but the purse went to another
singer, who heard me singing the song over and over
again, and being called before me in the competition,
the shameful fellow sang not his own song, which was
worthless, but Abélard's. For such is the luck of the
luckless, my fate always, and finding myself penniless
I entered the army to help to win the Holy Sepulchre
from the Saracen. And here I am in France without
hope of finding a trouvère to engage me.

But in Palestine great adventures must have happened
to you? said Héloïse. Great adventures truly, he said,
but the whole afternoon cannot be spent in relating them,
and I am anxious to hear your story, Héloïse. You will

trust me with it? for all the while I have been telling mine I have been thinking how I may help you. But you have not heard of Abélard since the days you've been telling? she said. Were Abélard dead I should have heard of his death, Rodebœuf answered, and it seems to me that when I have sung at a few more castles where I am expected, I might undertake some journeys hither and thither, picking up news of Abélard, finding him at length, and bringing him to you. Your words bespeak a kind heart, Mathieu, said Héloïse, but if Abélard had not forgotten he would have come to me long ago. You wrong him, Héloïse. It may be that I do, she said, for my vow was that I should remain here till he returned to me, a priest. I have kept my vow, but has he kept his? Is he a priest? You will have to tell me more of your story, for I can make no good sense of it till you do, Mathieu replied. Why should you be here waiting for Abélard to return to you a priest? That story none knows but myself, she answered, but lest you should think me a foolish woman who dreams, I will tell it to you; and she related that she had besought him not to marry her in Brittany, saying that women have always been the undoing of men since Eve, our mother, and not wishing to bring ruin upon the world again, I recalled all the stories I could remember, and though he could not deny the truth of any he still persisted, and we went to Paris together and were wedded.

A sad journey it was, and all the while of it I knew we were riding towards our misfortune, for, worst mistake of all, Abélard chose that the marriage should be kept secret. As if his marriage could be kept secret. Often I said to him: The marriage of Abélard cannot be hidden from the world; nor was it hidden from anybody. Within a few days it was common talk. My uncle made it public.

But why should I tell you any more? said Héloïse,
stopping suddenly. The Comte pressed her to tell all,
and the impulse to tell the secret she had kept hidden
in her heart so long being upon her, she said: I never had
any wish but Abélard's renown, and seeing that my uncle
was determined upon his ruin, the thought grew in me
that we must undo our marriage; and for this purpose,
I said to myself, I will return to my old convent and he
shall become a priest, for outside of the Church there
is no advancement for any man, however great a genius
he may be. Abélard was adverse, but one night it fell out
that my uncle in wine and anger gave way to such violent
words and threats that I left the house in the rue des
Chantres and ran to Abélard's lodging. How came it
about, and who said the first word, who the second or
the third, I have no memory, but it was for his sake
that I came hither at the break of day next morning——
And you have been here ever since? the Comte interrupted. Yes; and till yesterday I believed in his return
to me. But to-day it seems to me that belief is dead.
You have lived here, the Comte said, in that black Benedictine robe, for nine years, accepting a life that is not
yours, for a man's glory. But I have brought him no
glory, she replied, only misfortune; yet I live among idle
prayers, wandering through a life of rule, my life a sort
of dazed stupor, no more than that. In the glamour of
the day I laugh and talk like another, but in the night I
weep, asking myself again and again if he have forgotten
me, if he will return, if all be not a mad dream, if it
will ever end. If I sleep he comes to me in dreams, but
before the moment of our joy he disappears, and I sit
up in bed scared, watching the grey window-pane.

This sudden and precise realisation of what her life
had been for nine years, and which it still was, swept

away all memory of the Comte de Rodebœuf, and his voice startled her when he spoke, saying: I will seek Abélard. But Abélard, she cried, knows where I am. If he have not forgotten me he would have come hither or sent a message. Have you not told me, the Comte said, of a covenant—— That he may not come hither till he be a priest, she replied. He may still be seeking a bishop to ordain him, not an easy thing for a man convicted of heresy to find. But if this be so, why am I here? Why does he leave me here? Your eyes seemed to promise a search for him yesterday, but in sending you to seek him out I am breaking the covenant; and there may be a reason for this silence. But you would not live and die without knowledge of him? Mathieu said, and after waiting for an answer he began to try to persuade her out of her scruples, saying that his tongue confirmed the promise that his eyes made yesterday. The thought is your own, obey it, she said, since it was sent to you, and on these words they turned into the orchard, unable to bear the melancholy of the river any longer. There's no river, he said, so melancholy as the Seine, for it winds oftener, a deep, silent current, with hardly any eddy in it. The sisters like to come here to watch the boats going by, Héloïse replied, and it's pleasant to see the barge appear, its red sails filled with a west wind; but I am always sorry when it goes away down the river, for I know it is only going away to come back. I do not know why I am sorry for the barge; sometimes I think that I am sorry for everything, for even the old dead barge lying in yonder bed of rushes. But I must not give way. You'll forgive me, knowing how long I have waited. And yet . . . You have been here till a river flowing through the pleasant lands of France brings you unhappiness, Rodebœuf answered. But your son comes to you, leaping and singing through the orchard; he at least is happy. At this moment perhaps, but he is always craving for something, Héloïse said, with a faint smile. But where hast thou been, my little son, and why comest thou hither singing thy father's song so joyously?

I have come from the village, mother. May I tell Comte de Rodebœuf about the gittern that Raoul plays so beautifully? It came from a shop in Paris where one can buy gitterns and flutes and viols and many more musical instruments than I can remember the names of. And from another shop, mother, thou canst buy the swords and the shields and the armour that the Crusaders wear when they go away to Palestine to fight for the Holy Sepulchre. I should like to be a Crusader and sail in a ship down to the sea, and cut off the heads of many Saracens. When may I go to Palestine, mother? And when wilt thou take me to the shop to buy the gittern? And if thou canst not leave the convent, mother, may I go to Paris with the Comte de Rodebœuf? Ask the Comte if he will take thee, Héloïse answered. Will you take me to Paris, sir? the child repeated. For I do want to see Paris. Now which is thy heart set on, he asked—Paris or Palestine; and which wouldst thou like the better, to go to Paris with me or with thy father? So many questions silenced Astrolabe's loquacious tongue, and soon after the Comte Mathieu de Rodebœuf took his leave of Héloïse. Will he take me to Paris to see the lute-maker, mother? cried Astrolabe. Yes, I think he will, she answered; and the boy ran up the orchard to tell Rodebœuf that on the whole he preferred the gittern to Palestine, and Héloïse had to call him several times before he would return to her.

Why may I not go to Paris with the Comte de Rodebœuf? he asked. Come to thy lesson, she answered, a

little wearied by his reiterated requests. But Astrolabe
was unable to fix his attention on hexameters that day;
at every moment he would break into telling of the wonderful instruments that the gleemen played. Girard's bagpipe is in the shape of an animal that wears its house on
its back, with four little feet to walk on and a head no
longer than my thumb. Thou dost not believe me, mother,
but Girard would not have told me a lie; we don't have the
animal about here, but it is common enough in other parts.
Thou believest, mother? Yes, and what then? Well,
Astrolabe continued, the bag of the pipe is sewn into the
shape of that animal, while the other end of the pipe
is carved. Floriant's bagpipe is in the shape of a serpent
that he winds round his body; and just as if his mother
remembered all the minstrels who had taken part in the
entertainment given in the quadrangle, he continued:
Bernard can dance while he plays the gigue and the
organistrum with seventeen strings, to the sound of bells,
and he composes jigs to suit the psaltery. Mother, if
thou canst not go to Paris with me thou must come to
the village and hear Bernard mimic the sounds of birds.
There is no bird he can't copy, and so well that the bird
thinks it is another bird of the same kind as himself
calling to him. But Denis could do that too, Héloïse
answered. He could in a way, Astrolabe replied re-
flectively, but he couldn't pretend to make an attack on a
castle, and he was too old to jump through four hoops,
and I don't think that he ever said he could play on the
gittern and the mandore. I must have a gittern, mother,
for one has to learn these instruments early when one
is young, just as I am, else it is difficult to learn them
later.

But I heard thee say that thou wert going to be a
Crusader. Can't I be both, mother, gleeman and Cru-

sader? Well, there is plenty of time for thinking, Astrolabe, for children do not go to the Crusades. Oh, but
they do, mother, they do, for I have seen them passing
in processions, boys with banners, and boys swinging silver censers and singing hymns. So thou wouldst as lief be
a Crusader as a gleeman? she asked Astrolabe, and was
drawn almost into a meditation by the thought that her son
was beginning to pass from her. Can't I be both? the child
repeated. Do gleemen never go to the Crusades, mother?
Is father in Palestine, and if he isn't, why shouldn't he
come here? Will he never come? I should like to see
father. Héloïse did not answer, and afraid that he had
vexed his mother by his desire to see his father, he said:
but I don't want to see father, for he hasn't been good
to thee. Thou mustn't say thy father was not good to
me, Héloïse answered. Why does father leave thee here
among a lot of womenfolk? the child asked. I am here,
Héloïse replied, for I am a nun, and thy father is a
priest; at least I believe him to be one. But I don't
want to live here shut up with a lot of women, the child
answered; I'd as liefer fight for the Holy Sepulchre. But
thou'rt a child, Astrolabe. Haven't I told thee, mother,
that children are going to the Crusades? Cherriez's boy
went yesterday, he blurted out. But who has been talking
with thee, telling thee that thy father was not good to
me, and that he is in Palestine? I didn't say father was
in Palestine, only that if he were not, that—— The child
hesitated, and Héloïse ended the sentence for him: He
would come hither; so say the gleemen in the village,
where thou hast been, Astrolabe, despite thy promise. As
Astrolabe did not answer, a great fear, come from a passing thought, laid hold of her that Astrolabe, having a
musical ear, might be taken away by the gleemen, kid-

napped, leaving her without a son to show Abélard when
he returned, for she had not yet given up hope.

There was a cause, a reason for his absence, and she
fell to thinking of Mathieu's journey to Brittany, and
continued to think of Mathieu's chances of bringing Abélard back to her till she remembered that she must get
a promise from Astrolabe not to go to the village inn
again. Mother, thou art always asking for promises.
But art thou not always asking things from me? she
enquired. But thou'rt my mother, and he clung to her
robe with a pretty, affectionate movement. But if I
don't go to the inn I shall not learn to play the gittern,
and I do want to play it; it is much merrier than the
vielle, and lighter to carry. And before his mother could
answer him he begged for leave to go to the village, for
I do want to go so much, mother. And when she asked
him why, he answered quickly: To play my organistrum,
mother; and when she asked why he didn't care to
play it in the convent, he answered: You're all thinking
of your prayers, not of me. O, that is sad, indeed, she
replied, and in the village thou wouldst find eager ears?
There may be some gleeman about the inn, mother. And
to provoke one of his unexpected answers she spoke of a
quiet wood as a better place for music than an inn yard.
But one can't play without listeners, he said. Mother,
thou knowest that, and art teasing me. But the wood,
she replied, is full of birds, blackbirds, thrushes, and
these will come down from the branches and hop close
to listen to thee. Will they? he asked coseningly, and
after meditating a little while he asked if blackbirds and
thrushes could tell whether the rote be well played. Astrolabe, thou'st heard them, and spoken to me of their singing, many times. And thinking to embarrass him with a

question, she asked if the birds could sing as well as they do if they weren't little musicians.

Astrolabe did not answer, and his mother smiled; and thinking that she had puzzled him fairly, she told him of a short, stocky, little bird with a red breast darker than the robin's, and a thick bill, that could be taught to whistle tunes correctly. As correctly as I can, mother? Very nearly, she answered. And this is no joke thou'rt putting upon me, mother? No, darling; no. And if I play the rote long enough and well enough, will the little bird come down and sing me his own tune? The bullfinch has no tune of his own, like the blackbird and the thrush, dear, but he will sing to thee the tunes that are taught to him. I will teach him father's tune, he replied, and to hide her emotion from him she spoke of the rabbits and hares, which like music too, so it is said, and will come out of their holes to listen. But rabbits and hares don't sing, mother. No, but they like music; and to amuse herself and him she related stories of serpents that came out of their holes to listen, and that there was once a piper who played so well that all the rats followed out of their holes. But didn't they bite his legs, mother? No, they followed his piping and he led them down to the river, and they were all drowned. But why did he do that? asked Astrolabe. Wasn't it cruel to lead the rats that loved his music to the river to be drowned? But there was a plague of rats in that town, said Héloïse; they were eating up all the food, leaving nothing for the men and women and children. So they had to get rid of the rats, the child said; and if I played my rote as well as the piper played his pipe, would the rats follow me to the river? Ah, but thou mustn't go to the river. Now there it is again, mother; always something that I mustn't do.

A bell rang; Héloïse caught her boy up in her arms, kissed him, and said: Now I have thy promise not to go to the village? and reading in her son's face that her promise would be obeyed her heart was eased. Mother, I'll not go to the village, he said, and she forgot her fear in the delightful thought that while she was praying in church her little son would be in the green wood by the river-side, playing to the demure and speckled thrush, so like a nun, and to the gay and sprightly blackbird that cocks his tail, flaunting himself in the sun, chattering like a gleeman when in luck's way.

CHAP. XXXVII.

SISTER AGATHA, Astrolabe said, let me through the gate, for I have given mother my promise not to go to the village but to the wood by the river-side; and he began to tell Sister Agatha of the birds that would follow him home, the bullfinch singing his father's melody (if he was sure of finding one); the thrush and blackbird he knew he would see, but the bullfinch—could she tell him where he might be certain of finding one? A sister came to take charge of the portress's lodge, and during their casual talk Astrolabe passed out of the gate and crossed the fields forgetful of the thrushes and blackbirds that would certainly give ear to his minstrelsy, his thoughts set on finding a bullfinch. A stocky little bird with a short bill and a red breast darker than the robin's, he said, and before sitting down to play he wandered round the wood, discouraged by the rattling little tune that the chaffinch kept repeating high up in the pines, saying to himself: That bird could never learn my father's song, for the song he sings is always the same, he repeats it like a lesson. And he threw sticks into the tree to frighten

the bird away, for with that going on always, he said, my
bullfinch (should I find one) will not be able to listen
to my father's song.   Now do bullfinches hop about in
the hedges, or are they out in the branches of the trees?
And he wandered round the little wood, full of many
kinds of trees, with dark places in it, hollows that he did
not dare to venture into for fear he should meet fairies
or dwarfs, or giants, but kept on the outskirts of the
wood, where the trees grew thinner, within view of the
fields, casting his eyes into the darkness of the branches
overhead, for it was there he was certain that bullfinches
perched when there were any.   A blackbird ran along
the ground and chattered as it dived into the dell that
Astrolabe did not dare to enter.   Now that that bird is
gone, he said, I will try what I can do with the two
thrushes yonder.   The speckled birds ran in and out of
the ferns that were uncurling in the interspaces, picking
as they went, stopping now and again, afraid to approach
too near to the little musician.   He played his father's
song twice over and waited for the thrushes to begin to
sing it.   They uttered no note of song, but watched him
with enquiring eyes, taking courage every now and then
to pick a worm, and it was in the hope of distracting their
attention from dinner that he struck up again the same
tune; but, instead of coming nearer, beguiled by the
music, as his mother had told him they would, the thrushes
flew away.

If the birds won't come, maybe a rabbit or a hare will,
and he played on and on.   A squirrel came down a tree
trunk and he was encouraged, but the squirrel ran up the
birch-tree and disappeared, and so Astrolabe was left
alone again.   He played on, and did not know how many
tunes or minutes had passed when the sound of a dry
stick breaking under foot nearly frightened him to his

feet, for the thought of a giant or a dwarf coming out of the dell was in his mind. But on turning his head he saw neither one nor the other, but a very old man, bent with years. He may be a dwarf who has put on a false beard, Astrolabe said to himself. But don't dwarfs wear beards? And he was about to take to his heels when the old man called him and said: Do not run away, my dear child, but let me listen to thy music, for never have I heard anybody play the organistrum as well as thou. O, sir, said Astrolabe. Thou doubtest my words? the old man replied reprovingly. No, I do not doubt, the child answered, but I wish you had heard Denis, sir. It was he who taught thee? the old man asked. Astrolabe nodded, and a sudden mood of shyness falling upon him, he rose to his feet to go; but the old man called him back, and the two stood facing each other, and the child, not knowing what words to say, said (seeing a long stick in the old man's hand with a crook at the end): a shepherd, sir? Yes, indeed, replied the old man; a shepherd. But where are your sheep, sir? the child asked. My sheep follow me. As well they might, Astrolabe said, for I am sure, sir, you're a good shepherd. At which the old man smiled, and turning away from the boy he went to the edge of the wood, and looking across the field he said: My sheep will find me when they have done feeding, a remark that seemed strange to Astrolabe, for there were no sheep in the field. And he was about to ask the old shepherd if it would not be well for him to go in search of his sheep, but if he did that the old man might never come back, and he wanted ever so much to play to him, for he was tired of playing to thrushes and blackbirds, and bullfinches were nowhere about. Do you know, sir, a stocky little bird, that can learn tunes and repeat them truly? The old man said that he had

heard of bullfinches that could whistle tunes.   And the
child's thoughts passing from bullfinches to himself broke
the pause: Would you like to hear me play, sir?   I would,
indeed, the old man answered, and never did Astrolabe
play to anybody that listened so well as the shepherd, for
he sat, his eyes fixed on the boy, his feet crossed, his
elbow resting on his knee, his chin in hand, his beard
flowing through his fingers.   And when Astrolabe had
played two or three pieces, he said: Now tell me, who
was thy master? for a good one he seems to have been.
And bubbling over with excitement, Astrolabe told the
story of Denis coming to the convent pursued by wolves,
and of his departure in the springtide and the finding of
him dead by Cherriez, the gardener, his organistrum by
his side.   And it was he who taught thee to play it? the
old man said again, his eyes fixed intently on the child.
Yes, and the pipes, and on the gittern a little at the inn,
for we have no gittern.   But it couldn't have been Denis
that wrote the beautiful song that thou hast just played
to me?   Why couldn't it have been? Astrolabe asked.
Denis wrote music.   But was it? said the old man.   No,
it was my father, years ago; a prize song, mother tells
me, that he wrote for the Comte Mathieu de Rodebœuf,
who came in a barge from the Holy Land.   And one story
leading to another, it came to pass that Astrolabe mentioned that his mother was a Benedictine nun in the
convent of Argenteuil.   A nun, said the old man; then
thy father is dead?   We don't know, Astrolabe answered;
mother says he is not, but she hasn't seen him for many
years.   One of these days we shall see him, however, for
the Comte de Rodebœuf is sure to meet him again in his
travels, and he will tell him where he will find us.   And
you too, sir, if you should come upon Pierre Abélard, tell
him that we are here, and that he will hear me sing and

play the song he wrote for the Comte Mathieu de Rodebœuf.

I have travelled a long, long way, the old man answered,
and meet everybody on my rounds, and when next I see
him I will tell him all you say. So you know my father?
He composes the best songs in the land of France, the
old man replied. Do you know one? the child asked, and
the old man sang a song which seemed to Astrolabe like
the song that Rodebœuf had taught him. And who may
you be, sir? he asked. I am, the old man said, Jesus
Christ, come again upon earth to beg those who believe in
me to fare to Palestine for the rescuing of my Sepulchre
from the Infidel. But the Sepulchre has been rescued
from the Infidel, my Lord Jesus, Astrolabe answered, as
you must well know, sir. But the Infidel has begun to
get the upper hand of the Crusaders; more are required,
not to fight but to pray. Prayers are powerful and I'd
sooner have my Sepulchre won back to the Christians by
prayers than by swords. If I could follow the other
little boys and be a Crusader with them, I would pray
all day and all night, and I will ask mother to pray, too,
so that when I leave her she will know that I am praying
for the same thing. She taught me the story of the Lord
Jesus when I came to the convent. I said prayers only
when mother was with me, but now I have met you, sir,
I shall think only of prayer. Thou'rt a good boy, that I
can see, the old man said, and wilt be able to win other
children to pray, and to go to the Holy Land itself to
beg Saladin to withdraw from the country of Jerusalem.
But mother says it is a long way, Astrolabe answered,
and the old man told him that children were assembling
at Saint-Denis, a town on the other side of Paris, and
that if he followed the Paris road he would meet the
wagoners going thither, who would take him, for it is

too far for thy tender legs, he said. But, good sir, I mean
my Lord Jesus, I cannot leave my mother. When I was
on earth did I not say, dear child: Leave thy father
and mother, leave all thy goods and chattels and follow
me? Am I to leave my mother? If thou wouldst win
honour and glory, little man, go to Saint-Denis, and say
that I bade thee go thither. I have not yet told thee that
Saint-Denis is the burial place of the great martyr
Dionysius, one of the seven holy men who came to France
and baptised many. But like all those who loved me,
he was beheaded in the reign of Valerian after much
cruelty and torment, and was thrown into that very river
thou seest over yonder, into the Seine. But so great was
the power of God that his body rose to the surface, and he
swam after his head, which he captured without much
difficulty, and walked with it in his hands to the place
in which he wished to be buried. Did you not tell me
that Saint-Denis was on the other side of the Paris road?
I did indeed, dear child. But is not that a long way for
a man to walk, carrying his head in his hands? Astrolabe
asked, and was answered that the saint accomplished this
great feat by the power of God, to whom all things are
possible.

And along what roads do the wains pass that are taking
the children to Paris for the Holy Land? Astrolabe asked,
and before the priest could answer Astrolabe was telling
how Cherriez's son fell into a sickness, for, being the
only son, his mother and father would not allow him
to join the children's pilgrimage. The boy's parents had
no thought for my suffering on the Cross. Did you suffer
more than the robbers, sir? My sufferings compared with
theirs were as seventy is to seven. But you died before
them. I lost my temporal life, the old man answered,
and as if to stop further questions, he said: The wain

goes by about this hour at the corner of the lane, and all thou'st to do is to hold up thy hand and the wagoner will draw rein for thee. Soon after the rumbling sounds of wheels were heard, and the priest and Astrolabe started running. But the driver's eyes were turned from them, and the wain, full of children swinging censers and singing hymns, passed out of sight. We have missed the wain, but it will pass again to-morrow; and now I must go and look after my sheep; I stayed too long listening to thy playing. Whereupon he went away, leaving the child, who returned to the convent very unhappy, trying to recall his father's song, the one the old man had sung for him. But it eluded his memory, which was unlucky, for he could not tell his mother that he had met Jesus Christ in the wood till he remembered the tune, for the first thing his mother would ask him would be to sing the song, and she wouldn't believe that he had forgotten it, for he never forgot a tune. Sister Agatha's keys were nearly always at her girdle, but she left them on a nail sometimes and went away on an errand, but that didn't happen often. He would rather die than that his mother should think him a wicked boy, and if it had been anybody else than Jesus—a priest, for instance—he wouldn't have listened. But Jesus must be obeyed, and his thoughts turned again to the convent walls. The ground is higher down by the river and softer than elsewhere, he said to himself, and once on the other side I've only to run up the lane. But which hour of the day shall I choose? he asked himself, concluding that to go early in the morning, after Mass, would give him some two or three hours' start of Cherriez, who would be sent after him. More than three, he added, for he's a hungry man about midday, and will not go after me till he has had his dinner.

CHAP. XXXVIII.

ON hearing that he was not in the convent the conviction
pierced Héloïse that she would not see her son again,
and Madelon's words that they would find him in the
inn singing and playing to the gleemen rang hollow in
her ears, but she had to go thither, and for a moment it
soothed her to hear that there were no gleemen in the
village—the last had left some days before. He may be
in the wood, she said. What wood? asked Madelon, and
Héloïse told her that she had given him leave to play to
the blackbirds and thrushes. Yes, and to the bullfinch,
she cried. But I have no heart for talking. But, dear
mistress, he would not loiter in a wood, not till this hour.
A wolf! Héloïse cried, and the wood was searched in
vain for traces of him. No wolf has been here, Madelon
said, and the women stood staring at each other till one
of the peasants who had followed them spoke of the
children that the priests were urging to fall into the ranks
for the Holy Land. If he has fallen in with one of the
wains that take them to Saint-Denis, then we have lost
him, she said. The gleemen might have yielded him back
to us for money, but the priests will not. We must seek
him in Saint-Denis, Madelon, and appeal to the Archbishop. The King shall hear of this, Héloïse cried, and
it was in a frenzy of grief that she came before the
Prioress to ask her for leave to seek Astrolabe among the
crowds of children the ecclesiastics were collecting at
Saint-Denis. Yes, to Saint-Denis thou shalt go, said
the Prioress, and Cherriez to all the villages whither he
may have strayed. Yes, that is so, the distracted mother
answered; and as soon as the door closed behind her
the convent went to prayer, for though all the nuns knew
in their hearts that the Church was calling the children

to help the Crusaders to complete the conquest of the
Holy Land, they could not but think that the Sepulchre
might be won without the sacrifice of their boy.

The mothers, the choir, and the lay sisters joined in
prayer, and the prayer was the same on every lip, that
our Lord's Sepulchre might be restored to Christendom
without Astrolabe being sacrificed. It seemed as if God
could not do else than spare him, so united was the
convent in supplication, and when Sister Agatha opened
the door to Héloïse her words were: Hast thou found him?
Héloïse wailed. He has not come back to us, Sister
Agatha continued. Cherriez has searched all the villages.
We shall never see him again, Héloïse cried, unless he
has joined some gleemen, who will bring him back at the
end of their round; that is all the hope we have left to us.
I have searched among the children assembled at Saint-
Denis for the pilgrimage, and have much to say to the
Prioress. You will find her in her room, Sister Héloïse.
It is Héloïse returned to us, Mother Ysabeau said. Hast
found him? the Prioress cried from her chair. He is not
amongst the pilgrims, unless they have hidden him; and
she fell to telling of the scene she had witnessed at Saint-
Denis, parents crying for their children, wringing their
hands, tears running down their cheeks, appealing to the
priests and bishops, but never getting an answer save the
ready-made one: The children have vowed to go to Jerusalem to exhort Saladin to yield the tomb of the Lord
Jesus to those who believe in him. But the children, I
answered them, cannot take vows to leave their parents.
Even so, the Pope may liberate them from their vows.
We cannot, was the reply we got, hearing mutterings that
none but heretics would seek to prevent children from
obeying the Divine Will which had fallen on the city,
on town and village, finding its way into isolated hamlets,

setting the children's feet on the road to Marseilles, where they would embark for Palestine.

On these words Héloïse fell into a chair overwhelmed, unable to complete her story except in broken sentences: to wit, that she had heard it said that it would be a worse evil to keep the children back than to let them go, for those that were detained against their will died of their longing to serve Jesus. Amid stories of miracles and prophecies she had struggled through the dense throng assembled at Saint-Denis to pray beside the relic of him who recovered his head from the flood and carried it in his hands to the place where he desired it to be buried. And to satisfy the curiosity of the Prioress she told of banners embroidered with the Cross and ecclesiastics swinging censers, saying that she seemed to hear her boy's voice in the hymn, *Veni Sancte Spiritu,* and that she had tried to get through the throng, but was pushed back. Doubts were cast on my robe—no true Benedictine nun would ask for her child back, it was said, at most she is a widow who has taken the veil, and therefore no true bride of Christ.

A cloud gathered on the Prioress's face and she asked some questions, learning that her letter had obtained lodging for Héloïse and Madelon in another convent of their Order. But when my quest was made known, Héloïse said, I encountered dark looks in the convent, and always the phrase: Why seek him whom it is the will of God to take from thee, Sister? It surprises me to hear that the Prioress of a Benedictine convent should regard so little a recommendation from the convent at Argenteuil, Mother Ysabeau replied dryly; we are not all of the same kind; this pilgrimage falls cruelly on parents, and we are sorry for Héloïse, her loss is also our loss, but she'll remember later that if God has taken her child from her, it was for

His own good purpose. He may, Héloïse said, have joined
some company of gleemen. In that case he will soon
come back to us. A smile glided into Mother Ysabeau's
face, and she remembered with satisfaction that she had
always been opposed to the admission of vagrants into the
convent. If the gleemen have taken him he may return
to us, Mother Ysabeau replied. But how will he return?
soulless, I fear; these gleemen are the off-scourings of
the world; but if he join the pilgrimage he will be returned
to us hereafter, for all eternity. Theology is easier for
childless women than for parents, Héloïse answered passionately, and I have no heart to argue with you that we
need not lose our children that they may gain heaven;
enough it is to remind you that Mary was afflicted and
wept at the foot of the Cross. Sister Héloïse is right,
the Prioress interposed, for it may be doubted if God
placed the maternal instinct in us so that we may deny
it, and as she says, Mary—— It was far from me to say
that a mother's love should be put aside, trampled on,
Mother Ysabeau interrupted, but are we not taught
resignation to God's will? There is always a seeming
conflict, the Prioress answered, between the spirit and
the flesh. We are as God made us, half spirit, half flesh;
our instincts as much as our souls are the will of God.
And have we not got it on the authority of the Evangelist
that Jesus called from the Cross to his mother: Mother,
behold thy son? Even if we could we must not put our
instincts aside, lest God should deem us unworthy of
His love without them. I am going too far, maybe; such
questions as these we cannot decide ourselves, we should
refer them to our spiritual guides. It was so with me
when the news of my dear husband's death reached me.
My sister said that I must remember he died fighting for
the Holy Sepulchre and that we should meet in heaven;

but it was hard for me to think that years and years would pass without my seeing him. My sister lost her husband soon after, and then her grief enabled her to take pity upon me.

Mother Ysabeau and Héloïse listened, knowing well all that the Prioress had to say and that her exordium would not be completed in less than ten minutes, and for about that time she followed wandering memories until at last she could remember no longer why she had started out on a long story which, it occurred to her suddenly, she must have told before. I am afraid I've told that story already. I have wearied you both. I have been a little more prolix than usual this morning. The nuns protested, but the Prioress said: It is kind of you to bear with an old woman's memories, especially Héloïse, who has her own griefs to attend to now.

Héloïse took these words as permission to absent herself; and as she descended the stairs her thoughts turned to Mother Ysabeau, whom she caught sight of going from the schoolroom to the novitiate. And then her thoughts turned suddenly from the hated nun, for the sight of the library awakened her to a sense of loss. It was in the library that she used to teach Astrolabe Latin. The Æneid lay on the table (Sister Josiane had not returned it to the shelves) and dropping into a chair she fell to thinking of the good progress he was making in Latin and French, a startled look coming into her eyes, for she might never see him again. But this could not be; he would come back to her, unless he was murdered, and who was there to murder him, and for what reason? None. But if he were in that procession he might perish by the roadside, drop out overcome by heat and dust; and in her imagination she saw the white dust rising from the road, for there was no breeze in the air. How he will suffer from the heat of the way, she said, if—— But he may be with trouvères and gleemen; if so, there was hope. Her thoughts melted away, and when she awoke from her reverie the first thing that came under her eyes was the story she had written for him, *Peronnik the Fool,* the sight of the manuscript bringing back the intimate hours of her life—mother and son sitting side by side, teacher and pupil, and after a little while she remembered him sitting on the edge of the well singing so beautifully that all the nuns came to the windows to applaud their little serenader. But afraid that he might fall backwards into the well, she had scolded him. Had she known that he was going to be taken from her she would not have scolded him. It seemed to her now that she was always scolding him or answering: No, darling, no. How often had she spoken these words. But all was different now; if he'd only come back he might do what he liked— tease her from morning to evening. How happy she would be to answer: Darling, yes, but have care, lest——

But she would never hear his voice again. She might never hear him sing, or speak, or sigh, or cough. It might well be that he was afraid to return lest she should scold him for going to the village. Why had she forbidden this innocent enjoyment to him? He liked music, it was a gift that came to him from his father, and if he'd only return she would let him spend whole days in the village, yes, whole days, if he would only come back. But was it gleeman or priest who had robbed her of him? Unable to resist the impulse, she fell upon her knees suddenly and prayed that he had gone away with the gleemen, for if so he would return to her, telling her joyfully of all the instruments he had learned to play, the gittern, the lute, the psaltery. He had wanted her to take him to Paris to buy a flute. If he would only come back she would buy him three flutes, and she almost swooned in the joy it would be to clasp him to her bosom once more, feeling his warm body in her arms, his knees against hers. To kiss him, ah, to kiss him; but he was gone— gone—gone, and these words sounded very dismal in her ears.

Once more she fell to thinking. Looks, words, gestures floated up to the surface of her mind, and quarrels long forgotten. The worst pain of all was the thought that she had never loved him. She had loved him, but not enough, and her conduct towards him seemed full of mistakes. Of course she had tried to teach him, and perhaps her rule was severe; and once again she turned to the past, dredging it in the hope of bringing up some cause that would explain why he had run away. It might be to escape from the nuns, for boys of that age look to men rather than to women; ever since the minstrels came to the convent he had spoken to her of men, asking her why she lived in a convent, why she was a nun, and if she would go on being a nun always. So she must not blame him, for it was not for lack of love of her that he had left her, but for weariness of the convent, which lay upon him heavier than it lay upon her, and very often it lay upon her very heavily indeed. It was her vow to Abélard that had enabled her to bear the convent life for so many years, but her boy had not pledged himself to anything, and it was natural that he should say to himself: Mother would not take me to Paris to buy a flute, what harm to go away in a boat with the trouvères and gleemen for a week, for a month, for two or three? Mother will grieve, of course, and be frightened, but I cannot do else. The river might have tempted him, she said; every child likes a boat and a sail.

Her hope was that it might all have happened as she imagined it happening, and these hopes caused her almost dead life to quicken; but as her hopes faded her life became empty as a shell, and it often seemed to her that she was no more than a ghost, so detached was she from all worldly ties. The nuns had prayer; some believed in heaven, some were afraid of hell, but she had no thought for these beliefs, less now than ever. So she fed upon her grief from day to day, finding her way instinctively to the room that Astrolabe had lived in, spending many hours alone there. All other rooms were naught to her; but the pillow on which he had laid his head was a reality that she could appreciate, even comprehend, and returning from his bed she stood looking across the quadrangle, noticing the roofs, for he had often spoken to her about them, telling her of the eaves under which the swallows had their clay nests. One of the things that made him such a delightful companion was that he was always curious to see and to hear. Why do the swallows come, and whither do they go, and why do they return? he often asked her, telling that he had tried to feed them with bread, but the sparrows ate all the bread. Swallows, she answered, live upon flies, and he would have had it from her why one bird could eat what another could not. Her memories of him filled her eyes with tears, and turning from the window she opened a drawer, and taking out the clothes he had left behind, she examined them to see if they wanted mending. Few they were and scanty enough, but he might be glad of them if he returned; and she began to mend them, forgetful for the moment that he had run away and might never return to her.

But not many stitches did she put into his hose when a road full of hot dust stretching forward through a country of red hills rose before her eyes, with a throng of children in it, the weak ones falling out of the ranks. At last the children came to a great, deep, silent river, and the boat that was there to take them across it was laden to the gunwales when it pushed away from the bank, to be overwhelmed by a tree floating down the current. She uttered a cry and stared about her, returning to her senses quickly, thankful that she had been dreaming—a waking dream without any truth in it, she said, but bad enough while it lasted. She continued her sewing mechanically for a while, but before long the pilgrim children appeared to her, this time in a forest filled with lurking wolves, and with Astrolabe's hosen again slipping from her fingers, she sat watching the evening sun shining on the tiled roofs opposite, her soul uplifted in prayer that he had not been beguiled by the hope of winning the Sepulchre from the Saracen. There were three linen tunics that needed mending, and she was glad to come upon a rent in the surcoat he wore over them.

The days went by, the same thoughts returning as she sat sewing, and then it seemed to her that she had grieved enough and could grieve no more. She descended to the refectory, and was glad that the meals were eaten in silence. The nuns rose from their places and left the chapel on different errands, Héloïse returning to the room in which her son had lived, to continue the mending of his garments. But if he have jumped into a barge and gone with gleemen down to Normandy, and is singing with them from town to town, from castle to castle, he will not return for months, perhaps for years, and the cloak that I am now mending will be too small for him! She picked up the cloak from the floor, where it had fallen, and continued her sewing till a sudden thought entered her heart, and it seemed to her that the pain she suffered was greater than any pain she had felt before. It flung her upon her knees, and she prayed that whither her son was gone might be made known to her. But of what good to me is the truth? Be he with Crusaders or gleemen he is lost to me. Another outburst flung her on her knees again to pray that Abélard might not return till his son was given back to her. But would the hope help her to bear with the agony of living? (she had borne the drudgery till now), and it seemed to her that she must turn to poison or knife for release, till she said unto herself that death would be no sufficient escape for her. She must live to tell him the story, else he would execrate her memory. He must not think ill of me, and rather than that should happen I will endure this convent life still a little longer. As she stood thinking how she might redeem herself from blame when she and Abélard came face to face, the quiet of the convent began to awaken her to a still deeper sense of her loneliness. I am forgotten even by the nuns, she said, remembering suddenly that since her return from Saint-Denis she had lived more as an oblate in the convent than a true member of the community. The Prioress, who had known much grief in her life, allowed her the privilege of solitude, and whole days passed without a knock; but now one came, and she heard Mother Hilda's voice asking for admission, which she gave gladly, for Hilda's voice would enable her to put aside her memories, and her troubles for a little while. But all about her was the litter of her sewing, and to avoid questions, she said: The weather has been very fine for the last few days. Shall we not go out and enjoy it together? It was for that I came hither, Mother Hilda answered, and the two nuns descended the stairs, but before they had crossed the threshold into the open

air, one of the sisters came with a message from the
Prioress: The Prioress is waiting for you, Mother Hilda,
in her room. All the mothers are there, and she will be
glad to see you too, Sister Héloïse, a little later. We
were going for a walk together, Héloïse answered, and
Mother Hilda, interrupting sharply, said: I cannot keep
dear Mother waiting; I am sorry. And she went away,
leaving Héloïse in the broad walk leading from the
orchard to the river to watch the swallows. Thousands
were in the air, and the birds recalled Abélard's words:
It seems as if the birds took pleasure in flight. Do we
not take pleasure in walking? she had answered. A simple
answer, truly, but they had found pleasure in it, for they
loved each other then. But now! Now I have nobody,
neither lover, nor husband, nor son, not even this black
Benedictine robe; and she had begun to consider the
mockery of it when the sound of footsteps on the gravel
behind her caused her to turn. It was Sister Agatha
bringing with her the Comte Mathieu de Rodebœuf, the
trouvère. Thou hast found him? Hast seen him? she
cried. He is in Brittany, Rodebœuf answered. But of
whom art thou speaking? she cried, almost hysterically,
and he answered: I am speaking of Abélard, who is in
Brittany. In Brittany, she answered, with his people?
A great light of joy came into her face; she looked like
one transfigured; but soon the light dimmed a little and
she said: But Brittany was never near to his heart, though
he came from thence. In Brittany he cannot be. No;
thou art mistaken. Mistaken! he said, and he told her
of gleemen who had wandered to a monastery built on a
cliff-side and sung some songs in the Abbey of Saint-
Gildas to Abélard—— Who is the Abbot? Héloïse cried.
Yes; and who, on hearing the songs, which were his own,
asked the chief gleeman if he knew the trouvère who had

written them, to which the gleemen answered that the
songs were sung everywhere in France. But they must
not be sung here, Abélard replied, for they are my own
songs, composed before calamity brought me to repentance. By the stories the gleemen told me, I judge that
the Abbey of Saint-Gildas stands in a wilderness of rocks,
seaweed, surge and screaming gulls. He has gone into
the wilderness, Héloïse said, to repent of sins committed
with me. Philosophy, of which he was the divine master,
laid aside, poetry and music forsaken; well indeed might
he speak of calamity. No more do we know about him
than the story I heard from the gleemen, Rodebœuf said.
For what purpose, Héloïse asked, should they tell you
lies? None that I know of, he answered. Why should
gleemen wander to coasts out of the path of gleemen? she
questioned. And why should Abélard have gone thither?
Because all men wander. Be it so, thy business is to find
him and to bring him hither. But he knows where I am,
and he comes not, for he has repented and prays that he
may not remember me. But go to Brittany, Mathieu, and
tell him that I am weary of waiting in this convent. I
will go, Rodebœuf answered; and the moon under which
the swallows are flying now will not have waxed and
waned twice before I am back with news of him. Your
tidings, good or evil, will make an end to the present, she
said. The Prioress is waiting for me in her room. I bid
you farewell.

She looked back to see him hurry away, and stopping on
the stair she said to herself: The time has come for me
to tell why I am here. Is it thou, Héloïse? Yes, it is I,
she answered; my excuse for having kept you waiting,
dear Mother, is that the Comte de Rodebœuf was here
with news of Abélard. News of Abélard, the Prioress
repeated, and what may his tidings be, dear child? But

before Héloïse could answer, the Prioress's thoughts had
returned to the peril in which the convent stood, and
she began to tell it, but was stopped suddenly by a
woman's curiosity to hear of a returned lover. News of
Abélard! she said, breaking off suddenly almost at the
outset of her own story, and Héloïse related as much
of hers as it seemed to be her duty to tell.

You are pained, dear Mother, as indeed I knew you
would be, to hear that I have been living for nearly nine
years with a lie in my heart always and often on my
lips. The Héloïse you knew is not the true Héloïse, and
it pains me as much to tell that I came hither to wait for
Abélard as for you to hear it. But it was not in thy
mind to live with Abélard again, Héloïse? It was, dear
Mother, for to do so was the promise between us, and
it could not be else, he being he and I being I. The
Prioress did not answer at first, and when her words came
they were gentler than those Héloïse expected. I know,
she said, how God has wrought woman's life cunningly
into her love of man. We do not think outside of our love.
But I am fain to believe, Héloïse, that you are telling a
tale against yourself, and harshly, when you say that if
things had come to pass as you wished them, you would
have put vows aside and lived with Abélard in sin. Nor
can I believe that he, as a priest, would have connived.
Blundering there must have been on both sides. My
story pains you, Mother, but I could not keep it from
you any longer. We fall into sin, Héloïse, for the flesh
is weak, almost unwittingly. But to plan a sin, to live
amongst us, looking forward month after month, year
after year, Héloïse. The old nun sat looking with implor-
ing eyes, and Héloïse answered her: It may be that I
have not sinned against God though against the Church,
Against God and not against the Church? the Prioress

repeated. But how can that be? Heresy is on your lips,
Héloïse, and nothing is more terrible than that, worse
even than sin. The Church, dear Mother, received her
wisdom from God in the beginning and still receives wisdom from him, century after century; but though the
Church cannot err, God being with His Church always,
we must not forget that God is above the Church and sees
into the heart as even the Church cannot see, judging
men by their hearts, for the sin is in the intention rather
than in the act. One moment more, dear Mother, and I
shall have done. Abélard's teaching is as I have often
told it to you. He may be wrong in the eyes of the
Church, but being sincere in his belief, he may be right
in the eyes of God. His heart, I know, was without
guile, for it was I who persuaded him against marriage
in Brittany, and, when in obedience to him I came to
Paris with him and was married, I went to him, saying:
Thou seest that all that I told thee has come to pass.
Fulbert, my uncle, is making known our marriage to all
the world, and if a great philosopher is not to be lost
to the Church, this marriage must be undone; and there
is but one way to undo it—by my taking the veil. Then
thou'lt be free to enter the priesthood and make an end
of heathendom. Abélard has put it to Bernard again
and again: Faith may be enough for those who have
faith, but how would you bring the heathen into the
Church except by reason? To these questions Bernard
has never found an answer, and Abélard has replied to
his silence: By neglecting the Infidel thou'rt neglecting
the work of God, for has he not said: Go forth and preach
to all men? You came to my convent that a philosopher
might be saved to the Church? That was indeed a
thought that God might have put into your mind, but
you tell me that—— Without my love of Abélard, Héloïse

interrupted, I should not have been able to live here for nine years, as I have said, with a lie in my heart always and often a lie on my lips. God, who looks into the heart, knows that I have suffered. The Comte Mathieu de Rodebœuf came to-day with tidings of Abélard, who is now in Brittany, the Abbot of Saint-Gildas, and therefore I judged that the time had come for me to make confession to you. For me to remain here any longer—— But you're not leaving us? Why should I remain? Though there was neither son nor lover, I could not. But there are both; I must seek my son first, and then my husband. You said, Mother, that you had a story to tell, if you do not deem me unworthy to hear it.

Only this, Héloïse, that it is not necessary for you to leave us; we are all leaving Argenteuil in a few days, for the Pope acquiesces in our expulsion from this house and these lands. But we thought—— Héloïse answered. Ah, yes, the Prioress interrupted, we all thought that the Pope would revoke that Bull; but Suger, the Abbot of Saint-Denis, has influence with the Pope and with the King, and we shall have to leave here within the next few days. But the bishops and the clergy will oppose so cruel an act, said Héloïse. We cannot reckon upon their help, for Suger has made out a good case against us, and in reply to further questions from Héloïse, she related that Suger, while a novice in the monastery of Saint-Denis, made himself acquainted with all the details of the charters of that monastery, and undertook to prove that the lands of Argenteuil belonged to his monastery and should be restored to it. The charter goes back to the time of Clothaire III., and it appears certain that the donators left these lands to the monks of Saint-Denis, who, however, made so little use of them that Charlemagne took them over and gave them to his daughter, Theodrade,

and Adelaide, wife of Hugh Capet, built the convent. A
hundred years went by, and now the riches of the convent
have excited the cupidity of Suger, who, as I have said,
Héloïse, has influence with the Pope, Honorius II., and
with the King, and he has never ceased to try to dis-
possess us. The deeds make it clear that Hermenric and
his wife, Numana, gave these lands to the convent of
Saint-Denis and that Louis the Debonair decreed they
should return to this convent after the death of his sister,
but the Normans sailed up the Seine and pillaged and
destroyed Argenteuil; and under Hugh Capet the monks
omitted to claim their rights. But now, after two hundred
years, they are pressing their claim, and it has come to
pass that the house we have lived in so long, and the
lands about it, have to be given back. So you see, Héloïse,
there was no need for you to decide to leave us. Some
of us will go to other convents, some to their parents and
friends. But there are some here who have no parents
and no friends, and what will become of them? cried
Héloïse. The monks of Saint-Denis, by never exercising
their rights, have lost their rights in these lands. The
present Abbé of Saint-Denis has the ear of the King and
the Pope, the Prioress said. But you, dear Mother, are
the widow of Godfrey de Châtillon, and you come from a
family as great as the one that you entered by marriage,
and the King would not sacrifice the aristocracy of his
kingdom to please a greedy prelate and infamous monks,
the irregularity of whose lives is—— If the lives of
the nuns at Argenteuil, the Prioress answered, were irre-
proachable, the claim of the monks might be set aside.
But our convent, alas, is far from being blameless.
I am reproached by the nuns and clergy, and by myself
for having yielded in many instances where I should have
been firm, the nuns saying to me that they had vowed

to obey certain rules and that these they would obey, but none other; and in fear lest the harsh rule would prevent rich postulates from joining our Order I acquiesced, added to which ill-health, sorrow, grief for my husband's death, weighed me down, poisoned my life. I was a broken old woman when I was selected to the priorate of this convent for my rank rather than for personal reasons. I should have refused the honour that was imposed upon me, but my will failed me then, as it has failed me often. Tears rose to the Prioress's eyelids, and it was a long while before the old woman could resume her narrative.

The year and the season that Madelon came to fetch thee are well in my mind. Was it not then that we were all going to Argenteuil to see Paula's baby, now a growing girl employed in the laundry, who is thinking of entering the religious life. That scandal was not forgotten when another fell upon us. Sister Agnes left us for a gleeman, so it is said by her enemies, but none knows with whom she fled. Sister Angela left us last month in the belief that the beauty of her hair would convert Saladin to Christianity. The beauty of her hair! Héloïse repeated. That Saladin's redemption should come through the gold of her hair was the story she told me, the Prioress answered, and when I reasoned with her she said that she had seen Saladin in a dream, his dark straight hair like ebony and his body pale as gold as he lay asleep in a tent. And leaning over to hear his dream Angela heard from him that the East was longing for union with the West, and that the gold of the morning and the gold of the evening should undo the knot. But what knot? Héloïse asked. The Sepulchre, I understood her to mean, the possession of which has caused war to arise between the East and the West. My hair, she said, is the golden

West and his body is the golden East, and the mingling of
the two will cause all the trouble of the West and the
East to end. On these words she raised her veil, and the
hair she had let grow fell about her. I reasoned with
her and told her of the great distance, and she said the
children had gone, and if they could, she could. But
on her way thither it would seem that she met a gleeman
returned from the Holy Land; and now I am being re
proached for having admitted gleemen and their shows
into this convent. Thou hast it all in mind, Héloïse?

I have indeed, dear Mother. And the next scandal,
mine own, is beginning: a Benedictine nun is about to
leave her convent for a monk. We are not all-powerful
in our own lives, Mother, as you know well. Only God
is that and He wills it all, a terrible God in this world
and crueller in the next, so it is said. When the thunder
muttered and crashed yesterday, I said: The earth is
afraid of God in her very entrails, and when I saw the
lightning shiver I said: The skies tremble with fear of
God. The Scriptures tell us that we must fear God—
and who does not?—Death himself slinking into the tomb
silent from fear of God. She had thrown herself by the
Prioress, and, rising from her knees, she said: All we
know of God is injustice; and the Pope finds it easier to
yield to Abbé Suger than to resist him.

Women come and go from convents, the Prioress answered, and babies are born; but worse than the sins of
the flesh are the sins against faith, and a great charge
of witchcraft is directed against us and has proved our
undoing more than Paula's baby. Sister Angela is now
selling charms and potions and casting horoscopes in the
fairs. Worst of all, two of our schoolchildren have begun
to wrangle and bear witness one against the other till it
seems beyond our wits to separate truth from lies. Some

truth there must be in their sayings, for both are agreed on certain facts. That Stephen was unwise in allowing them into his house there can be no doubt. The first to go thither was Adèle, and her adventures, whether false or true, excited Lucille to stay longer in the confessional than she need stay, and to go to the priest's house by night. Her story is that he took her to the garden of a herbalist, a trader in spells and charms and amulets, whither peasants assemble for the worship of Satan, who is wheeled in, in effigy, horns and hooves and tail, all and sundry falling down before him. We asked Lucille why people should pray to Satan, and she answered that she had put that question to the folk, and got for answer: We have prayed to God long enough to redeem us from the tyranny of the nobles; we are perishing of hunger, of disease, and if God will not help us perhaps the devil may. When questioned further, Lucille said that the devils who accompanied Satan seemed like nuns disguised as devils, the thought behind being that our nuns here escape by night to these pagan festivals to worship Satan, and to commit in his honour and to obtain his aid, all sins natural and unnatural in the shubberies and arbours with whomsoever lays hands upon them. So it is Lucille, that blue-eyed, flaxen-haired child, who tells these things? said Héloïse. Who has not only seen, but who has participated in this worship, in her imagination or in reality, that is what we do not know, the Prioress answered. Mayhap she only heard of devil-worship, picked up wandering stories; stories are going about of men and women who have lost their memory of all things and collect in groups about village fires, and assemble in the woods for strange rites brought back from Palestine, which is stranger still; unbelievable it is that returned Crusaders should have brought this evil into the country.

Saladin's magicians are charged with it. We live in
strange times. In strange times indeed, Héloïse answered,
when a convent chaplain brings children to pagan festivals. For why does he bring them? the Prioress continued; for that Saladin's magicians ordained that the
defilement of the consecrated Host is essential to procure
Satan's help. And how is the Host defiled? Héloïse
asked; does Satan participate? Satan is a priest, the
Prioress answered, so it is said, and the perversion is so
great that the Host—— I cannot bear to repeat the child's
words, and if she has seen nothing of what she tells us,
then indeed she is possessed of Satan. Is their sin pardonable in the eyes of God, Héloïse said, if they believe
that Satan can help them, or should I say more pardonable
than if an unbeliever committed the sin? Whereat the
nuns fell to thinking.

CHAP. XXXIX.

THE sound of wrangling voices reached her in the
passage, and when she entered the community-room, in
which were all the choir sisters, Mother Ysabeau said:
You have come, Héloïse, from the Prioress, who believes
everything these wicked children, Adèle and Lucille, are
telling against each other and our chaplain, Stephen?
A group formed quickly round Héloïse and Mother Ysabeau, and the wrangle increased in noise, everybody anxious to speak but not to listen, till one of Lucille's detrac-
tors gained the ear of the community with news of
Lucille's withdrawal of the statement that Stephen had
taken her to the village to worship Satan. Lucille's de-
fenders denied quickly that the child had ever said she had
worshipped Satan, only that she had been taken to the

village at night by Stephen. Of that there could be no
doubt, and proof did not lack that prayers were offered
to Satan in a herbalist's garden.

What did not seem clear was why Stephen should
have taken Lucille and not Adèie; and the wrangle continued, the disputants saying the same thing again and
again, till everybody was wearied of the rigmarole and
waited for some new fact.

And the debate slumbered until Sister Mechtilde returned to the community-room. She was at once surrounded. Which of the children has confessed? was the
question put to her, and an enumeration of punishments
that might be applied in order to procure a confession was
passed from mouth to mouth, each nun demanding severer
tortures. But, said Sister Mechtilde, however we may
punish the children, and frighten them with tales of the
rack and thumb-screws, we shall not get the truth from
them, for they do not know it themselves. At these words
the community-room became instantly silent. All crowded
to hear. That is my belief, continued Sister Mechtilde.
The children have been playing at ghosts, frightening
each other, walking about in white sheets with faces
whitened or blackened out of human resemblance; they
were joined by some of the novices; Sister Marcella and
Sister Ursula led them up and down the passages, and
after frightening others, dreams began to awaken them
out of their sleep; from telling each other their dreams
and the stories that have come into the convent of the
doings in the village, a tale of a nightly visitor arose.
For a long time the children did not know who this
visitor was, but suddenly he became Stephen, and the
children began to tell of how they had found Stephen in
their beds and waked up too late. So you think, Sister,
said Héloïse, that the stories Adèle and Lucille are telling

against each other and against the convent are all illusions, and that no ghost seeks the children in their beds? It may have been, Sister Mechtilde answered, that it was the novices who played the prank of visiting the children in their beds. Else we must believe that Stephen bribed our portress Agatha or climbed into the dormitory by a rope ladder. It seemed as if their chaplain, Stephen, was acquitted of all evil doings by the nuns themselves. For of Agatha's integrity they were sure; the rope ladder and their chaplain climbing up by it into the dormitory at midnight, when the owls were hooting, did not seem to unriddle the story in which they were all caught, nuns, children and chaplain, one which would leave the nuns homeless and might conduct poor Stephen to the stake.

The burning of Stephen was a sad thought, but some nuns had fallen to thinking of what was going to become of them, of the days that lay ahead, when they would have to face angry relatives, who would look upon them as extra mouths to feed; others, who were to be scattered through different convents, were thinking of the unpleasantness of life among hostile nuns and under rules that they had never promised to obey. The convent lot seemed irretrievable indeed. It was Sister Josiane who broke the sad pause that had fallen upon the community-room: Those of us, she said, for whom our persecutors will find convents are fortunate, and those who have fathers, mothers, brothers and sisters, and even cousins, who will give them a welcome, however short and scanty, are fortunate. But some of us are alone in the world, and some there are who, for one reason or another, will find small mercy from the Church. Sister Paula's incontinence will be urged against her, and though the same blame cannot be cast upon me, my knowledge and admiration of the works of that great man, John Scotus Erigena, will be remembered. We are in truth a most unfortunate community. Her words struck terror, and the silence that succeeded her words became in a few moments a piercing that none could endure. Before she could speak again a babble of nuns began, and then little groups of three or four nuns formed; sometimes a single nun walked across the room, in the hope of catching the ear of a casual auditor, and every one of these nuns was hot with anger against Suger and the monks of Saint-Denis. The gleemaiden was not enough for old Abbot Adam; he despised her, a nun was heard saying, and then a little nun said: I heard Angela say something like that once—that man's love of woman was something the world lived upon, a necessity, but a woman's love of woman was more detached—purer; and understanding her a little, I said: Yet if I were in great trouble it would seem to me more natural to go to a man for help. Whereat she looked at me gravely; it is not so with me, she said; I would go to a woman. She said she would let me into the secret, but she has gone away to live with a gleeman, a returned Crusader, and I shall never know it. The door opened; and it was Sister Agatha come to say that Abbé Suger was in the library and wished to speak with Sister Héloïse. To speak to me? Héloïse asked, and she looked towards Mother Hilda and Mother Ysabeau. Yes, Sister Héloïse, Sister Agatha replied; he wishes to speak with you. We have seen him, Mother Hilda answered, many times within the last few weeks, but were not able to get better terms from him than promises to find us convents. But shall I see him? Héloïse asked. It may be on some privy matter he wishes to speak to you, Mother Ysabeau answered. But I do not know him, said Héloïse, and she left the community-room expecting

to come upon the great Abbot lost in admiration of their
library, looking up and down the shelves.   But he was
pacing the room like a wolf in a cage, and she recoiled
inwardly from the thick-set man who came to greet her
enveloped in a brown-yellow robe tied by a rope around
his middle.   His tonsured head offended her, so like a
religious brag did it seem, and her aversion for his bony
yellow forehead, finely cut aquiline nose, and watchful
eyes, was so instinctive that she withdrew her hand from
his fat grasp, betraying, or almost, her aversion.   Her
hatred was that of a Benedictine nun for a man who had
come to rob her convent and disperse the sisters through
different convents, leaving the residue to shift for themselves, but deeper than her hatred was her dread of him,
for she was sensible of his power even before he began
to speak, and after the first words she knew that to
withstand him she must summon all her courage to her
aid.

So were they in the first moments, but ridding her
voice of all resentment, she said: Will you sit down, Abbé
Suger?   He thanked her, and while finding a seat for
himself and drawing it forward to within pleasant speaking distance, he talked to her about the long walk from
Paris—two leagues at least, along dusty roads, a remark
that compelled her to ask him if he drank wine or water.
Water, he said, and while waiting for the water he began
to tell her that he had asked to see her rather than the
Prioress, Mother Ysabeau, or Mother Hilda, for he had
talked to them during the week unprofitably.   To talk
profitably, he said, one must start from certain facts
accepted by both parties as a basis for discussion.   And
not being able to persuade them to accept our expulsion
as unavoidable, Héloïse answered, you—— I would
have you accept it as irrevocable, Suger interrupted, for

his Holiness, the Pope, and the King have ordered it. But all discussion between me and the mothers declined into a wrangle; I could not persuade them to start from certain facts, and it was to avoid another profitless wrangle that I sent for you, Sister Héloïse, for the sake of your intelligence, which is known to everybody.

Héloïse's face darkened, and his voice assuming a stricter tone he began to tell her that his Holiness, Honorius II., and Louis VII. of France, and himself (if he might include himself), and the monks of Saint-Denis, whose Abbot he was, wished to make this expulsion from the convent of Argenteuil as little harsh as might be; and it is for yourselves, he added, to make the expulsion harsh or gentle. You think expulsions can ever be gentle, Abbé Suger? Héloïse said, ruing the words, for they did not seem to give her any advantage over their cruel enemy. She even thought that she descried a smile through his hairy lips, for in his reply there was a certain irony: He had no wish for an argument regarding the exact meaning of the word expulsion, his object being to avoid recriminations. The convent is going to be closed, he said, and the question comes if this can be done without causing a scandal. You would avoid scandal then? Héloïse asked. Of course we would like to avoid scandal, the monk answered, and shall avoid it in a great measure if we may reckon on your help, Sister; you are powerful in the convent and will be able to persuade the sisters not to butt, like silly sheep, against the rocks but to scale the rocks—— Like goats, Héloïse interjected. If the discussion be conducted on a basis of admitted fact, he said, that, come what may, the convent is going to be closed, much may be done to soften, to alleviate the lot of the sisters; also to avoid recriminations and a raking up of old scandals.

Abbé Suger waited for Héloïse to vent herself, but she sat saying nothing, and, dismayed somewhat by her silence, he continued: I was sorry not to have seen you when you were at Saint-Denis. Forgive me for recalling to your memory the loss of your son, who I would like to think will be returned to you, for it would be sad indeed if all the children engaged in this pilgrimage, inspired to do so by the words of Our Lord Jesus Christ— out of the mouths of babes and sucklings cometh forth wisdom—should never return to their parents. But you do not think, Abbé Suger, that these children will ever reach Constantinople? I hope indeed they will, and Jerusalem too, and that many will return, else we should not have yielded to their importunities. I am without news of your son, but if he be with the procession that started from Saint-Denis some three weeks ago, it may be that a quick messenger might overtake the procession; and one child more or less would not matter to the pilgrimage, which is sufficiently numerous. You would bribe me by promises to get back my son? We should avoid, Sister Héloïse, such words as bribe, for the use of them will make it hard for us to come to an agreement; and moreover the word bribe has no meaning at all in the proposal that I am making to you. I cannot promise to get back your son for you, I can only promise to help. There is no bribe in a promise, I am asking you to save your sisters much unnecessary hardships by your counsel—— By not trying to withstand you? Héloïse interrupted. By not trying to resist the closing of the convent, he answered; for if you resist and create scandal we are powerless to help you. The orders of the King and the Pope must be obeyed. If we are thrown out of this convent, Héloïse said, we shall have to beg at the doors of the churches in our Benedictine robes. That is the scandal,

Sister Héloïse, we wish to avoid, he replied. You would have our lands, she said, and would have us come to terms, and I am asked to make them pleasant and agreeable. And you will not? Abbé Suger said, rising. Am I to understand that my appeal is vain? If the Pope dispossesses us of our lands and our convent he might at least absolve us from our vows, Héloïse replied; is not that so, Abbé Suger? The sisters of Argenteuil, he answered, do not ask to be absolved from their vows. Sister Angela—— I thought, Abbé Suger, we were to avoid wrangles and recriminations. I have not reproached the monastery of Saint-Denis with the sins committed in the days of the late Abbot; and you might have observed the same reticence regarding any sins that may have been committed in my convent.

We will not enter on a long chapter of the reformation of convents and monasteries, said Abbé Suger. No, it would be time wasted, Héloïse answered. And now tell me, has a date been fixed for our expulsion? A few days more remain, he replied. In a few days then, Héloïse said, we shall be begging at the doors of Notre-Dame. An old enemy of yours, Abbé Suger, my husband, will, I hope, come to help us in the days of great trial that you are preparing for us. You do me wrong, Sister Héloïse, for my first act of administration was to befriend your husband, Pierre Abélard, for the late Abbot, whom he denounced on many occasions in public and in private, was striving at the time of his death to compel Abélard to return to his monastery, from which he had escaped; and he might have succeeded if death had not intercepted his project. I would lay no claim for what I did to obtain freedom for Abélard to live and to teach outside of his monastery, but since you have chosen to speak of him, I may be permitted to tell you that he owes his liberty to me, as indeed he will tell you when he comes to your aid.

Touched in spite of herself, Héloïse turned different eyes on Abbé Suger, who, perceiving the advantage, began to praise Abélard, whom he held to share the truth equally with Bernard, adding: neither being possessed of the whole truth, that being with God. I have not heard of Abélard for nine years, Héloïse answered sadly. For nine years, Abbé Suger, I have waited without knowledge of him. He left me to become a priest; is he one? No, he is not a priest, and may not be ordained. The persecution continues? Héloïse said. No persecution but the law that we read of in Deuteronomy. You know it. In Deuteronomy? Héloïse asked. How can the laws of ancient Israelites control the life of Abélard? Have you forgotten the text, Sister Héloïse?—He that is wounded in the stones, or hath his privy member cut off, shall not enter into the congregation of the Lord. Abélard, the father of my son, is not a eunuch. Your meaning is far from plain, Abbé Suger. To quote again, the Abbé answered (this time from the New Testament), our Lord says—for there are some eunuchs which were so born from their mother's womb: and there are some eunuchs which were made eunuchs of men: and there be eunuchs which have made themselves eunuchs for the kingdom of heaven's sake. Abélard has not imitated Origen? Héloïse asked. No; but there are some eunuchs that were made eunuchs of men. The pallor that overspread Héloïse's face frightened the Abbé, and he caught her by the arm, but she drew herself abruptly away from him. During these nine years you have waited, the story must have reached you? he said. No story has reached me, and I have waited, asking myself day by day why he did not come. But, Abbé, tell the story, which I do not believe

It was one night, he said, not many nights after he had
put you into this convent—— But he did not put me
into this convent, she interrupted; I came hither of my
own free will. It was one night, he said, soon after your
coming, by your will or by his, that Fulbert, your uncle,
bribed Abélard's servant to let two hirelings into his
house by night, and seizing him, to satisfy Fulbert's
revenge, they cut the stones from him. By others it is
said that your uncle yielded to ecclesiastical influence,
for as you know, Sister, there are many who believe that
Abélard is no friend of the Church, and who would turn
to any means to prevent him taking Orders. The story
you tell, Abbé, is too fearful, too horrible, to be true;
and it is not true. Ever since I came into this room and
met you face to face I suspected some dire purpose in
you. You would kill me, and for that purpose have
invented this cruel lie. Go out of my sight—go. And
without more words the Abbé left her.

CHAP. XL.

IT was late in the evening, about an hour after Abbé
Suger had left the convent, that the nuns began to remember Héloïse and ask themselves if she had succeeded in
getting better terms for them than the Prioress had been
able to get—a lease, mayhap, that would outlast the lives
of the present community—a sort of rushlight hope, a
faint flicker that came and went, but still a hope, and
they begged Mother Hilda to seek out Héloïse, who was
not in the parlour and must be in the library. And going
thither, Mother Hilda came upon Héloïse, sunk in a sort
of stupor in which there were no thoughts, only pain. No,
Mother; no. I cannot talk to you about my thoughts;

let me pass. And pressing past Mother Hilda and through the nuns assembled in the passage, she answered them: No terms; let me pass, let me pass, and the nuns began to ask each other what had fallen out. She has shut herself into her cell, and gives no answer to my knocking, a nun said, re-entering the community-room, and Mother Hilda answered: Had she news that would help we should have heard it from her whatever may be her woe, and whilst Mother Hilda was speaking there rose up in Héloïse a feverish belief that Suger had lied to her for some purpose of his own; and in a whirl of thought she sought to guess his purpose, discovering none that satisfied her, the most likely being that he was afraid of Abélard's intervention, for she had told him that news had come to her of her husband. If not that, he had lied out of sheer revenge for her refusal to help him, mayhap; and then, like one who has climbed to a height and looks over the edge, she said: But if he should have spoken the truth! Another messenger came and she had to recover enough calm of mind to go to the Prioress to tell her of Abbé Suger's attempt to bribe her to use her power in the convent to persuade the nuns to allow the closing of the convent without protest. But, Héloïse, thy face tells a tale. Mother, put no questions to me if thou wouldst not see me mad. And without another word, in a strange silence she withdrew to her cell, this time sure that none would come to torment her.

If it should be true! But it cannot be true. The world is full of horror, but not that—it cannot be. It cannot be; it cannot be. Every hap is within the will of God. And she seemed to understand suddenly, in a blinding flash, why the peasants turned from God to the devil. But if the plot be true, it is well invented, she said. But it isn't true; it cannot be true. And she believed it to

be a lie well planned to humiliate her and compel her
to come to his terms.　To make me feel that nothing
mattered, and my life being at an end, it would be well
to save myself further trouble.　A lie well planned to
break down my self-respect—to kill it; or a plan to
enslave me, to oblige me to accept any mercies he might
be disposed to allow me.　But if he were to restore my
son to me for my services!　He is afraid of a scandal, and
it may be that I did not do wisely in refusing his offer.
Astrolabe in hunger and thirst fallen by the roadside
alone, deserted, no one to bring him water to sup.　But
the Prioress did not believe in Suger; she herself did
not, and had done well to promise nothing.　But is there
any woman so unfortunate?　Can it be? she asked once
more, and in a strange quiet of mind suddenly fallen
upon her she began to examine Suger's lie, feeling in
stinctively that she could not reconcile the story he had
told with her knowledge of Fulbert's character.　Fulbert
was shut up in a selfishness which, from long habit, had
become himself, sending me to school, she said, on the
day of my mother's death lest I might disturb by my
presence the even flowing of his days, and sending Madelon to fetch me home because he feared my father's
ghost.　A selfish man, but not a wicked one, he would
not allow me to return to school for admiration of my
Latin speech; liking, she continued, to sit opposite to
me in the evenings, both of us reading by the fire.　In
her memory of those hours her thoughts softened towards
her uncle, and an amusing incident returned to her mind,
one that showed his selfishness exactly as she understood
it.　He always asked her if she liked the leg of the
chicken or the wing, and she answered: The leg, so that
he might have all the breast to himself; but one day,
to disclose his selfishness, she said: I will take a wing,

and he gave her the wing, but with a cry that would have
been childish in a child.

But apart from a selfishness which always had its own
way with him, he was kind to her, and her thoughts fell
back on the friends he had summoned for music to his
house. He liked music, but he had thrown open his doors
to the world, after they had been long closed to it, for
her sake, and in the midst of her grief and torment of
soul she gained a little respite, remembering Madelon
and herself in the kitchen preparing the cakes that were
to be distributed, and choosing the wine that she invited
the guests to partake of. The rival philosophers had
brought an end to those little assemblies, and the winter
intervened; a terrible winter it was, and many of the
incidents of that winter rising up in her mind delayed the
inevitable return of grief. Grief hushes like a wind and
breaks forth again in the mind like a wind. And her
mind calm between the gusts of grief, she remembered
the end of that winter, and how Fulbert had asked Abélard to come and lodge in his house, for he wished her to
be well instructed; and it was not true, as Madelon had
once said, that he asked Abélard to lodge in his house
for the sake of the money that Abélard would pay him.
Her Uncle Fulbert was full of faults and failings, but
he was not a man of crime, and would not have dared to
seek such a vengeance upon his niece's husband, for
Abélard had wedded her in Fulbert's presence and the
presence of witnesses. No, it was not true that he had
devised this vengeance. But Suger had spoken of a
conspiracy among the canons of Notre-Dame. Was there
one amongst them who would tell Fulbert that Abélard
was a spreader of heretical doctrines, one who would
avoid imperilling himself in heresies (he had found himself imperilled in one but would avoid heresies for the

future)—that he would avoid saying any words (who was more skillful in words than he?) that his enemies might lay hold of—and that in this way he would procure himself ordination; and that once ordained his talents would raise him to a bishopric, and if the devil should favour him well he might be raised to St. Peter's chair.

So might they have spoken to Fulbert, and Fulbert, a vain and foolish man, might have given ear to them. It may be all like that, she said, starting to her feet, or it may be but an invention of Abbé Suger to wring all courage out of my heart, to stifle my love for Abélard, to throw me back upon nothingness. Rodebœuf has gone to Brittany to find Abélard; he will bring him back, and I shall learn the truth from Abélard. And if it be that Suger has lied, he will take me in his arms.

CHAP. XLI.

A CARRIAGE came to take the Prioress to her sister at Arras, and with her went Mother Ysabeau and Mother Hilda, for Suger had managed to find homes in different convents for all the choir and lay sisters who wished to remain religious, and only five nuns were left behind, Sisters Héloïse, Josiane, Paula, Agatha and Madelon, an oblate. These waited to be expelled by Suger's henchmen and bailiffs, their choice being to put Suger to the shame of throwing five Benedictine nuns into the public road. And once in the road it was their intention to follow it to Paris to live by begging at the portals of Notre-Dame, perhaps at the doors of Suger's own church, Saint-Denis, till Abélard arrived from Brittany. Héloïse was sure that he would come to their rescue, and encouraged the sisters of her company to bear with fortitude the few weeks of privation that lay before them. We

must not acquiesce in this expulsion, she said; and when
Suger's henchmen and bailiffs came, saying: If you do
not leave this convent, our orders are to put you upon the
road, Héloïse answered: We know that those are your
orders. Whereupon the bailiffs seized the nuns, carried
them out, and forced them on to the road, after which
they locked all the doors. We have to obey orders, ladies,
but we are free to give you seats to Paris in our carts,
if it be to Paris that you be going. At the instiga-
tion of Héloïse the nuns refused these conveyances, and
after six weary miles they arrived in Paris, and not
knowing where they would sleep that night, the five
nuns took their station in front of Notre-Dame, and
told their story to the passers-by, getting quickly from
them enough money to pay for food and lodging. For
the laity, Héloïse said, are more charitable than the
clerics. Nor did their luck cease with the money that
was put into their hands. A pious woman said: I do
not want your money; my house is open to you till you
find one of your own. And to her house they went and
lived in it for many weeks, faring every morning to Notre-
Dame and to Suger's church at Saint-Denis, thereby
bringing discredit on this prelate, and returning with
enough money for their daily wants, putting the words
into their hostess's mouth that they were costing her
nothing. For such was her complaint, and they answered:
We shall soon have money enough to buy ourselves a
house, for Abbé Suger's cruelty has caused everybody
to put his hand in his pocket; our story is well known
now and there is nothing against us. And their hostess
answered them: It has all come about as if by the will of
God; his hand is in it. And she told a story of the
unseen Providence that had guided her to the church
that day, at which they marvelled greatly.

A week passed by and then another week, and still another, charity continuing to feed the nuns unfailingly. They brought back some small coins every day, and these Héloïse was counting when the door of the kitchen opened and a monk crossed the threshold and stood, his eyes fixed upon her. On seeing that she did not recognise him, for he stood against the light, he raised his hood, and the surprise was so great that for a moment she felt like dying, and leaned against the wall gasping, to fall into Abélard's arms at last. Neither could speak, nor were words needed; it was enough for each to know that each was with the other. So thou hast come at last, broke from her sighing lips. So thou hast come, she repeated, and checked the words on her lips: After nine years, for she was now awaking from her almost swoon and would not have the sweetness of this meeting jarred by any untoward word, any word that he might appre- hend as a reproach. Is it thou, Abélard? Is it thou? she repeated, clinging to him as if afraid that her senses deceived her and that the illusion might pass, leaving her alone in the nothingness that she dreaded. Yes, it is Abélard, and thou art Héloïse. The words came again to her lips: Why didst thou stay away so long? but she checked them instinctively, almost without being aware of them, so great was her ravishment; and still speaking out of it she passed her hands through his hair, drawing tresses from his face. Grey hair! she said, and this time the words broke from her: Why didst thou stay away? A long story that is, he answered, smoothing her hair. Not a grey thread in it, he continued; thou art the same, Héloïse, and thou hast been through much trouble, I can read it in thy face; but thine eyes are the same. Look at me like that again; keep thine eyes upon me, for they are what I remember best of thee, thy grey, earnest, spirit eyes that cloud like the sky and that clear like the sky. Abélard, it seems that I never loved thee till this day. But thine eyes wander from me; thou art tired and would sit. Yes, he answered, I am very weary, but glad to see thee. Only glad? she repeated. Is there any other word? he asked. Let me sit down, for my feet are aching, and there is a little giddiness that will soon pass away. Thou'lt not mind if we speak but little for a few minutes? Come, give me thy hand, Héloïse, so that I may know that thou art with me.

She gave him her hand and sat watching his lined face and his greying hair—a monk come out of the wilderness, she said; weary, hungry, and thirsty, no doubt. We have some wine; it will revive thee. And releasing her hand from his she fetched it; and hungry too, no doubt? I am too weary to eat, he answered, but will drink. As he sipped the wine she brought him, he told her of his arrival yesterday at Argenteuil, and how to his surprise and grief he found the convent closed. Why grief? she asked, and he answered her: because I was eager to see thee. And then he related, in the broken words of a man overtired, who fetches his words with difficulty, that he had slept in the inn that night but gained little rest; for I was overtired, and my sleep was short and starting. And despite thy tired limbs thou hast come to me? And have been seeking through Paris for thee, he interjected, at last to find thee; that is enough. But let me loosen thy cloak, she said; let me relieve thee of it. And he let her do as she wished, and from his aching feet she drew the worn shoes.

Let me bathe the feet of the weary traveller, she said. Again he let her do as she wished; and when his feet were bathed, and he had eaten and drunk, something of himself returned to himself, and he asked her: Where am I? She told him, and seeing his eyes going to the money she was counting, she said: That money was gathered this morning at the doors of Notre-Dame. So it is to find thee begging that I have come from the Abbey of Saint-Gildas. Of what concern may it be to thee or to me that I beg, since thou hast come to me again? O, Abélard, I have longed for nine years to see thee, and the recompense is great enough for what I have suffered. But thou hast suffered, and the story will be told when thou art rested. So after the expulsion, he answered, of the nuns from their convent, thou camest to Paris to live by begging with three or four or five of the sisters. Some of the sisters have returned to their parents, she answered, some have found other convents to receive them; and she waited for him to speak, but his words seemed to die out of his mind, and she watched him earnestly, with fear in her heart, afraid to speak, thinking that it might be that he had returned to her only to die in her arms. He will be better after food, she said, and began cooking. In the midst of it she heard him humming to himself some old tune of other days, and to hear him, she returned from the hearth, for in her heart he was a singer always, though in her intellect he was a philosopher always.

The sound of his voice brought back the first months of their love story in the company-room in the rue des Chantres, and so intense were her memories that at first she did not hear which song he was singing. Not one of his own, she said, recovering herself suddenly, for she knew all the old songs. A light broke upon her face, and she said: He is singing snatches of the song that the gleemen sang at Étampes. He looked up, and seeing her in her black Benedictine robe he said: In those days the gleemen sang to a false friar and to false nuns,

and now the false has become the true. And they sat recalling their memories of that delightful journey, till at last Héloïse said: Let us not think of what is behind us, but of what is in front of us now that we are together again. Let the past be forgotten, its joys and its griefs, to which Abélard made no answer; and she thought that mayhap she had said something not to his liking, though how that could be she could but faintly understand. And anxious to regain the mood which chance words had lost to her, she asked him to tell her the story of his exile in the monastery of Saint-Gildas, among rocks where the tides are moaning always if they are not crashing. Tell thee the story of my exile? he said. It is a long one, and to be understood must be told from the beginning. When thou art rested thou'lt tell it, she said. I am rested enough now, he answered, and it had better be told.

Thou hast heard of my trial for heresy at Soissons and my condemnation to burn my book whilst reciting the Athanasian Creed and to be imprisoned in the monastery of Saint-Médard? So much of my story must have reached thee. That thou wert tried for heresy and condemned and thy book burnt, that much of thy story was brought from Paris to Argenteuil by Stephen, our chaplain, but he could not tell us how the plot against thee began, the causes of it, and who began it. The beginnings of the hatreds that were raised up against me are to be found in my success in the school, which surpassed that of any other teacher. After leaving thee at Argenteuil my triumphs were greater than ever I had known before. But, Abélard, when we parted did I not tell thee that thy triumphs were within the Church and not without it? How often did we not say: there is no advancement for any man outside of the Church? We follow, Héloïse, the way that is open to us; sometimes it is a path and sometimes it is a road, and on leaving thee my thoughts were set upon discovering for myself a close and humble life, obedient to the Church in wrong as well as in right, vowing that not till the mitre was placed on my head would I teach that faith and reason should walk together, hand in hand, each dependent on the other, twin sisters, always with their eyes set on the ultimate goal which is man's knowledge of God. But my renown closed the way to me. That was the way we chose together, but everywhere was I claimed the true teacher, and when I opened a school, my school emptied, as before, all other schools. I fled from renown, but it followed me, till wherever I went there were houses too few for my disciples and pupils to find lodgings.

Canst blame me, Héloïse, that being what I am, I taught that which was within me to teach, theology? And to theology I added the study of secular learning, thereby bringing to my school new disciples, new pupils. It was secular learning they desired to learn from me, and it was used by me as a bait to attract them to the study of the true philosophy, according to the method attributed by ecclesiastical history to the greatest of Christian philosophers, Origen. And as the Lord seemed to have gifted me equally for the teaching of profane as well as sacred history, pupils continued to flock from every side to hear me. The schools, as I think I have said before, emptied before me. This could not happen without exciting the hatred of the masters, and it became the need of all to seek my overthrow by every means within their reach. As I have said, I withdrew from Paris, and this withdrawal was taken advantage of by two of my inveterate enemies. Why, they asked, does he teach secular learning, he who is not in Orders? And why does he teach philosophy? And still oftener they said that it was wrong for one not in Orders to teach theology. Thou seest, therefore, Héloïse, that their plans were to exclude me from all teaching, for, not being in Orders, I should not teach secular learning, and for the same reason I should not teach theology. And these enemies of mine never ceased to urge these reasons for my exclusion upon all bishops, archbishops, and abbots—in a word, upon everybody in the ecclesiastical hierarchy.

It was about this time that I was attracted above all by the thought of making plain the fundamental principles of our faith by analogies, and to do this I composed a treatise on the unity of the divine Trinity for the use of my pupils, who asked for human and philosophical reasons. They said that they did not seek for vain words, and that nobody could believe what he did not understand, and that it was ridiculous to preach what one did not understand oneself. The Lord himself reproved the blind men for leading the blind. My treatise was written and generally approved of, for it seemed to answer all questions, even the most difficult, and in proportion as the gravity of the subject was appreciated, greater was the admiration it called forth, thereby infuriating my enemies, compelling them to discover means for my overthrow. Albéric and Lotulfe took the lead, and they were powerful, having a school at Rheims; and by their reiterated suggestions they at last succeeded in obliging their Archbishop, Raoul, to call upon Conan, the papal legate, to assemble a Council at Soissons, and to invite me to bring thither my celebrated treatise on the Trinity.

It is a long, long story, Héloïse, he said. She waited for him to say that he would postpone telling it, or that,

however long it was and wearying to tell, he must tell it.
But he said nothing more, and she sat watching, anxious,
for he seemed to have faded away out of himself again
till little seemed to remain of Abélard in the man sitting
by her. And this being the second time that his wits
seemed to have left him, she was alarmed and began to
ask herself if she should run and call for help. As she
was about to do so he began to speak, telling that if a
man sins it were better to leave God to punish or forgive
him as He pleased when the time came, and for him to
apply himself instead to learning rather than censor-
ship. But what does he mean? she asked herself, trembling. And again breaking the pause, Abélard continued:
Men hate the truth, for few are of the intellect, whereas
all are of the flesh; and not knowing the truth well, or
being unable to accept it then, as perhaps I am still
unable to accept it, I told the monks that one day, while
reading in their library, I had come upon a passage in
the venerable Bede's commentary upon the Apostles, in
which the author says that Denys l'Areopagite was
Bishop of Corinth and not of Athens. But nothing that
I could say could have annoyed the monks more than
this, for their boast was that the founder of their Order
was Denys l'Areopagite. The truth did not seem to concern them in the least—it was their interest and pride
that the founder of their Order should have been Bishop
of Athens—and without giving a moment's thought to
Bede's statement they declared him to be an impostor,
and that Abbot Hildun was worthy of belief, saying that
he had been to Greece and verified the fact, placing it
beyond all doubt. One of the monks begged me to say
which I thought was most worthy of belief—Bede or
Hildun—and I answered that Bede, whose writings were
accepted by all the Latin Church, seemed to me a more

considerable authority. Thou'lt hardly believe it, but
my simple desire to make plain a truth set the monastery
on fire, as it were, and from the lowest monk to the high
est they were agreed that I had been from the beginning
the plague spot of the monastery. And they ran to the
Abbot to tell him what I had said, who of course was
glad to find me in a trap, for he feared me even more
than his monks. He called a council of the monks and
I was threatened, this time not with a charge of heresy
but of a historical untruth which, in his opinion, amounted
to an attack not only on the monastery but on the Crown
itself. Nor could he see any way of dealing with me
but to send me to the King to be punished. My answer
to his threats was that I was ready to submit myself
to judgment if I could be proved to be guilty; but
I was not listened to, and the end of the story was
that three or four monks took pity on me, and with
their help I escaped one night and took refuge in the
domain of the Comte de Thibaud, whom I knew to be
kindly disposed towards me, having heard of my misfortunes.

I tell this story, Héloïse, thinking that thou'lt see the
significance of it. Those who are addicted to the truth—
who love it and seek it on all occasions—find little favour
among men. Well, to continue my story. One day it
fell out that the Abbot of Saint-Denis came with several
of his monks to the castle to speak with the Comte upon
some personal matters, and hearing of their visit I went
to the Comte and begged him to use his influence with
the monks to obtain permission from them for me to be
allowed to live as a monk wherever it might please me
to live. The Abbot and his monks asked for some time
to consider the question, and withdrew, saying that their
answer would be given before leaving. At once it became

clear that they were opposed to granting our request,
for very soon they were reminding each other, hypo-
critically, of course, that so great a personage as myself
was of great value to their monastery and that they could
not hear of my leaving it and enrolling myself in another
Order, for to do this would be to cast a slur on the monastery of Saint-Denis—to degrade it, and that they
would dishonour themselves by so doing. No, they could
not grant our request, and they left—the Abbot declaring he would pronounce a sentence of excommunication
against me if I did not return at once, and against the
Prior (I forgot to say that there was a Prior on the
Comte's lands) for sheltering me. He was for the time
being my host and guardian. The Comte, too, feared
excommunication if I remained, and it is hard to say
what would have befallen me if the Abbot's death had
not rescued me from him. He died soon after; and was
succeeded by Suger.

It is an implicated and bitter, intricate story, Héloïse,
and of what use can it be to go over it again? But I
must hear it, she answered; omit no detail, I beg of thee,
and Abélard, acquiescing in her wish, related how he
had approached the Archbishop of Meaux, who seemed
to be well disposed towards him, and to wish that an
end and surcease should be made of the obligations he
had incurred towards the monastery of Saint-Denis; he
had reason to know that the King and his Council would
approve of his request, and that the new Abbot would
not oppose it, for Suger was anxious to purchase the
King's pardon for the irregularities of his monastery
while under the rule of his predecessor, by submission
and the payment of a large ransom. It may have been
to enable them to pay this ransom that the monks of
Saint-Denis revived the old charter granted to them by

Clothaire III., which, as thou knowest, had been in abeyance for at least a hundred years. So it all came to this—Suger and his monks agreed to grant me my freedom and that I might go and live as it best pleased me to do, so long as I did not join another Order, conditions that were drawn up in the presence of the King and his ministers; and I withdrew penniless to the neighbourhood of Troyes with a single friend and disciple, an Englishman, a poet, to some barren fields, and we two together raised from reeds and clay a sort of oratory, our chapel it was of the diocese, dedicated to the Holy Trinity with the consent of the Bishop, and there, hidden and believing myself forgotten of the world, I often said at daybreak when we rose from the clay on which we rested: Hilary, we can say, like David, lo, then would I wander far off and remain in the wilderness.

But, Héloïse, my story wearies thee. Abélard, thou hast forgotten much to think that I am indifferent to anything concerning thee; and vowing that her face should not again betray her, she begged him to continue his story. But how much better I could listen if he would speak the words: The story that may have reached thine ears about me is not true. At these words she would leap into his arms, and the story of their past sufferings would be a pleasant story for the fireside. But if it were not true, why had he not come before? The thought almost forced a cry from her lips, and that he might not read her face, she hid her face in her hands.

So thou seest, Héloïse, hard as thy lot was in the convent of Argenteuil, mine was not easier. I know nothing, she answered, of the hermitage at Troyes, but my heart goes out to thank Hilary for his devotion to thee. And were ye long together? she asked, jealousy rising in her voice. Not for long! peace is never long in my life,

and very soon disciples came from afar, leaving towns
and castles, to live in a desert in huts that they built
with their own hands, never regretting the delicate food
they had left behind as they munched black bread and
watercress; as I walked by night, I often said: They
sleep better on the moss than on feather beds, and my
thoughts turned to the Essenes sleeping peacefully in
the huts by Jordan.   We have often talked about the
Essenes, who left towns and villages to live in huts on
the eastern bank of the Jordan, living on the produce
of their gardens and the milk from their yoes, speaking
rarely, hiding their heads under white hoods.   Thou canst
not have forgotten, Héloïse?   I have forgotten none of
thy words, she answered, and Abélard continued to tell
that the number of disciples multiplied, and that there
was peace at Troyes, till envy began to stir his enemies
to hatred; and with the same voice of dangerous fascina-
tion that had thrown her at his feet, he continued to speak
of the peace of the desert, asking why it was that the
Pythagoreans avoided all that could flatter the senses,
living like the early Christians in deserts, not forgetting
to tell how Diogenes came to Plato and roused him in
his rich bed with a foot covered with mud, and that Plato
rose, and in agreement with the advice of the sage withdrew from the town and chose an abandoned pestilential
country-side as the most suitable for his academy, so that
the continual care of his health might calm the rage of
his passions, and his disciples should not know other
joys and pleasures save those of learning.

It was with the bodily ear she heard him, for in her
soul a voice was crying: Will he tell me if Suger's story
be true?   But instead of speaking the words which she
desired, which he was afraid to speak, he told her that
the world contrives always to thrust itself between men

and happiness, and that our poverty, which gives us happiness, robs us of it in the end. For as the number of my disciples increased, he said, the difficulties of life in the wilderness multiplied, and to supply our wants there was no other way for me except to open a school of philosophy. To get my living I had thought of returning to the world to beg, but to beg I was ashamed, and dig I could not, having tried and failed, for though digging is never spoken of as an art, it is an art in this much, that it must be practised from boyhood. My disciples said: We'll undertake to relieve you, master, of all bodily needs. Food and clothing we will bring and you will give us divine philosophy, and we shall profit greatly in health by prescription of the great air and in learning, and our minds will advance, keeping pace with yours always as far as may be.

We spoke and lived like the philosophers of old, and there being a disused quarry on a hill-side near to our oratory, we often repaired thither on fine evenings for discourse. A spacious place warmed by the sunset, the semblance of a ruin, it was, with stone seats for those who chose to sit, and passage enough for those who would walk back and forth, with creeping plants falling like curtains over the edge above us, and pine-trees pointing to the sky. Daws and choughs nested in the clefts, and very often men and birds were talking together. I have pleasure in recalling that place, for our best hours were spent there. Yet, as often happens in this life of ours, the ruin and misfortune that awaited us was discovered there by one of our number—a sort of Judas, but an unwitting Judas—the architect of our oratory, and one more devoted, mayhap, than all the others, who said one evening: Master, how easily that stone could be detached and cut to the form of a sculptured group above the portal of our church. And I said: The stone could be detached, but what group wouldst thou cut upon it? The group, he said, is set forth by the stone itself. And he called me to follow the lines that he pointed out, of three figures, the Father, the Son, and the Holy Ghost, but which I could not see, though he averred they were distinct to his eye. Some of the disciples saw the Father, some the Son, but none saw the triptych clearly from the first but the sculptor. A little chipping, he said, will make it plain to all. And before long he wrought the three divine Persons out of the stone, with the Father in the middle, in a long robe with a stole crossed over his breast, the ends tucked under his girdle. His cloak extended from his shoulders over the other two Persons, and from its buckle hung a gold band, bearing these words: Filius menus et tu. On the right of the Father was the Son, but without a girdle; He carried his hands in the form of a cross over his breast and a ribbon bore the words: Pater meus et tu. The Holy Ghost, in a like robe, held His hands crossed over His breast, and His legend was: Ego utriusque spiraculum. The Son wore a crown of thorns, the Holy Ghost a crown of wild olives. The Father's crown was closed, in His hand He held a globe, signifying empire, and the Son and the Holy Ghost watched the Father, who alone was sandalled. An assemblage of the country-side was needed to bring the stone from the quarry to the church, at first dedicated to the Holy Trinity, now placed under the protection of the Holy Ghost and called the Paraclete, in memory of myself come thither as a fugitive, who, in the crisis of my despair, found peace and consolation and divine grace. My enemies were seeking an excuse to attack me, and began at once to ask if it were seemly to consecrate a church to the Holy Ghost rather than to the Father. It should have been dedicated to the Father, the Son or the entire Trinity.

Héloïse heard Abélard start out with an argument in a way that she recognised as characteristic of him, and knowing him as well as she did, Héloïse did not seek to interrupt the flow of logic which he could not restrain, so natural was it to him. She heard many quotations from Saint Paul, and the case he made out against his accusers was an excellent one. But why does he put himself to all this trouble, she asked, to prove himself to be in the right before one whose heart cries always: thou art the right, and known by me from the beginning, since thy voice called me out of myself; and now, listening to the thrice-beloved voice, she regretted nothing, for she knew now that the story he was telling her was the story of a man to whom a thought was more imperative than health or wealth or glory.

Wherever there is great love, there also will be found pity, and she apprehended more clearly than ever that the man whose destiny she had accpted as hers could spare no faintest shade of his thought. His thought is himself, and next to his thought, I come, she said, and fell to listening once more to the beautiful voice and to the abundance of words that had led half the world away, herself more than any other. She began to listen again, for he was now telling how he had sent some Dialogues of Plato, and a rare book, the *Elevatio Theologica,* by Proclus, to be copied by a skilful scribe in the abbey of Clairvaux; and in this story, Héloïse saw Abélard as plainly as she did in the carving of the bas-relief and the dedication of his church to the Holy Ghost rather than to the Trinity or the Son, together with the indignant Bernard and another fanatic, Norbert, who ran about France foretelling the coming of Antichrist and stirring up persecution against all those who seemed to him a danger to faith and unity.

Though they had nothing else in common, they were united in hatred of me and of learning, Abélard said. It would seem to them that Christianity rested not upon a rock of learning but upon the mud-banks of ignorance; and ever since they met they had not ceased to speak against me and impugn my teaching, and wherever they go their aim is to discover some act of mine, which would justify them in bringing a charge of heresy against me. Whilst I was at the Paraclete tidings reached me almost every week of something that had been said against me. I call God to witness I never heard of a synod of ecclesiastics that the thought did not cross my mind: they are meeting now to consider my case. A man bears with his enemies easily for a time, but at length he begins to feel himself like a hunted animal. Whichever way he goes the hounds are on his track; they seem to be getting nearer, and at last he swings himself over a cliff's edge to escape them—a thing that I often longed to do myself, dreaming myself out of Europe in the midst of some idolatrous country, where at least I should not have to teach philosophy for money.

But, Abélard, Héloïse said, returning to her conception of Abélard's character—that the source of his misfortunes was his love of truth—Abélard, thou dost defame thyself worse than thine enemies do. How is that? he asked, for his mind had been away, and he returned to the actual present with difficulty. The thought of money was never in thy mind, Abélard; thou didst teach philosophy for philosophy's own sake, and I will not hear thee defame thyself. It may be that thou art right, he answered, and that the money I received was but an accident. It was indeed, she said; the love of truth was

always thy lode-star. And now tell me what brought thee
to Saint-Gildas—to Brittany. To a monastery, he added,
hung like an eagle's nest among rocks; to savage monks
whose language I do not speak and whose wants I cannot
fulfil. Drink and food they claimed from me for themselves and their wives and families, and we were persecuted by a lord of that country and robbed by him. The
ocean thunders around the rocks and the gulls scream;
a country without laws, a savagery. What evil providence drove thee thither? she asked, and Abélard, his
voice dropping to one of gentle sadness, related that the
monastery, founded by Chilperic I., lost its Abbot, Harvé,
in 1125, and that the monks were deputed by Conan IV.,
Duke of Brittany, to go to France, and these, having obtained the consent of the Abbot and monks of Saint-Denis,
came to the Paraclete. And all being dark about me—
not a single light showing anywhere—I set forth with
them for Brittany and have borne as best I might with
them. But thou wilt not return? Héloïse said. Rodebœuf, he continued, came to Saint-Gildas and told me of
thy life at Argenteuil and of the danger of the monks of
Saint-Denis possessing themselves of the buildings and
lands belonging to you. The thought of the abandoned
Paraclete came into my mind as a refuge for you. But
now that we have met after these many years we shall
not part again, she said. It cannot be that thou hast
come from the uttermosts of Brittany to leave me again.
Thy life and my life are but one life now, as they should
have been, without hope or joy except what each may
bring to the other. Our lives are twain as before, Héloïse.
Then it is not for me that thou hast come, but for thy
son? For my son, whom I saw but once; where is he?
Did Rodebœuf not tell thee what befell him? Another
misfortune then has befallen us both, Héloïse? Is our

son dead? We know not if he be dead or living, Abélard, but he has gone from us. He may return.

Tell me thy story, Héloïse. And when she had finished telling it, he said: That boy, if he had lived, might have made the twain one. Then he will return, she said. There is no returning from those pilgrimages, he answered. If there be no returning, she replied, thou wilt give me another son. That may not be, Héloïse. So the story Suger told me is the truth! God has spared us no misfortune, she cried, falling over against him, and when he strove to lift her from her knees, she wept the more. He took her in his arms and kissed her, but his lips frightened her, and she could not bear the touch of his hands; and the violence of her grief was such that she did not know the cruelty she was guilty of till he released her, saying: Héloïse, it would have been better had I stayed in my monastery amid the rocks than to come hither to see thee grieve like this. How often didst thou say to me: Thy love for me is but passion, mine is above passion, for it is not with my body alone that I love thee but with my soul, with my spirit, with my intellect. The very words, Héloïse, but now when I return I find no consolation in thee but hard hands that repulse me. Héloïse, can it be that I have been mistaken in thee and that thy love was not what I thought it, but passion and desire of my glory, mayhap, that a ray of it might fall upon thee? It would seem that this is a truth. Héloïse, it would have been better that I had not come hither. And yet to die without seeing thee again, I could not, or my son, him whom I shall never see!

If I weep, Abélard, it is from shock, out of which I shall come the same Héloïse as thou knowest; out of it I have come already, and strong enough to bear without flinching the story of thy misfortune. Suger was not

lying then. Ah, it was the mutilation that kept thee
from me these nine years. Shame of it kept thee away.
Art thou not culpable even as I was when my grief took
all reason from me for a few minutes? For nine years
thou didst leave me to mourn, but I make no complaint,
for thou hast returned. Only tell me that now we shall
be united, that our lives shall be one, and that the misery
of hope is at an end. But why this silence? It was
shame that kept thee from me? How little thou knowest
me! Speak, Abélard, for thy silence is worse than any
story, worse than any grief we have met with; and we
have met with many, more than enough. Speak. It is
as thou sayest, Héloïse; it was shame kept me from
thee, and misfortune, always on my track, is upon it still,
for now I come to thee to learn that our son has been
taken from us. Is there no end to our misfortune? There
is an end to it if thou canst remain with me, she replied;
and I would hear all, for all thou hast not yet told. Thou
wouldst hear of the mutilation, when and how it came to
pass? Two weeks after leaving thee in the convent at
Argenteuil Fulbert's hirelings bribed my servant and
broke into my lodging, held me, and the mutilation was
accomplished. After it I lay in pain of body and shame
of mind, saying to myself: Héloïse I shall never see again.
How little thou knewest thy Héloïse, she answered, her
tears falling upon his hands. Never shall I see her, I
cried, during the night and day, and prayed that I might
die and escape the shame of it. But death did not come
as was expected, and my soul said to me: Bury thyself
in a monastery. Mine enemies have robbed me of love
and glory; and it was for that I put on the monk's cowl
in the monastery of Saint-Denis. My enemies have indeed
brought about my overthrow. They have not, she answered; my love thou hast and wilt always have it, and

thy glory is assured, for is it not true that the vanquished to-day is to-morrow's victor, and vice versa? It may be that the truth triumphs in the end, he said. Let us be faithful to one another, she cried, for we have none other to be faithful unto. Abélard, let us be faithful to one another. We may not live together, Héloïse, for, despite his mutilation, it would be said, he creeps back to his mistress. What matter, she cried, what is said of thee or me? Yes, Héloïse, it matters; it matters much what is said. A struggle still awaits me against the all-powerful Church, and we may not live together, Héloïse.

Then indeed, Abélard, thy coming is not well for me or for thee, for I had as lief never have seen thy face again. Do not speak so, Héloïse, we must live our lives to the end. I must return to my abbey among the high rocks over against the Western Ocean, and the oratory that my disciples built for me in a desert at Troyes, near to the banks of the Arduzon, will be a shelter for thee and the nuns who have come with thee from Argenteuil to Paris. Héloïse, do not weep, for it breaks my heart to see thee. I thought that there was more strength in thee and that thou couldst bear with finer fortitude a hard lot.

She did not answer, and he watched her fall into a trance of grief, out of which his words could not awake her, and from which she did not awaken till the sisters pushed the door open and crossed the threshold, stopping at the sight of Abélard. My husband, Héloïse said, rising, and Abélard answered: My sister in Jesus Christ.

CHAP. XLII.

FROM Héloïse to Abélard:

To him to whom my body and temporal life belong, as my immortal life and soul belong to God. When thine eyes read these words, Abélard, thou'lt remember that I have never been disobedient to thee, that thy will has always been my will; and such it would be to this day, an undivided, mutual will if misfortune had not robbed me of my strength to obey thee, the only strength that I ever sought to possess or that seemed to me to be of any value. But the strength that empowered me for nine years is not with me to-day. I am no longer the Héloïse whom thou knewest; indeed I know not what I am beyond that I am nothing, having lost the hope of seeing thee again, for thou denyest thy presence to me. A consolation it would be to know that thou livest in thy monastery pitched above the sea, but that is not enough; with thee I could continue the pilgrimage, without thee I cannot. I must go. These words will torture thee when I am gone; I know it, and would spare thee all suffering, for, like myself, thou hast suffered enough. But I must brave thy disapproval, and though it is hard for me to do this, I must do it, for there is no reality, nothing in life for me but thou; I am dead to all other pleasure and my life is over and done in the heart of God; and like the poet I would that the black fate overhanging me should fall quickly, suddenly. He asks for hope to soothe our fears, but hope has been taken from me, and my soul is reft of all save dread of thy disapproval, of the words: Why did she leave me when I needed her most? But if such a thought come to thy mind, I pray thee remember that I sought thy fame, thy glory and thy genius always, and that I am leaving thee in the belief that, released, thy

genius will flourish again. In justice to me thou'lt not
forget that I tried to dissuade thee from marriage, saying that it was honour enough for me to be thy mistress,
thy concubine, and that I called to thy mind the names
of the women who brought about the downfall of great
men. I knew them all, for the terror of my soul was
always that I might find myself among them in the end.
In trying to dissuade thee from marriage I was pleading
my own case, but thou wouldst not hearken, though thou
knewest the truth and stifled it in love of me. Thy mistake was to desire me wholly, for in this world God's
gifts are partial. Clasp nothing, not even love, too
tightly, lest love die in thy embrace. But since those
days in Brittany thou hast pondered my words, for I find
them in thy lamentations. In telling the story of Jephthah thy thoughts were on me, and in the lamentations
of Israel for Samson thy thoughts were on thyself:

O, woman, thou the eternal scourge of great men:
thou wert made to destroy them. The first among you
struck down the father of mankind and gave the cup of
death to the race.

Who was holier than David, who more prudent than
Solomon, and unto what blind folly did women not lead
them! Who, amid the strongest, was broken like Samson,
the strongest of all!

Thy lamentations and thy love songs have reached me.
The love songs are echoes of a time gone by, the lamentations tell that, released, thy genius will flourish again; and
so I do not leave thee hopeless after all. But again I
hear thy voice reproving me, saying: She has divided
herself from me for ever by disobeying God's law. But
who shall say that in speaking to Moses the words: thou
shalt not kill, it was God's thought to forbid man to take
his own life? Was not his law raised up against man

killing his fellow? So indeed we may understand the
law, for has not our Lord Jesus Christ said: Love thy
neighbour as thyself. But God's laws are not fully revealed to our understanding, and so imperfect are our
natures that each must explain God's law to himself and
to herself. And knowing what my strength is and the
burden of suffering he has put upon me, I dare to put my
trust in his inclement clemency. Thy genius was a gift
from him which he would protect, which he would save
for his unknown purposes; and in this belief I find courage as Jephthah's daughter did, but unlike her I do not
ask for two months' reprieve, but that my death shall be
prompt, as is the promise of the phial. Be strong, Abélard, read this letter with firm hands, without tears, remembering that Jephthah placed his sword against his
daughter's bosom without fear. Her story will still the
reproaches which I dread. Once more I beseech thee to
put no blame upon me, and to think well that all that
has been had to be for reasons unknown to us. I was
brave in my way and thou wast brave in thy way. But
our hardihood has served us nothing, so it seems, unless
indeed my death releases thy genius from the constraint
my life put upon it. Thou art stronger than I am and
wilt endure thy life to the end, but being a woman I
cannot bear with mine any longer. Ah, Abélard, would
that it had been otherwise.

Her pen had flowed on without stopping, and might
have flowed on for some lines longer, but a footstep interrupted her thoughts, and looking up, she saw Abélard.
What is this? he said, laying his hand on the phial. Give
it to me, she cried. He let her take it and without answering, he took the letter and began to read it aloud to her.
So thou wouldst be divided from me for ever, he said, for

that thou'rt unable to endure a few more years of grief
for eternity's sake? This phial of poison would set to
rest thy troubles here, whilst robbing thee of heaven.
What are our troubles here compared with the troubles
of those on the other side who were disobedient to God's
commands? We might not be divided, Héloïse answered.
Which means, he said, that thou wouldst face hell with
me rather than heaven without me? Abélard, there is
no heaven for me without thee. Then away with the
poison, he said, and bear with thy life for the sake of
eternity; and let us dedicate to God whatever years remain
to us to live, and so gain a happiness to which there will be
no end. A wiser course that is, for what joy would there
be in heaven for me without thee, Héloïse? Will our
lives in heaven be as our lives were in the days that have
gone? she asked. Wilt thou be given back to me whole?
We know but little of heaven, he answered; only this for
certain, that heaven is happiness. Earthly pains may
differ from eternal pain, but happiness is the same in
heaven as on earth. Is that, she asked, an answer to my
question? It is, he answered, for since we shall be happy
in heaven, the means of enjoying our happiness must be
given back to us—— It is said by some that at the last
day we rise with the body that we are now wearing, and
it is said by others (by Origen, my predecessor in mutilation and in suspicion of heresy) that although our present
flesh dies it holds within it a root, a seed, from which
springs our heavenly body. It may be as thou sayest,
Abélard, as Origen and many others dreamed, but he
parted with his manhood to escape from sin. Not to
escape sin, Abélard said, but to escape suspicions of sin,
and was reproved for it by the Church, for we must not
escape from sin or suspicion of sin by such gross means
as Origen took. Sin is not of the flesh but of the spirit,

and he who is not aware of the sin does not sin. But it
would seem that once more I am dropping into a heresy,
a thing that in this world seems hard to escape from if
one thinks at all. But Origen, she said, was ordained,
though he castrated himself. The Church was laxer, he
answered, in those days than now. I am Abbot of Saint-
Gildas, and will die Abbot without hope of other advancement, for outside of the priesthood the Church has no
higher office than Abbot. My enemies have succeeded.
No bishop would ordain me for valid reasons, and hope
has ended for me in this world. It would seem that hope
has ended for thee, also, since thou sayest herein that
thou canst not love any other. Life without love is a
weary burden for us to bear, and a useless one too, if
henceforth our adventure be not heaven, so throw the
poison into the street; spill it into the mud. Obey me
for thy sake and mine, and accept the Paraclete—be its
Abbess—and we will go thither with the sisters who have
remained faithful. I have no heart but to do thy bidding,
Héloïse answered; and in the midst of remembrance that
he had never heard her sob like this before, Abélard
too felt tears trembling on his eyelids ready to overflow
them, but he forced them back, saying: I will leave thee
now, Héloïse, and go out in search of the hackneys to
carry us over the first stage of our journey.

She heard the door close behind him, and rising to her
feet her eyes fell upon the phial of poison. He had said:
Empty it into the mud of the street, and opening the door
she did this, and awaited the return of the sisters, who
came back soon after from Notre-Dame, shaking their
money-box so that Héloïse could see how successful their
begging had been. It matters not, she said, we are leaving Paris to-morrow; and she told them of the convent
that Abélard was going to put them into, and of the hack-

neys that would come for them, and the long ride thither. News indeed this is, said Josiane, and our money-box might as well have returned soundless as with all this chinking of coin—she rattled it again. And they slept that night disquieted by dreams, dozing and awaking quickly, till they were awakened by the trampling of hooves under the windows and remembered that the journey would begin with their dressing. On throwing open the casement Héloïse saw Abélard on a chestnut hackney, and there were five others all of the same kin, stout, compact ponies, with large bushy tails and manes, wilful eyes, tiny hooves, and shaggy fetlocks. The five nuns rode on pillions, Abélard deeming a pillion more suitable to their religious garb and less tiring to women than riding astride. Agatha, Josiane and Paula, having little habit of horseback, would be barely able to keep astride on a pony, he said, and even when they were securely strapped in upon a pillion, he had to turn to them with words of encouragement, saying they were not to feel afraid if their ponies put back their ears, for that meant wickedness. He promised them that they should rest at noon, and in this hope the nuns rode across the Little Bridge into a silent country of shrivelled hedges and grey fields, with the hill-sides shrouded in grey mist. As they ambled the hooves of the hackneys rang out from the frozen clods, and all seeming to be going well Abélard turned in his saddle, crying to them that they must not clutch at their bridles, for the ponies will not trip if you allow them to look after themselves. But my pony will go too fast if I do not hold him in, Josiane answered. And my pony will follow Josiane's, Agatha cried out. And I shall be left all alone, for my pony is lazy, said Madelon. Your ponies will settle down to their amble, Abélard replied, and will

be loath to leave each other; nor will they pass us on
the road.

And when another league was accomplished without a
bolt, a runaway, or a fall, Abélard felt compelled to turn
in his saddle to remark that the ponies were now travelling in good order, and that they would reach an inn at
noon where they would rest. He heard the three sisters
speaking together and his heart smote him, for he felt it
would be hard to keep silence any longer, and if he spoke
to Héloïse at all he must speak of greater things than
the mere accidents of the road. There was no way of
escape from speaking of what was on their minds, for
each knew that the journey they were engaged on was the
last they would undertake together. For as soon as he
had established her Abbess of the Paraclete, which he
would do without doubt—the Bishop of Meaux, being a
friend, would offer no opposition and would obtain sooner
or later the approval of the Pope—he must return to
Brittany and never ride to the Paraclete again, lest his
enemies, seeing him going thither, should mock and jeer,
saying in their beards: the old wether still hankers after
his yoe. So they would speak of him, being pitiless, and
he sought for words whereby he might break the news to
Héloïse that they might hope for nothing in this world,
but that God would recompense them in the next for
unmerited suffering. A shade came into his face, for
Héloïse had suffered, he feared, without much belief in
an eternal recompense; yet she had ceded to his prayer
not to take poison but to put her faith in God and
live her appointed life however empty it might be. It
would be lonelier for her than for him, for he still cherished the hope that divine philosophy would prevail in
the end, bringing all the world into God's fold. Faith
was the antique shepherd, Reason was the new. But

Héloïse had not philosophy, and if he were taken from her was he sure that she would be able to endure life? and if she were not, then indeed they would be separated. Then he put to her the question: What hast thou done with the poison? and she answered that she had emptied the phial into the street's mud. For having obeyed thee, Abélard, always, I was moved not to disobey thee in the end, for to do so would spoil all; and he answered that she had done well, saying (knowing well that it would please her to hear him say it): Heaven would not be heaven for me without thee; thou wert my heaven on earth and wilt be my heaven hereafter, if we gain heaven. As all hangs on that, let us devote, as I said before, whatever years of life remain to us in gaining heaven. It was surely wisdom to spare no pains to accomplish our love, for when we meet in heaven there will be a fulfilment of love such as has not befallen us here; though our love was very great on earth, it will be greater in heaven. Wherefore I am taking thee to the Paraclete, to the solitude by the banks of the Arduzon, for it is not in castles hung with silk, overlooking parks graced with noble trees and terraces, that the soul turns to God, but in solitude 'mid rocks and sand where there is nothing pleasing. But be not afraid; the lands of the Paraclete are smiling, pleasant lands compared with the rocks that overhang the Western Ocean whither my lot lies. And Héloïse answered him: The banks of the Arduzon will be welcomed by me, for to my ears the echo of thy voice will linger among the rocks of the hill-side, and my eyes shall find the footsteps that the earth has allowed to pass into nothingness. For man hath a memory and an imagination, and to our ears and eyes thou wilt be present always; we shall say to one another: All this is not wilderness, for here he worked and lived. All about us is his handiwork; before he came this coun-

try was known only to robbers and wild beasts. Thy lot
will be hard at first, he said, but it will become easier with
time. She answered: thou wilt write and establish a
rule for me and my nuns to follow? And they journeyed
on again, arriving at the inn tired, all of them: Josiane,
Agatha and Paula so tired that it was late next morning
before they started again on their journey. A missel
thrush sang on a bare bough. A song out of season, Abélard said. The moist morning deceives him; and he fell
to thinking of the winter in which he and Rodebœuf wrote
the songs that they were to sing when they started forth
at the end of April, stopping at the various castles for
festivals of song and jousting in the lists.

At noon the sky was blue, the sun was shining; larks
rose wet-winged from the fields singing, and in a little
while (four hours later), the day was declining, and
riding through the dusk they saw great companies of rooks
flapping home through the sky, making for some rooky
woods about a nobleman's castle. The birds came in
thousands, and then there was a lull, a talking, a great
shuffling of the branches, as the pilgrims rode beneath
them. Again the sky was filled with rooks; at every
opening of the trees they caught sight of late-comers,
and in the blue gloom of the wintry evening, in the hour
that is not day nor night, the bats zigzagged round byre
and barn, flying almost in the faces of the travellers, casting shadows on the moonlit road and then disappearing
in the mist.

There were still some miles to ride before they reached
the next village, and Abélard and Héloïse rode immersed
in the sad belief that their lives were wasted and that
their last hope was heaven. Abélard believed in heaven,
therefore Héloïse believed, and, united at last, they rode
to Troyes, thinking how they were to live out the few

years that remained for them to live, thereby gaining an
immortal happiness, the letters germinating in their minds
as they rode, hints of them appearing in their talk as
mile after mile went by.

But it would be vain indeed to record their lives and
their talk further, for the rest of their lives and their
speech are on record.

END OF VOL. II.